INORGANIC
LABORATORY PREPARATIONS

GERT G. SCHLESSINGER, Ph.D.

Department of Chemistry

Gannon College

CHEMICAL PUBLISHING COMPANY, INC.

212 Fifth Avenue · New York 10, N. Y.

1962

© 1962

CHEMICAL PUBLISHING CO., INC.
New York   N. Y.

Printed in the United States of America

INTRODUCTION

This book is the result of extensive personal experience and the supervision of laboratory work in inorganic chemistry at the University of Florida.

The background of the average chemistry student even in simple inorganic preparations is, on the whole, far from complete. His training in this basic branch of chemistry ordinarily consists of perfunctory courses in general chemistry, and in qualitative and quantitative analysis. In these subjects, with the inevitable prepared solutions and solid "unknowns," the undergraduate is left with the vague feeling that inorganic chemicals originate in bottles!

Admittedly then, none of these courses serves to train the student in the fundamental techniques and problems of preparing inorganic chemicals. This is in direct contrast to the study of organic chemistry in which laboratory work is extensively stressed. The point is reached in the student's training where he can no longer think of preparative work except in terms of the chemistry of carbon compounds.

This book is intended to fill this void in the student's training and practical experience by supplementing the usual course in theoretical inorganic chemistry on the level of college seniors and university graduate students with a carefully selected and tested collection of compounds which can be prepared with relatively simple equipment and inexpensive materials. Every experiment is designed to familiarize the student with some special aspect of inorganic theory.

iii

Due to the diversity of approaches in the presentation of advanced inorganic chemistry from the standpoint of both textbook and classroom, this manual has no theoretical discussion preceding each experiment. It seemed that an advanced work of this kind would be most versatile in scope if instructors or students, themselves, were to outline the underlying principles. In this way the book also becomes far more useful to research workers and industrial chemists.

The experiments are given in as much detail as seems to be consistent with the student's previous background in practical work. It is tacitly assumed that he will be familiar with all the basic techniques of the laboratory such as the manipulation of sensitive solids and liquids, procedures for distillation and crystallization, as well as the proper drying of substances. Any laboratory manual of organic chemistry will be of help as a guide in these respects.

The subject matter is so organized that the instructor can inject his own modifications such as arranging the necessary apparatus, preparing beforehand a batch of some special reagent needed, the scaling up or down of quantities to be prepared, or the utilizing of the finished products in further syntheses and research work.

Most experiments are supplied with selected references to stimulate the student's reading of the original literature. Information has been borrowed freely from the following supporting texts: *Inorganic Syntheses; Experimental Inorganic Chemistry,* by W. G. Palmer; *Laboratory Methods of Inorganic Chemistry,* by W. Biltz (translation by Hall and Blanchard); and *Lehrbuch der analytischen und präparativen anorganischen Chemie,* by G. Jander and H. Wendt. There are lists of cognate preparations at the end of many procedures which employ similar or slightly modified techniques, thus giving the chemist a choice of experiments based on comparable principles. A number of the procedures also serve for the preparation of intermediate compounds which are to be used elsewhere, especially in the section on coordination complexes.

It is to be noted that most of the compounds have been deliberately chosen because they are not commonly found on the laboratory shelf. For example, barium and ammonium permanganates are listed instead of the common potassium salt; and similarly, antimony sulfate was chosen rather than sodium sulfate.

It is hoped that this policy of selection, particularly in the chapter on *Salts,* will arouse the student's interest in, and awareness of, the diversity and fascination of the reactions and compounds of other elements besides carbon.

The outline of experimental topics and compounds is quite arbitrary but it has been found to serve the useful purpose of setting a trend in a semester of laboratory work. For convenience, the procedures in each section are listed alphabetically and are marked with asterisks; one for the simplest experiments to four for the most difficult ones.

Noting that old textbooks and manuals of inorganic chemistry are heavily thumbed in the pages dealing with Werner complexes, I have diligently attempted to satisfy this interest on the part of experimenters by devoting a relatively large portion of the text to this engaging subject. Much of the work calls for the use of ethylenediamine *(en)* and *dl*-propylenediamine *(pn),* to illustrate bidentate coordination, because these materials are cheap and readily available. In the category of polybasic amines, diethylenetriamine *(den),* triethylenetetramine *(tet)* and dipropylenetriamine *(dpn)* have also been added for the same reasons.

Grateful acknowledgement is made to my wife and to Sister Mary Edith Lange of Gannon College for assistance in the preparation of the manuscript; to Dr. H. Alsentzer, of the University of Pennsylvania, for first arousing my interest in the preparation of inorganic chemicals; and to Union Carbide (Petrochemicals Division) for their generous supply of polyamines.

Any suggestions and corrections from the users of this text will be most welcome.

Gert G. Schlessinger

July 1962

CONTENTS

ABBREVIATIONS

B—W. Biltz, *Laboratory Methods of Inorganic Chemistry*, 2d Ed.; Wiley, New York, 1928.

I—*Inorganic Syntheses*, McGraw-Hill, New York, 1939–1960.

J—G. Jander and H. Wendt, *Lehrbuch der Analytischen und Präparativen Chemie*, 3rd Ed.; Hirzel, Stuttgart, 1959.

P—W. G. Palmer, *Experimental Inorganic Chemistry;* Cambridge University Press, 1954.

en—Ethylenediamine: $H_2NC_2H_4NH_2$

pn—Propylenediamine: $CH_3CH(NH_2)CH_2NH_2$ (*dl* mixture)

dpn—Dipropylenetriamine: $H_2NCH_2CH(CH_3)NHCH-(CH_3)CH_2NH_2$

den—Diethylenetriamine: $H_2NC_2H_4NHC_2H_4NH_2$

tet—Triethylenetetramine: $H_2NC_2H_4NHC_2H_4NHC_2H_4NH_2$

*, 1 to 4—Increasing order of difficulty of experiments

INORGANIC
LABORATORY PREPARATIONS

INORGANIC
LABORATORY PREPARATIONS

Chapter 1

METALS

I. Antimony from Stibnite *

$$Sb_2S_3 + 3Fe \longrightarrow 2Sb + 3FeS$$

An intimate mixture of 25g stibnite, 11g iron powder or filings, 2.5g anhydrous sodium sulfate, and 0.5g charcoal is placed in a covered crucible and heated about 20 minutes with a Meker burner so that the fusion mixture softens but does not quite melt. This is determined by momentarily stirring with an iron rod. The melt is allowed to cool and the crucible is broken. A mass of crude fused antimony weighing about 15g is found at the bottom; this is mechanically cleaned and then washed with hot water.

Reference: B:25; J:352.

2. Chromium by the Goldschmidt Process ***

$$Cr_2O_3 + 2Al \longrightarrow 2Cr + Al_2O_3$$

Fifty grams of C.P. chromium oxide are thoroughly dried by heating in a clean iron dish over a Bunsen flame for about one-half hour while stirring with a file, then cooled and mixed intimately with 25g of powdered dry potassium dichromate and 27g of 15–30 mesh aluminum powder (a). [CAUTION: Shake the mixture in a stoppered bottle; *do not grind it in mortar*.] Seventeen grams of this mixture are mixed with 7.5g of barium peroxide and 0.75g of Al powder (b). An ignition mixture of the same weights of BaO_2 and Al is also prepared.

A layer of (a) is placed in a clay crucible about four inches in diameter and six inches deep. The thickness of the layer should be ½–¾ inch and well tamped down. A ¾-inch

1

diameter test tube is placed in the center of the crucible to provide a shaft and the rest (85g) of mixture (*a*) is poured around it and packed down well. The test tube is then carefully worked out and (*b*) is poured into the open shaft. The rest of the hole is filled with the ignition mixture and pressed hard, spreading the excess on top of the entire charge. A 3-inch piece of clean magnesium ribbon is carefully inserted in the center and the crucible is half embedded in a pail of sand. The ribbon is lighted and the operator must step back.

When the spectacular reaction is over the crucible is allowed to cool, then broken, and the regulus is mechanically freed of metal (about 20g) from adhering impurities. Sometimes the chromium is isolated as several smaller globules. The purpose of the dichromate is to raise the reaction temperature of the charge.

NOTE: In order to avoid an accident, if the reaction in the crucible does not seem to start, wait at least three to five minutes before going over to examine the reaction mixture.

COGNATE PREPARATIONS

2 a. Manganese from Pyrolusite ***

$$3MnO_2 \longrightarrow Mn_3O_4 + O_2$$
$$3Mn_3O_4 + 8Al \longrightarrow 9Mn + 4Al_2O_3$$

Eighty grams of native manganese dioxide are ignited for one hour at 800°–900°C to convert the ore to Mn_3O_4. This oxide, weighing about 65g, is mixed with 22g of granulated aluminum and tamped into a crucible, leaving a hollow depression on the surface of the mixture into which 2g of magnesium is packed. A 3-inch fuse of Mg ribbon is inserted and the charge set off in a sand-filled pail, preferably outdoors. The regulus of manganese weighs about 20g.

The pyrolusite is first ignited to the oxide of lower valence because the latter reacts much less violently in the process.

2 b. Crystalline Silicon ***

$$3SiO_2 + 4Al \longrightarrow 3Si + 2Al_2O_3$$
$$2Al + 3S \longrightarrow Al_2S_3$$
$$S + O_2 \longrightarrow SO_2$$

The reaction mixture consists of 90g of dried sand, 100g of aluminum powder and 120g of flowers of sulfur, all thoroughly mixed and placed in a clay crucible imbedded in sand. The reaction is started with a thin layer (about $\frac{1}{8}$-inch) of Mg powder and a fuse of Mg ribbon. Much sulfur dioxide escapes during the process: the necessary heat is generated by the reaction between the aluminum and the sulfur. The broken pieces of slag are treated with water under the hood to hydrolyse the aluminum sulfide; the hydrous aluminum oxide and crystalline alumina are easily separated from the grey-black metallic regulus and smaller globules of silicon.

The metal is allowed to stand with concentrated hydrochloric acid for several days with occasional renewal of the latter until all the excess aluminum has dissolved, leaving a loose mass of silicon leaflets. The crystalline mass is boiled for two hours with more of the acid, drained, and then transferred to a platinum or plastic beaker. The product is treated with 10ml portions of concentrated hydrofluoric acid [CAUTION: Corrosive!] until no more silica dissolves and then drained, washed well with water, and dried at 100°C.

$$Yield = 20\text{--}25g$$

2 c. Crystalline "Boron" (AlB$_{12}$) ***

$$B_2O_3 + 2Al \longrightarrow 2B + Al_2O_3$$

Proceed as for silicon, using 50g of dry boron trioxide, 75g of sulfur, and 100g of aluminum. About 7.5g of black metallic crystals (which scratch glass) are obtained. The thinnest crystals show a dark-red color by transmitted light.

2 d. Molybdenum

$$3MoO_2 + 4Al \longrightarrow 3Mo + 2Al_2O_3$$

Molybdenum dioxide (MoO_2) is prepared [4, 5] by ignition of the trioxide MoO_3 in a stream of dry hydrogen at 450°C for three hours. A combustion tube and circular oven (see No. 14) are used. It is not necessary to remove the remaining traces of the trioxide with gaseous hydrogen chloride for the purposes of the Goldschmidt process.

Eighty grams of the molybdenum dioxide and 21g of aluminum are used and worked up as under chromium (No. 2). A regulus of about 50g of metal is obtained with a purity of 98%. With smaller quantities the yield drops due to excessive volatilization of the product. The metal contains traces of aluminum and silicon.

A useful time-saving device in igniting aluminothermic charges is the so called "ignition-cherry" which is readily prepared as follows:

Ten grams of aluminum powder and 40g of fine barium peroxide are mixed by *shaking* with 7g of powdered potassium chlorate. The mixture is kneaded with collodion into balls about one gram in weight, and a 3-inch piece of Mg ribbon is inserted. These spheres are then inserted into a small depression on the top of the reaction mixture.

References:
1. B:17ff; J:351
2. GOLDSCHMIDT, *Ann.*, 301:19 (1898).
3. BILTZ, *Ber.*, 41:2634 (1908).
4. BILTZ AND GÄRTNER, *Ibid.*, 39:3370 (1906).
5. FRIEDHEIM AND HOFFMANN, *Ibid.*, 35:792 (1902).

3. Lead from Litharge by Carbon Reduction *

$$PbO + C \longrightarrow Pb + CO$$

Twenty-five grams of litharge are mixed well with 1.5g of very fine charcoal and heated over a Meker burner in a large covered crucible for about one-half hour. The molten lead is poured into a clean iron dish and allowed to cool. Yield about 20g.

COGNATE PREPARATION

3 a. Copper from Copper (II) oxide *

$$CuO + C \longrightarrow Cu + CO$$

Eighteen grams of copper oxide and 3g of charcoal are used; the directions for No. 3 are followed. The red-brown powder (which is tinged with black if reduction has been incomplete), is stirred repeatedly with water to float off any carbon and then warmed on the steam bath, adding several 50ml portions of $3M$ hydrochloric acid until all the excess oxide has dissolved, leaving the orange-brown copper.

$$Yield = 12–14g$$

Reference: B:15; J:352

4. Tin from Cassiterite by Cyanide Reduction *

$$SnO_2 + 2KCN \longrightarrow Sn + 2KCNO$$

Twenty grams of finely powdered native stannic oxide and an equal weight of potassium cyanide (mixed in a mortar) are heated in a crucible over a Meker burner for about one-half hour.

The button of tin is cooled, washed with 25ml of water, and this extract is reserved. The metal is rinsed thoroughly with hot water. Some samples of ore are not readily reduced.

$$Yield = 12–15g$$

The 25ml water extract contains potassium cyanate (see No. 40) which may be isolated by mixing with 50ml of 95% alcohol and filtering.

COGNATE PREPARATION

4 a. Antimony from Sb₂O₅ or SbOCl *

$$Sb_2O_5 + 5KCN \longrightarrow 2Sb + 5KCNO$$
$$2SbOCl + 2KCN \longrightarrow 2Sb + 2KCNO + 2KCl + (CN)_2$$

Equal weights of antimony pentoxide and pure potassium cyanide are treated as above. The regulus is washed with hot water for the removal of impurities.

To prepare antimony oxychloride, 50g of antimony trichloride (No. 77) are stirred well with 35ml of water and allowed to stand for 2–3 days. The white product is filtered off, washed with 50ml of 95% alcohol and with the same volume of ether. The material is dried at 100°C.

$$Yield, about 36g$$

Basic antimony chloride is fused with twice its weight of cyanide as in the preceding sections. Yields of antimony are about 85%.

References:
1. B:20, 22; J: 351.
2. WILLARD AND MCALPINE, *J. Am. Chem. Soc.*, 43:801 (1921).
3. GROSCHUFF, *Z. anorg. Chem.*, 103:164 (1918).
4. HÖNIGSCHMID, *Ibid.*, 136:264 (1924).
5. VAN BEMMELEN, *Ibid.*, 33:290 (1903).
6. MONTIGNIE, *Bull. soc. chim.* (5), 14:378 (1947).

Chapter 2

OXIDES

5. Barium Peroxide **

(I)

$$Ba(NO_3)_2 \longrightarrow BaO + 2NO_2 + \tfrac{1}{2}O_2$$
$$2BaO + O_2 \longrightarrow 2BaO_2$$

Twenty-six grams of barium nitrate are placed in a large covered crucible and heated with slowly rising temperature to a dull red color (about 500°C) for about one-half hour. After cooling, the mass is broken up quickly into small lumps and transferred rapidly to a weighed combustion tube. The tube and contents are weighed to determine the amount of barium oxide present and then heated in a circular combustion oven at about 450°C in a steady stream (about 3 bubbles/sec) of air which has been dried by passing first through caustic soda and then through concentrated sulfuric acid. After cooling in the air current, the tube is weighed; the increase in weight should correspond to one-tenth the initial weight of the BaO, otherwise the material must be reheated again in oxygen using a slightly higher temperature (500°C).

Yield almost quantitative

(II)

$$Ba(OH)_2 + H_2O_2 \longrightarrow BaO_2 + 2H_2O$$

Barium peroxide may also be prepared in the wet way by the following method:

Thirty grams of barium hydroxide are agitated with 500ml of distilled water in a stoppered Erlenmeyer flask at 14°C until no more of the alkali dissolves. The mixture is

7

then filtered by suction into 25ml of *fresh* 3% hydrogen peroxide. The barium peroxide 8-hydrate that forms is first dehydrated *in vacuo* over P_2O_5 in a desiccator, and then at 100°C in a drying pistol with the same dehydrating agent.

$$Yield = 2.5–3.0g$$

COGNATE PREPARATIONS

5 a. Strontium Peroxide *

Five grams of anhydrous strontium nitrate (or the equivalent weight of the 4-hydrate) are dissolved in 50 ml of 3% hydrogen peroxide and mixed with a solution of 7 ml of concentrated aqueous ammonia in 100ml of water. The peroxide 8-hydrate is converted to the anhydrous compound by heating it at 300°C for about 4 hours in dry CO_2-free oxygen, as described under the procedure for barium.

$$Yield = 2.5–3.0g$$

5 b. Calcium Peroxide 0.4 and 8-Hydrate *

To prepare the 8-hydrate, 11g of calcium chloride 6-hydrate are dissolved in 5ml of water and treated with 50ml of fresh 3% hydrogen peroxide and then with 7ml of concentrated ammonia solution in 100ml of water. If this procedure is carried out at 55°C, or if only 30ml of water are used for the ammonia at 20°C, the four-tenths hydrate is obtained. Palmer may be consulted for more details.

Yield, about 4.5g of the 8-hydrate and 3.0g of the 0.4-hydrate

References:
1. B:102; P:177, 178.
2. RIESENFELD AND NOTTEBOHM, *Z. anorg. Chem.*, 89:405 (1914).
3. TRAUBE AND SCHULZE, *Ber.*, 54:1626 (1921).

6. "Bismuth Pentoxide" *

$$2Bi(NO_3)_3 + 6KOH \longrightarrow Bi_2O_3 + 6KNO_3 + 3H_2O$$
$$4KOH + Bi_2O_3 + 4K_3Fe(CN)_6 \longrightarrow Bi_2O_5 + 4K_4Fe(CN)_6 + 2H_2O$$

Twenty grams of freshly powdered bismuth nitrate 5-

hydrate are slowly added to a mechanically stirred solution of 50g *potassium* hydroxide in 100ml water at the boiling point. Heating is continued for 15 minutes with stirring and then 20g of well-ground potassium ferricyanide are added over a period of 5–10 minutes. After the addition, agitation is maintained for 5 minutes longer and then 400ml of water are added. The residue is washed thoroughly by decantation after settling, drained well, and stirred continuously for one hour with a mixture of 200ml of water and 20ml of concentrated nitric acid. The deep purple material is filtered off after cooling, washed with cold water and then dried *in vacuo*. The powder so produced contains about 4% active oxygen ($Bi_2O_3 \cdot Bi_2O_5$—3.33%) (Bi_2O_5—6.45%).

Yield = 6g

References:
1. P:316.
2. HAUSER AND VANINO, *Z. anorg. Chem.*, 39:381 (1904).
3. GUTBIER AND BÜNZ, *Ibid.*, 48:162 (1906); 50:210 (1906); 52:124 (1907).
4. SCHOLDER AND STOBBE, *Ibid.*, 247:392 (1941).
5. WORSLEY AND ROBERTSON, *J. Chem. Soc.*, 117:63 (1920).

7. Chromium (III) Oxide *

(I)

$$K_2Cr_2O_7 + 2NH_4Cl \longrightarrow Cr_2O_3 + 2KCl + N_2 + 4H_2O$$

Thirty-seven grams of potassium dichromate are mixed intimately with an equal weight of ammonium chloride in a clay crucible and heated with slowly rising temperature over a Bunsen flame in the hood until no more vapors are given off. The contents are cooled and powdered. The material is washed by decantation with successive portions of boiling water until no more test for chloride is obtained, then filtered and dried for several hours at 105°–120°C. The filter cake is reground and dried again overnight. The product is a loose green powder which is not attacked by acids or alkalies, especially after ignition.

Yield almost theoretical

(II)

$$(NH_4)_2Cr_2O_7 \longrightarrow Cr_2O_3 + N_2 + 4H_2O$$

Ten grams of ammonium dichromate are placed in a small heap in a large (8-inch) porcelain basin. A red-hot iron wire is touched to the material; the reaction spreads throughout the mixture with incandescence and sparks and is soon completed. The loose green product is extracted with hot water until the washings are colorless and then dried at 100°C. The yield depends entirely on the completeness of the ignition; if considerable quantities of orange dichromate remain in the basin, the entire mass is reheated in an upright clamped flask until decomposition is complete.

Reference: B:63.

8. Copper (I) Oxide *

(I)

$$2CuSO_4 + 2NH_2OH \cdot HCl + 6NaOH \longrightarrow Cu_2O + N_2 + 2NaCl + 2Na_2SO_4 + 7H_2O$$

In a 2-liter Erlenmeyer flask a solution of 55g of copper sulfate 5-hydrate is mixed with one of 25g of hydroxyl ammonium chloride (No. 55) in 125ml water. While cooling the mixture in a cold water bath and swirling well, a solution of 40g of sodium hydroxide in 750ml water is added. The precipitate is allowed to settle and the supernatant liquid is poured off. The oxide is transferred with a little water to a smaller vessel (250ml) and washed by repeated decantation until the rinsings are chloride-free, then suction filtered and the residue washed with 95% alcohol and with ether. The product is dried in warm air.

Yield = 13.5–15.5g

(II)

$$CuSO_4 + 2NaOH \longrightarrow Cu(OH)_2 + Na_2SO_4$$
$$Cu(OH)_2 + KNaC_4H_4O_6 \longrightarrow KNa[Cu(C_4H_2O_6)] + 2H_2O$$
$$4KNa[Cu(C_4H_2O_6)] + N_2H_6SO_4 + 2NaOH \longrightarrow$$
$$2Cu_2O + 4KNaC_4H_4O_6 + Na_2SO_4 + N_2$$

Seventy-five grams of potassium sodium tartrate (Rochelle salts) are mixed with 75g of sodium hydroxide in 600ml of warm water and 50g of copper sulfate 5-hydrate are dissolved in the liquid to give a deep blue solution

(Fehling's) of the copper tartrate complex. A solution of 7–8g of hydrazonium hydrogen sulfate (No. 54) in 100ml of hot water is added slowly with stirring, and the entire reaction mixture is heated to the boiling point with continuous agitation. Heating is maintained for about 10 minutes; the blue color should have completely disappeared and given way to a brick-red precipitate of product. The material is allowed to settle and the supernatant liquid is decanted. The residue of cuprous oxide is washed repeatedly by decantation with water until free of sulfates and then isolated as in (I).

$$\text{Yield} = 14\text{g}$$

$$(\text{III})$$

$$2CuSO_4 + Na_2SO_3 + 6NaCl + H_2O \longrightarrow 2Na_2CuCl_3 + 2Na_2SO_4 + H_2SO_4$$
$$2Na_2CuCl_3 + H_2SO_4 + 4NaOH \longrightarrow Cu_2O + Na_2SO_4 + 6NaCl + 3H_2O$$

Fifty grams of copper sulfate 5-hydrate and 100g of sodium chloride are dissolved in 600 ml of boiling water. One hundred and twenty grams of sodium sulfite 7-hydrate (or 60g of the anhydrous salt) are added with stirring; a colorless liquid is finally produced after the initial formation of a greenish precipitate. The reaction mixture is cooled somewhat and is poured slowly into a solution of 40g of sodium hydroxide in 200ml of water. A yellow precipitate is formed immediately which slowly turns reddish after thirty minutes of boiling with frequent stirring. The product is isolated as in (II). The yield is the same.

References:
1. B:63; P:127.
2. RUSSELL, *Chem. News*, 68:308 (1893).
3. GUNTZ AND BASSETT, *Bull. soc. chim.* (iii) 35:203 (1906).

9. Nitrogen (IV) Oxide ***

$$(\text{I})$$
$$As_2O_3 + 2HNO_3 + 2H_2O \longrightarrow N_2O_3(NO_2 + NO) + 2H_3AsO_4$$
$$2N_2O_3 + O_2 \longrightarrow 4NO_2$$

[CAUTION: Oxides of nitrogen attack rubber. Stoppers must be coated with paraffin and *small* sleeves of rubber tubing used to join glassware. As the gas is very poisonous, all work with it should be performed in a hood.]

A 500ml flask is fitted with a dropping funnel and an out-let tube that leads first into an empty wash bottle, thence into a U-tube packed with glass wool, finally into a second empty wash bottle, which is immersed in an ice-salt bath at −15°C or lower. Forty grams of arsenic trioxide are placed in the flask and 50ml of concentrated nitric acid (D—1.4) slowly dropped in while warming gently. When evolution of gas has ceased, a gentle air current (2 bubbles/sec) is passed through the liquefied gas until the color has become a pure yellow-brown. The gas may then be distilled into a sealing tube or ampoule by allowing the wash bottle to warm up in the air. The boiling point of nitrogen (IV) oxide is 22°C. The residue in the flask is reserved for the isolation of arsenic acid (No. 86).

Yield about 80% of theory

(II)

$$Pb(NO_3)_2 \longrightarrow 2NO_2 + PbO_2$$

Lead nitrate is finely powdered and dried for several days at 105–120°C. The salt is gently heated in a flask fitted with a stopper and outlet tube leading through a similar series of wash bottles and traps as in (I). The liquefied gas is treated with oxygen and isolated as above.

(III)

$$2NaNO_2 + H_2SO_4 \longrightarrow 2HNO_2 + Na_2SO_4$$
$$2HNO_2 \longrightarrow N_2O_3 + H_2O$$
$$(NO + NO_2)2N_2O_3 + O_2 \longrightarrow 4NO_2$$

Large quantities of nitrogen (IV) oxide are best prepared by allowing 20% sulfuric acid to drop slowly into 40% sodium nitrite solution contained in an evolution flask and treating the evolved gas mixture as previously described.

The gas exists as a colorless or very pale yellow dimer below 17°C and deepens in color as the temperature is raised, until at 64°C both forms exist at equilibrium in equal amounts.

$$2NO_2 \leftrightharpoons N_2O_4$$

Above 130°C nitrogen (IV) oxide slowly decomposes to nitrogen (II) oxide and oxygen:

$$2NO_2 \leftrightharpoons 2NO + O_2$$

The process is complete above 154°C.

References:
1. B:61; J:358.
2. ADDISON AND THOMPSON, *J. Chem. Soc.*, 1949:218.
3. GUYE AND DRUGNIN, *J. chim. phys.*, 8:489 (1910).
4. SCHEFFER AND TREUB, *Z. physik. Chem.*, 81:308 (1913).
5. BODENSTEIN, *Ibid.*, 100:68 (1922).

Chapter 3

SALTS

A. BINARY COMPOUNDS

10. Anhydrous Aluminum Bromide **

$$2Al + 3Br_2 \longrightarrow 2AlBr_3$$

The ideal vessel for this experiment is a 250ml tubulated retort with a wide neck (at least 15mm in diameter). However, a distilling flask of similar size with a delivery tube 15cm long and 15 mm in diameter sealed on its neck may be used as a substitute.

Sixty grams of bromine, previously dried with concentrated sulfuric acid are placed in a small dropping funnel with a long delivery tube. The neck of the funnel is protected with a drying tube.

Ten grams of aluminum (30-mesh or turnings) are placed in the vessel. The funnel is fitted into a rubber stopper covered with aluminum foil and adjusted so that the tip of the funnel is about 50mm from the bottom of the vessel.

The bromine is added, drop by drop, slowly (½–1 hour) so that the reaction mixture remains liquid. Towards the end of the addition gentle warming is needed. The pale-yellow fluid bromide is then distilled (b.p. 260–270°C) directly into a wide-necked four-ounce glass-stoppered bottle fitted on to the side-arm of the flask or retort with a wad of dry glass wool; m.p. 97°C, b.p. 255°C.

Yield = 52–55g

[CAUTION: The compound fumes in moist air and reacts violently with water. White crystals.]

14

COGNATE PREPARATIONS

10 a. Aluminum Chloride **

$$2Al + 6HCl \longrightarrow 2AlCl_3 + 3H_2$$

Ten grams of aluminum turnings are used for the retort or flask which is swept out thoroughly with dry hydrogen chloride. The receiving flask of the apparatus is fitted with an outlet tube connected to a calcium chloride drying tube to permit the escape of excess gas. The inlet tube for the hydrogen chloride should lead well into the reaction flask, and terminate about 2–3 inches from the surface of the metal. The vessel is heated gently in a steady stream of gas until white vapors start to form. The gas flow is then increased somewhat and the flame raised slightly until all the metal has reacted. After cooling, the gas inlet tube is *quickly* removed and replaced by a waxed stopper; the chloride is then sublimed into the receiver by means of a small flame, and it may be further purified by resublimation in dry nitrogen. The product is white and extremely hygroscopic; b.p. 180°C.

Yield about 40g

10 b. Aluminum Iodide ***

(I)

$$2Al + 3I_2 \longrightarrow 2AlI_3$$

Eighteen grams of iodine, heated to about 180°C are sublimed over 60g of aluminum granules (about 10 mesh) heated at 500–525°C *in vacuo* or a slow stream of nitrogen or carbon dioxide. Several types of apparatus have been suggested [2,3] (these may be used also for FeI_3 and SiI_4). The almost white product sublimes into the receivers; a large excess of metal is used to ensure complete use of the iodine.

Yield about 75% of theory based on the iodine used

(II) **

Five grams of pure aluminum are refluxed with 20g of dry iodine in 80ml of carbon tetrachloride until the iodine color has completely disappeared. The solvent is distilled off after filtering the reaction mixture to remove any excess metal and washing the residue with 25 ml of carbon disulfide. All operations must be carried out in the absence of moisture. The pale yellow to light brown residue (free iodine) is dried *in vacuo* at 100°C; m.p. 191°C; b.p. 382°C.

Yield about 90%

References:

1. J:371; I, vol. 3:30.
2. I, vol. 4:117.
3. GRUBITSCH, *Anorganisch-präparative Chemie*, 415, Springer Verlag, Vienna, 1950.
4. BILTZ AND VOIGT, *Z. anorg. Chem.*, 126:50 (1923).
5. BILTZ AND WEIN, *Ibid.*, 121:259 (1922).
6. KLEMM AND TILK, *Ibid.*, 176:15 (1928).
7. NESPITAL, *Z. physik. Chem.* (B), 16:164 (1932).
8. GUICHARD, *Compt. rend.*, 145:807 (1907).
9. For reviews on the preparation of metal halides see: I, vol. 4:104; for the dehydration of metal chloride hydrates with thionyl chloride, refer to: I, vol. 5:153.

11. Bismuth Iodide **

$$2Bi + 3I_2 \longrightarrow 2BiI_3$$

Eight grams of finely powdered metallic bismuth are thoroughly mixed with 13g of iodine in a mortar and the mixture is then introduced into a 50ml Kjeldhal flask without touching the neck. Upon gentle intermittent heating with a small flame, a little iodine sublimes and this is driven from the flask by the burner. The flask is now clamped horizontally and by continued heating of the reaction mass, the product sublimes into the long neck of the flask as a spangle of black-brown crystals. The iodide is transferred without delay to a small dry tared vial and well stoppered.

Yield = 15g

Bismuth iodide prepared by precipitation with iodide from solutions of acidified bismuth salts (No. 76, II) must be purified by sublimation, preferably in CO_2 or N_2.

References:

1. B:77i; I, vol. 4:114.
2. SCHNEIDER, J. prakt. Chem. (2), 50:463 (1894).
3. BIRKENBACH, Ber., 40:1404 (1907).
4. DÖNGES, Z. anorg. Chem., 263:112 (1950).

12. Boron Nitride *

(I)

$$Na_2B_4O_7 + 4NH_4Cl \longrightarrow 4BN + 2HCl + 2NaCl + 7H_2O$$

Ten grams of powdered sodium tetraborate 10-hydrate are heated in a nickel crucible with a Bunsen burner until dehydration is complete ($1/2$–$3/4$ hour), as indicated by the cessation of escaping steam.

The product is ground with 10g of ammonium chloride in a mortar and this mixture is heated in a nickel crucible for one-half hour over the full flame of a Meker burner. The product is cooled and pulverized and extracted three times with 1N hydrochloric acid. The residue is boiled with 100ml of distilled water, filtered, and the white powder dried at 100°C.

$$Yield = 0.3–0.5g$$

(II)

$$B_2O_3 + (NH_2)_2CO \longrightarrow 2BN + CO_2 + 2H_2O$$

Ten grams of finely powdered boric oxide are intimately ground with 20g of urea and heated in a covered nickel crucible for about 30 minutes over a Meker burner with *slowly* rising temperature to a bright red heat. The cooled mass is treated as in (I).

$$Yield = 2.5g$$

(III)

$$2H_3BO_3 \longrightarrow B_2O_3 + 3H_2O$$
$$B_2O_3 + 2NH_3 \longrightarrow 2BN + 3H_2O$$

Eighteen grams of well-ground boric acid are thoroughly mixed with 35g of pure calcium phosphate [$Ca_3(PO_4)_2$] and gently heated in a crucible until no more water vapor escapes. When cold, the mass is reground and placed in a clay crucible fitted with a finely perforated asbestos cover, through the center of which a clay tube about 8mm in diameter leads almost to the bottom of the crucible. A moderate stream of dry ammonia gas (about 3 bubbles/sec) is led into the mixture, which is then heated under the hood for 45 minutes at bright red heat over a Meker burner. The fusion residue is treated with 100ml of boiling water and stirred continuously while just enough concentrated hydrochloric acid is added from a separatory funnel to dissolve the calcium phosphate. The mixture should be *barely* acid at the end of the neutralization; about 60ml of acid are required. The residual product is washed by decantation with 0.5N hydrochloric acid until free of calcium and phosphate ions, then filtered and dried at 100°C.

$$Yield = 80-90\%$$

A few percent of boric oxide contaminate the product in all three procedures. For the production of pure boron nitride from either boron bromide [4] or boron chloride [5] and ammonia, the original literature should be consulted.

The product is only slowly hydrolyzed by hot water but dissolves in concentrated mineral acids to an appreciable extent; hot aqueous sodium carbonate causes slow decomposition to borate and ammonia.

References:
1. B:94.
2. DARMSTADT, *Ann.*, 151:256 (1869).
3. MOSER AND EIDMANN, *Ber.*, 35:536 (1902).
4. STOCK AND HOLLE, *Ibid.*, 41:2095 (1908).
5. MEYER AND ZAPPNER, *Ibid.*, 54:560 (1921).

13. Cadmium Iodide (Auto-complex—Cd[CdI₄]) *

$$Cd + I_2 \longrightarrow CdI_2$$

(I)

Eleven and two-tenths grams of finely powdered cadmium metal are used; or the latter is prepared by allowing three rods of pure zinc to stand for 24 hours in a solution of 0.1M of cadmium sulfate (21g of the anhydrous salt,

28g of the 4-hydrate or 26g of the 8/3-hydrate) in 100ml of water. The zinc rods are then removed and the spongy cadmium is purified by decantation with boiling water.

The cadmium is heated on the steam bath with 24g of iodine and 50ml water in a flask with a reflux condenser until the metal has dissolved (about two hours). The resulting solution is filtered, evaporated first on the steam bath in an open dish to remove excess iodine, and then finally to dryness in a vacuum desiccator. Almost colorless, lustrous plates are obtained.

$$\text{Yield} = 32\text{--}35\text{g}$$

(II)

$$Cd + 2HI \longrightarrow CdI_2 + H_2$$
$$CdCO_3 + 2HI \longrightarrow CdI_2 + CO_2 + H_2O$$
$$CdO + 2HI \longrightarrow CdI_2 + H_2O$$

Eleven and two-tenths grams of the metal, 17.2g of the carbonate, or 12.8g of the oxide are dissolved in 50–60ml of constant-boiling hydriodic acid. Procedure and yield are similar to those in (I).

Cadmium iodide is soluble in such organic solvents as alcohol, ether, and acetone. The salt may be formulated as cadmium (II) tetraiodocadmate (II) to explain this behavior.

Reference: B:148.

14. Anhydrous Chromium (III) Chloride **

(I)

$$Cr_2O_3 + 3CCl_4 \longrightarrow 2CrCl_3 + 3COCl_2$$

Fifteen grams of green chromic oxide (No. 7) are placed in the center of a combustion tube and the latter is placed in a tube oven with temperature control. The exit end of the tube should have an opening of at least 10mm to allow for escape of sublimed hexachloroethane, which is formed as a by-product. [CAUTION: The experiment must be conducted in a hood because vapors of phosgene are poisonous.]

Fifty milliliters of carbon tetrachloride are placed in a

distilling flask fitted with an inlet for carbon dioxide. The side arm of the flask is attached to the combustion tube. A slow stream of CO_2 is passed through the CCl_4, warmed to 50°C in a water bath, and the oven is heated to 450°C. At the end of about two hours, when all the carbon tetrachloride has disappeared, the tube is cooled in the inert atmosphere and the violet scales of product are collected.

Yield almost quantitative

(II)

$$2Cr + 3Cl_2 \longrightarrow 2CrCl_3$$

The apparatus described in (I) is used, employing 10g of pea-size lumps of chromium (No. 2) and chlorine gas from a generator or cylinder. The tube must be both heated and cooled in an atmosphere of chlorine at the beginning and end of the experiment. The temperature of the oven, the time of heating, and the yield are similar to those in (I).

To clean the combustion tube, stopper it at one end, clamp it vertically, fill it with dilute hydrochloric acid and a few pieces of zinc, and allow it to stand overnight.

(III)

$$CrCl_3 \cdot 6H_2O + 6SOCl_2 \longrightarrow CrCl_3 + 6SO_2 + 12HCl$$

Twenty grams of powdered green chromic chloride are placed in a small round-bottomed flask and 50ml of freshly-distilled thionyl chloride are added. When evolution of gas has ceased, the mixture is refluxed for two hours, the excess liquid evaporated off *in vacuo*, and the product stored in a vacuum desiccator over pellets of solid alkali for at least 12 hours.

Yield almost quantitative

The product obtained by (III) is hygroscopic and water-soluble, in contrast to the material from (I) and (II). It is light violet in color, and it must be kept out of contact with atmospheric moisture.

COGNATE PREPARATIONS

14 a. Chromium (III) Bromide **

(I)

$$Cr_2O_3 + 3C + 3Br_2 \longrightarrow 2CrBr_3 + 3CO$$

Fifteen grams of chromium (III) oxide (No. 7) and 6g of charcoal are ground together with just enough starch paste to yield a very viscous plastic mass. The starch paste may be prepared by boiling 100ml of water with about 10g of soluble starch until no more dissolves, decanting the solution from any undissolved material and allowing it to cool. The oxide-carbon mass is shaped into pellets 5–10mm in diameter and dried thoroughly at 100°C.

The brittle pellets are placed in an open combustion tube and heated for one hour at 500°C in a circular oven. The apparatus described in (I) under chromium chloride is used when the ignition is complete, except that 25ml of bromine (unwarmed) is substituted for the carbon tetrachloride, and the exit end of the combustion tube is fitted with a wide-mouth receiver that carries an outlet tube for the carbon dioxide. The reaction is maintained at 600–700°C until all the bromine has been volatilized; the dark olive-green scale of product partially sublimes into the cooler end of the tube and receiver in almost quantitative yield.

(II)

$$2Cr + 3Br_2 \longrightarrow 2CrBr_3$$

Method (II) for chromium chloride (No. 14) is used, employing 10g of chromium (No. 2) and 25ml of bromine as in (I), using the modified apparatus heated to 650°C. The yield is the same.

14 b. Chromium Iodide ***

$$2Cr + 3I_2 \longrightarrow 2CrI_3$$

Three grams of powdered high-purity chromium and 30g of iodine are used in an apparatus similar to that used for

aluminum iodide (see No. 10(b)). The metal is heated to
475°C during the reaction and the excess iodine is removed
from the black product by heating to 100°C. The yield is
virtually quantitative.

The anhydrous chromium (III) halides are almost unattacked by water; in the presence of a strong reducing
agent they dissolve rapidly. They serve as starting materials for a variety of coordination complexes.

References:
1. B:77d; I, vol. 2:193; *Ibid.*, vol. 5:153.
2. MOISSAN, *Ann. chim. phys.* (5), 25:408 (1882).
3. HANDY AND GREGORY, *J. Am. Chem. Soc.*, 72:5049 (1950).

15. Chromium Nitride **

$$CrCl_3 + 4NH_3 \longrightarrow CrN + 3NH_4Cl$$

Five grams of anhydrous chromium (III) chloride (No.
14) are placed in a combustion tube which is left completely
open at the exit end to allow the escape of the sublimed
ammonium chloride that forms. [Hood.]

The tube is set in a circular oven and a steady current of
dry ammonia (dried with lime) from a generator or cylinder is led in over the chloride. The oven temperature is
raised slowly to 450–500°C and held there until no more
fumes of ammonium chloride escape. After cooling, the
product is powdered in a mortar and re-ignited in ammonia
as described. Yield nearly theoretical. To remove traces of
unreacted chromium (III) chloride, the black product is
treated with 50ml of 3N hydrochloric acid and one-half
gram of granulated tin in the cold for about 15 minutes. The
excess tin is removed, the product washed well with water,
suction-filtered, and dried at 105°–120°. The nitride is hydrolyzed slowly by hot aqueous alkali.

References:
1. B:96.
2. BAUR AND VOERMANN, *Z. physik. Chem.*, 52:473 (1905).

16. Copper (I) Hydride *

$$2CuSO_4 + 3H_3PO_2 + 3H_2O \longrightarrow 2CuH + 3H_3PO_3 + 2H_2SO_4$$

Sixteen grams of copper sulfate 5-hydrate are dissolved

in 60ml of water and this solution is mixed with 20g of 50% hypophosphorous acid (or 30g of 30% concentration) in 400ml of water, and allowed to stand in a bath maintained at 30°–35°C for at least six hours. The red-brown product is filtered by suction (some material clings tenaciously to the reaction vessel as a shiny film), washed with water, and dried *in vacuo*.

$$Yield = 3.5–4g$$

The hypophosphorous acid may also be prepared by dissolving 15g of barium hypophosphite monohydrate in 400ml water, adding three milliliters of concentrated sulfuric acid and filtering off the barium sulfate to give a clear liquid. Twelve grams of sodium hypophosphite monohydrate in 400ml water and one milliliter of acid form an alternative solution suitable for use. The hydride decomposes to metallic copper and hydrogen on gentle heating.

Reference: B:65.

17. Recrystallized Lead Iodide *

$$Pb(NO_3)_2 + 2KI \longrightarrow PbI_2 + 2KNO_3$$

About ten grams of lead iodide are prepared by double decomposition from the requisite amounts of lead nitrate and potassium iodide (in slight excess) in a total of 200ml of water, filtered, and dried in the oven at 100°C.

Eight grams of the crude yellow product are added to two liters of boiling distilled water. The resulting solution must be kept at the boiling point throughout the subsequent filtration to avoid loss of product. The liquid is filtered through a large pleated filter paper which is placed in a funnel heated by a boiling water jacket. The combined filtrates are allowed to crystallize (preferably in ice overnight), then they are filtered and dried. The product has the appearance of shimmering gold flakes. The per-cent recovery from the starting material is calculated.

Lead (II) chloride and bromide may be recrystallized similarly, taking into account their solubilities at varying temperatures.

SOLUBILITY OF LEAD HALIDES

Salt	Grams per 100ml of water		
	0°C	20°C	100°C
Chloride	0.67	0.99	3.34
Bromide	0.46	0.84	4.71
Iodide	0.044	0.063	0.41

18. Green Manganese (II) Sulfide **

$$MnSO_4 + (NH_4)_2S \longrightarrow MnS + (NH_4)_2SO_4$$

Twenty grams of manganese (II) sulfate 4-hydrate are dissolved in 600ml of boiling water in a one-liter beaker. A steady current of dry steam is passed through the boiling solution and 150ml of ammonium sulfide solution (prepared by saturating 75ml of concentrated ammonia with hydrogen sulfide and mixing with 75ml of ammonia) are added *in one portion*. When the precipitate, which settles well, has turned a dark olive-green, it is washed by decantation with five 100–200ml portions of boiling water saturated with hydrogen sulfide. During each washing the precipitate is thoroughly agitated in the wash liquor by the current of steam. Traces of brown manganese oxides are formed during the process but these float on the surface of the water and are easily poured off.

The product is filtered on a large suction funnel, washed with alcohol and dried *in vacuo*.

$$Yield = 7.5g$$

Reference: B:89.

19. Sublimed Mercury (II) Iodide *

$$HgCl_2 + 2KI \longrightarrow HgI_2 + 2KCl$$

A solution of 13.5g of mercuric chloride in 150ml of water is mixed with one of 16.6g of potassium iodide in 200ml of water. The red mercuric iodide is suction-filtered, washed well with 100ml of water, and dried in a desiccator.

The dry material (about 22.5g) is placed in a 4-inch evaporating dish, embedded about three-quarters of its height in a sand bath, and covered with a 5-inch Petri dish (or watch glass). On heating the bath, the iodide sublimes as yellow vapors [CAUTION: poisonous!] which condense on the cover as a mixture of red and yellow prisms up to 2cm long. The product is removed by periodically changing the Petri dish or watch glass. Finally only a slight grayish residue of impurities remains behind.

$$Yield = 21\text{--}22g$$

The yellow modification of the product changes slowly to the red one; the process is hastened by scratching or tapping the crystals.

20. Red Mercury (II) Sulfide *

(I)

$$Hg(C_2H_3O_2)_2 + H_2S + NH_4SCN \longrightarrow Hg(HS)SCN + NH_4C_2H_3O_2 + HC_2H_3O_2$$
$$Hg(HS)SCN \longrightarrow HgS + HCN \text{ (partial equation)}$$

Thirty-five grams of mercuric acetate and 25g of ammonium thiocyanate are dissolved in 100ml of hot glacial acetic acid. A steady stream of hydrogen sulfide is passed into the solution until precipitation is complete and then the acetic acid is slowly evaporated with frequent stirring in an air bath. [CAUTION: In hood; hydrogen cyanide is evolved!] The initially black material turns slowly red as the acid boils away. To prevent the formation of a discolored product, overheating must be avoided and stirring must be maintained constantly in the final stages of the evaporation.

When all the acid has been removed, the material is cooled and 200ml of distilled water are added. The product is suction-filtered, washed with 95% alcohol, and then dried at 100°C.

$$Yield = 25g$$

(II)

$$HgS \text{ (black)} \xrightarrow[\text{(NH}_4)_2S]{\text{KOH}} HgS \text{ (red)}$$

From 13.5g of mercuric chloride in 200ml of hot water, black mercuric sulfide is precipitated completely by hydrogen sulfide. The residue is washed by decantation with boiling water until the rinsings are no longer acid. The sulfide is drained well, then 10ml of saturated ammonium sulfide solution and 12g of 20% potassium hydroxide are added to it. The mixture is transferred to a 50ml Erlenmeyer flask, stirred well, and the flask is placed in an oven at 50°C for one week, replacing the evaporated water and agitating the reaction vessel daily. At the end of this time the color should be bright red. The cinnabar is washed and isolated as in (I).

$$Yield = 11.5g$$

References:

1. B:88; I, vol. 1:19.
2. ALLEN, CRENSHAW, AND MERWIN, Am. Jour. Sci. (4), 34:351 (1912).
3. WEISER, The Colloidal Salts, pp. 94–96, 118–119, McGraw-Hill, New York, 1928.

21. Rubidium Triiodide *

$$Rb_2CO_3 + 2HI \longrightarrow 2RbI + CO_2 + H_2O$$
$$RbI + I_2 \longrightarrow RbI_3$$

A solution of 1.5g of rubidium carbonate is neutralized with pure 57% hydriodic acid (No. 89), avoiding an excess of acid. The solution is warmed to 60°C and 2.5g of pure iodine is dissolved in it by stirring. The mixture is allowed to cool and evaporated in the air to dryness.

$$Yield\ theoretical = (4.5g)$$

If desired, the salt may be recrystallized by dissolving in a little water at 60°C, suction-filtering, and drying in vacuo.

COGNATE PREPARATION

21 a. Cesium Triiodide *

The cesium salt, which is considerably less soluble than the rubidium compound, can be prepared similarly, using 1.9g of cesium carbonate as the starting material. The bulk of the cesium triiodide crystallizes when the initial solution is cooled in ice, and the mother liquor is worked up for further crops of crystals to give an almost theoretical yield = (5g).

Both salts are rhombic black crystals.

Reference: B:111.

22. Sodium Azide **

(I)

$$C_4H_9NO_2 + N_2H_4 + NaOH \longrightarrow NaN_3 + C_4H_9OH + 2H_2O$$

Forty to forty-three grams of sodium hydroxide are dissolved in 500ml of absolute alcohol by warming. The solution is cooled and either filtered through a sintered glass funnel or decanted to remove insoluble impurities. To the clear filtrate in a one-liter flask fitted with a reflux condenser (a ground-glass type is preferable) are added 60g of 85% hydrazine hydrate. The mixture is warmed gently on a steam bath and then 15g of freshly distilled n-butyl nitrite [1] are added through the condenser. The steam bath is removed and then 110g more of the ester are added as before at such a rate that spontaneous refluxing is maintained. The product precipitates during the procedure. To ensure completion of the reaction the flask and contents are heated on the steam bath 15–30 minutes after the addition. After cooling in ice, the product is suction-filtered and washed, first with four 25ml portions of ice-cold absolute alcohol, then with two similar volumes of ether. The white salt is dried in warm air.

Yield = 50–55g

(II)

$$2Na + 2NH_3 \longrightarrow 2NaNH_2 + H_2$$
$$2NaNH_2 + N_2O \longrightarrow NaN_3 + NaOH + NH_3$$
$$2NaN_3 + H_2SO_4 \longrightarrow 2HN_3 + Na_2SO_4$$

One and one-half grams of clean sodium are placed in a boat and inserted into a combustion tube mounted in a circular furnace. Bone-dry ammonia is passed through the apparatus which is heated to 350°C and maintained at this temperature for one-half hour. The tube is cooled in an atmosphere of ammonia. Nitrous oxide (either from a cylinder or from 20g of ammonium nitrate by gentle heating) which has been carefully dried by passage through two soda-lime and two sodium hydroxide U-tubes in series, is passed over the sodium amide at 190°C until vapors of ammonia are no longer evolved. If ammonium nitrate is used as the source of the gas, it is necessary to insert a vertical water-cooled condenser between the generator and the first drying tube to remove most of the water formed.

$$NH_4NO_3 \longrightarrow N_2O + 2H_2O$$

The sodium azide, mixed with the alkali, is dissolved in 20ml of water contained in a 50ml distilling flask which is fitted with a condenser and a dropping funnel. The condenser leads into a small filter flask containing 10ml of water. The solution is heated to the boiling point so that distillation just begins and then 15ml of 40% sulfuric acid are added drop by drop from the funnel. The distillation is continued until about five ml of liquid remain in the flask.

One milliliter of the aqueous distillate of hydrazoic acid is reserved and the remainder is exactly neutralized with $1N$ sodium hydroxide. The solution is evaporated to crystallization on the steam bath, then cooled, and the reserved hydrazoic acid is added to it. A volume of 95% ethanol double the volume of the contents of the dish is added to precipitate the sodium azide, the mixture is cooled in ice until no more crystals settle out, then suction-filtered, washed with ether and finally dried *in vacuo*.

Yield = 1.5–1.8g

COGNATE PREPARATIONS

22 a. Potassium azide may be prepared similarly using 65–70g of potassium hydroxide (85% purity).

Yield = 63–69g (Purity = 99%)

22 b. Ammonium azide is prepared by subliming an intimate mixture of 2g of dry sodium azide and 2.5g of dry ammonium nitrate at 190°C in a dry atmosphere for 40 minutes.

$$Yield = 1.5g$$

References:
1. A. VOGEL, *Practical Organic Chemistry*, p. 306, 3d ed., Longmans Green, London, 1957.
2. Org. Syntheses, coll. vol. 2:108 (1943).
3. B:112; J:367; I, vol. 1:77ff; *Ibid.*, vol. 2:136ff.
4. FRIERSON AND BROWNE, *J. Am. Chem. Soc.*, 56:2384 (1934).
5. DENNIS AND BROWNE, *Ibid.*, 26:577 (1904).

B. COMPOUND ANION

23. Ammonium Fluoroborate *

(I)

$$8NH_4F + 2H_3BO_3 + 3H_2SO_4 \longrightarrow 2NH_4BF_4 + 3(NH_4)_2SO_4 + 6H_2O$$

Sixty milliliters of concentrated sulfuric acid are mixed with 100 ml of water in an ordinary beaker and 24g of boric acid are dissolved in the warm solution by further heating. The solution is cooled slightly and then 60g of ammonium fluoride are added to the liquid in small portions with continuous stirring. Mechanical stirring is preferable. No appreciable amounts of hydrogen fluoride should be lost through volatilization during the addition. When all the fluoride has been added, the reaction is completed by heating for one-half hour on the steam bath, cooling in ice, filtering by suction, and draining well. The product is washed with about 50ml of acetone to remove acid.

$$Yield = 38-40g$$

The crude salt is generally satisfactory for most purposes, but it may be purified by dissolving it in 50ml of hot water containing 4ml of concentrated ammonia, heating to precipitate any silica, then filtering and evaporating.

(II)

$$2NH_4HF_2 + H_3BO_3 \longrightarrow NH_4BF_4 + NH_3 + 3H_2O$$

Thirty-one grams of boric acid are weighed into a 250ml beaker and covered with 57g of ammonium hydrogen fluoride. The mixture is stirred at room temperature until a clear liquid is obtained and then heated slowly on a hot plate or low flame. Slight gas evolution begins at 105°C and is fairly vigorous at 110°C. The mixture is maintained at 115–120°C stirring constantly with a thermometer. When the residue begins to solidify the thermometer is replaced with a clean iron rod. Stirring is continued until the opalescent product turns white and scarcely clings to the rod any longer. The temperature is about 125°C at the end of the reaction. The product is transferred to a watch glass and the remaining ammonia and water is driven off by heating in an oven at 140°C.

$$\text{Yield} = 52g$$

The product is recrystallized from 75ml of water and 6ml of ammonia as in (I).

COGNATE PREPARATIONS
23 a. Potassium Fluoroborate *

$$2H_3BO_3 + 8HF + K_2CO_3 \longrightarrow 2KBF_4 + CO_2 + 7H_2O$$

Under the hood, 6.2g of boric acid are dissolved in 25g of ice-cold 40% hydrofluoric acid (prepared by mixing 80ml of 50% acid with 20ml of water) in a plastic vessel, and the solution of fluoroboric acid is allowed to stand for 6 hours at room temperature to complete formation of the complex acid. The latter is then recooled and 6.9g of anhydrous potassium carbonate (or the equivalent amount of the bicarbonate or hydroxide) is added in small portions; much frothing accompanies the addition. The product precipitates immediately; the quantity of product suspended in water is deceptive, as many highly fluorinated salts have indices of refraction close to that of water itself. After being cooled in ice, the seemingly opalescent solution gives a 90% yield of white product which is dried *in vacuo*.

Potassium fluoroborate is also produced by dissolving 10g ammonium salt in ten times its weight of water and precipitating with 10g of potassium chloride in 40ml of water.

23 b. Sodium Fluoroborate is prepared similarly, using 5.3g of anhydrous sodium carbonate or its equivalent.

References:
1. I, vol. 2:23; P:208.
2. VORLANDER AND HOLLATZ, Ber., 65:535 (1932).
3. BALZ AND WILKE-DORFURT, Z. anorg. Chem., 159:197 (1927).

24. Ammonium Pentasulfide *

$$NH_3 + H_2S \longrightarrow NH_4HS$$
$$NH_4HS + NH_3 \longrightarrow (NH_4)_2S$$
$$(NH_4)_2S + 4S \longrightarrow (NH_4)_2S_5$$

Twenty-five milliliters of concentrated ammonia are saturated with hydrogen sulfide gas while cooling in ice. When no more gas is absorbed 25ml more of the ammonia water is added. The ammonium sulfide solution is warmed to about 35°C and then 25g of finely powdered roll sulfur are stirred in. When no more dissolves (½–1 hour), the yellow solution is filtered into 60ml of 95% alcohol and allowed to stand in a stoppered flask overnight in the refrigerator. The crystals are filtered by suction and washed with alcohol and ether. They are dried *in vacuo* over lime covered with a very small amount of solid ammonium chloride.

$$\text{Yield} = 40g$$

The product decomposes on long standing, especially in air, with the deposition of sulfur.

References:
1. B:106.
2. MILLS AND ROBINSON, J. Chem. Soc., 1928:2326.

25. Ammonium Tetrathiocuprate (II)

$$2NH_3 + H_2S \longrightarrow 2NH_4HS$$
$$2NH_4HS + CuSO_4 + 2S \longrightarrow (NH_4)_2CuS_4 + H_2SO_4$$

A mixture of 200 ml of concentrated ammonia and 50ml water is saturated with hydrogen sulfide while cooling in water. One-half of this solution is warmed to 40°C and 60g of finely powdered sulfur is added. When no more dissolves, the dark suspension is rapidly filtered into the remaining half of the original solution. A solution of 20g of copper sulfate 5-hydrate in 200ml water is added slowly through a dropping funnel while swirling the ammonium polysulphide mixture. As soon as a permanent precipitate of black copper sulfide forms, the addition is discontinued and the mixture is filtered immediately through a pleated paper into a flask. The latter should be almost completely filled with liquid. After the vessel and contents have been allowed to stand on ice overnight, the slurry is suction-filtered and the filtrate is reserved. The red crystals are washed with water or 95% alcohol and dried *in vacuo*. Then the filtrate is treated with copper sulfate as before, and the product is isolated again.

$$\text{Total Yield} = 25g$$

The salt dissolves in dilute alkali but is only slowly attacked by concentrated acids. When a fresh solution of the salt in $2N$ potassium hydroxide is treated with concentrated (30%) KOH, red potassium tetrathiocuprate (II) is precipitated.

References:
1. B:139.
2. BILTZ AND HARMS, *Ber.*, 40:976 (1907).

26. Antimony (III) Sulfate *

$$2Sb + 6H_2SO_4 \longrightarrow Sb_2(SO_4)_3 + 3SO_2 + 6H_2O$$

Twenty grams of finely powdered antimony (No. 1) are added in small portions to 200ml of hot concentrated sulfuric acid under the hood and the mixture is heated until all the metal has dissolved. The solution is allowed to cool thoroughly and is suction-filtered through a fritted glass funnel. The needle-like product is rapidly washed with two-40ml portions of glacial acetic acid, then with 50ml of ether. It is then transferred without delay to a vacuum desiccator and dried for one or two days over solid alkali.

$$\text{Yield} = 43g \quad (\text{Theory} = 44g)$$

The white material hydrolyzes instantly on contact with water or moist air to give basic products.

References:
1. B:130.
2. METZL, *Z. anorg. Chem.*, 48:143 (1906).

27. Barium Ferrate (VI) *

$$Fe + 2KNO_3 \longrightarrow K_2FeO_4 + 2NO$$
$$K_2FeO_4 + BaCl_2 \longrightarrow BaFeO_4 + 2KCl$$

Ten grams of iron powder (*not* filings) are ground in a mortar with 20g of dry potassium nitrate. The mixture is placed in a 125ml Erlenmeyer flask clamped at an angle in the hood. When heated with a small flame the mass becomes incandescent, giving off a shower of sparks and white fumes. The cold residue is rapidly extracted three times with 20ml portions of ice-cold water, all of which are immediately filtered through an asbestos mat in a Gooch crucible into 50ml of a 20% solution of barium chloride. After one hour, the red precipitate is filtered by suction through a hardened paper, washed with 95% alcohol and with ether, and then dried *in vacuo*.

$$Yield = 1.0g$$

The potassium salt is best prepared by the action of chlorine on ferric hydroxide in basic medium.

$$3NaOCl + 2Fe(OH)_3 + 4KOH \longrightarrow 2K_2FeO_4 + 3NaCl + 5H_2O$$

The ferrates are unstable in acids and have greater oxidizing power than do the permanganates.

References:
1. B:126; J:363.
2. I, vol. 4:164.
3. THOMPSON, OCKERMAN AND SCHREYER, *J. Am. Chem. Soc.*, 73:1379 (1951).

28. Barium Hypophosphite 1-Hydrate **

$$8P + 3Ba(OH)_2 + 6H_2O \longrightarrow 3Ba(H_2PO_2)_2 + 2PH_3$$

[CAUTION: The phosphine gas evolved in this reaction is a deadly poison. Use a well-ventilated hood.]

A 500ml round-bottomed flask is fitted with an inlet tube for nitrogen and an exit delivery tube leading into a dish of water. Twenty grams of barium hydroxide 8-hydrate, 5g of yellow phosphorus, and 200 ml of water are placed in the flask and a steady stream of nitrogen is led in to displace the air. The mixture in the flask is raised just to the boiling point and the flow of nitrogen is turned down to about 2 bubbles/sec. The start of the reaction is indicated by the evolution of white vortex rings of phosphoric acid, caused by the combustion of the phosphine above the surface of the water at the delivery tube. The temperature of the reaction mixture is maintained until the phosphorus has disappeared and no more phosphine is evolved (about 3–4 hours). A stream of carbon dioxide is led into the hot solution for 15–30 minutes to precipitate excess barium hydroxide. The solution is then filtered and evaporated on the steam bath to crystallization. After cooling and filtering, several more crops of crystals are obtained from the mother liquor. The product is dried in air.

$$\text{Total yield} = 7\text{--}10\text{g}$$

The slightly deliquescent sodium (1-hydrate) and anhydrous potassium salts are readily obtained by metathesis of the barium salt in hot water with the requisite amounts of sodium or potassium sulfate, removal of the barium sulfate that forms, and evaporation of the filtrate.

References:

1. B:135; J:361.
2. DULONG, *Ann. chim. phys.*, 2:141 (1816).
3. ROSE, *Pogg. Ann.*, 9:370 (1827).

29. Barium Nitrite 1-Hydrate **

$$Pb(C_2H_3O_2)_2 + Mg \longrightarrow Pb + Mg(C_2H_3O_2)_2$$
$$Ba(NO_3)_2 + 2Pb \longrightarrow Ba(NO_2)_2 + 2PbO$$

Fifty grams of lead (II) acetate are dissolved in 200ml of hot water and 5ml of glacial acetic acid and cooled to 40–50°C. Then 3.5g of magnesium ribbon is introduced in coils, each about one foot long. The temperature range is maintained by heating on the steam bath until no more gas is evolved (about one-half hour) and the ribbon is kept completely immersed by means of a bent glass rod resting lightly on the metal. To avoid compacting the lead sponge, the reaction mixture should not be shaken. Now the supernatant liquid is decanted and the sponge washed gently several times by decantation with hot water.

A solution of 10g of barium nitrate in 100ml of warm water is poured over the lead and the mixture is gently boiled for 1½–2 hours. A watch glass is used as a cover to keep the volume constant. The lead (I) oxide is cooled and filtered off. It is then washed with 10ml of cold water, and carbon dioxide is passed into the reheated filtrate for 5–10 minutes to precipitate a small amount of lead and barium carbonates. The solution is cooled and refiltered. The filtrate is then concentrated, first over a flame to 40ml, and finally on the steam bath to a pale yellow sirup which solidifies almost completely on cooling. The residue is triturated with 25ml of acetone and suction-filtered. The crystals are then digested for one-half hour under reflux with 120ml of 95% alcohol and 30 ml of water, filtered hot, and evaporated. Two crops of crystals are collected, washed with acetone, and dried over calcium chloride.

$$\text{Yield} = 6\text{--}7g$$

The nitrite is slightly deliquescent and should be kept in tightly sealed containers.

NOTE: If 32g of powdered lead are used in place of the prepared sponge, the yield is cut to 1g even after 24 hours of boiling.

References:
1. P:288.
2. ARNOLT, Z. anorg. Chem., 27:341 (1901).

30. Barium Permanganate ***

(I)

$$2MnO_2 + 2Ba(OH)_2 + O_2 \longrightarrow 2BaMnO_4 + 2H_2O$$
$$2BaMnO_4 + Cl_2 \longrightarrow Ba(MnO_4)_2 + BaCl_2$$

Forty grams of manganese dioxide are ground in a large mortar with 42g of barium nitrate and 125g of anhydrous barium hydroxide. The mixture is heated gently at first in an iron dish over a burner and then, with rising temperature, is fused to a dry green mass while being stirred with an iron rod. The material is chopped out of the dish and finely pulverized in a mortar. It is then stirred into one liter of boiling water, kept at 100°C, for five minutes, and suction-filtered hot. The filtrate containing excess soluble barium salts is discarded and the moist cake of barium manganate is suspended in 300ml of water.

As carbon dioxide decomposes the green manganate only very slowly in water, even at 100°C chlorine must be used for the oxidation.

The suspension is heated to 60°C and chlorine is passed in for one-half hour. Five grams of Celite are added and the purple solution is suction-filtered through fritted glass or asbestos. The clear filtrate is evaporated to crystallization on the steam bath and several crops of barium chloride are removed in this way. These should be washed with a very small amount of ice water and the washings added to the mother liquor which is finally evaporated to dryness.

The crude residue is a mixture of barium permanganate with barium chloride and it must be analyzed as follows:

One hundred and fifty milligrams of the product are dried at 105–120°C, weighed out to the nearest 0.001g, dissolved in 250ml of water at 85°C, and 10ml of $9M$ sulfuric acid are then added. The solution is titrated hot with $N/10$ standard sodium oxalate to the disappearance of the permanganate color.

1ml of $N/10$ sodium oxalate = 0.00375g of $Ba(MnO_4)_2$

After the percentage of barium chloride in the crude product has been determined by difference, it may be removed by metathesis with silver sulfate in calculated amount.

$$Ag_2SO_4 + BaCl_2 \longrightarrow BaSO_4 + 2AgCl$$

The impure material is digested in 250ml water with the required amount of Ag_2SO_4 at 60°C until the precipitate appears well settled (about 1 hour). After being cooled, filtered through asbestos, and evaporated, the clear filtrate is evaporated to dryness on the steam bath. It is placed in a dessicator to remove final traces of moisture. The yield is variable, depending on the purity of the MnO_2 and the success of the oxidative fusion, but it should be 30–50g.

(II)

$$4KMnO_4 + 2Ba(OH)_2 + 2Ba(NO_3)_2 \longrightarrow 4BaMnO_4 + 4KNO_3 + O_2 + 2H_2O$$

A mixture of 50g of potassium permanganate and 50g of barium nitrate in 500ml of distilled water is heated with efficient mechanical stirring. A 1-liter Erlenmeyer flask is used to allow for subsequent frothing. When the temperature of the solution reaches about 95°C, 100g of barium hydroxide 8-hydrate are added in small portions over a period of 15 minutes. Heating and stirring are maintained throughout the addition. The solution is now boiled with vigorous stirring for two to three hours longer; water is added periodically to keep the volume constant. The hot liquid should have only a relatively faint purple color at this point.

The mixture is filtered hot by suction through hardened paper and any purple-black product remaining in the reaction flask is transferred to the suction funnel with hot water. After washing with about 200ml more of hot water, the solid is drained well and dried at 100°C. The product is then used further as indicated in (I).

Yield = 84g (contaminated with a little barium carbonate)

COGNATE PREPARATIONS

30 a. Potassium Manganate (VI) **

$$2KMnO_4 + 2KOH \longrightarrow 2K_2MnO_4 + \frac{1}{2}O_2 + H_2O$$

Ten grams of powdered potassium permanganate are added to a solution of 10g of potassium hydroxide in 10 ml of water contained in a small evaporating dish. The mixture is now cautiously heated on a hot plate or a tiny flame and stirred *constantly* with a thermometer. It is advisable to mount an inverted powder funnel over the vessel during heating to minimize the possibility of accidental spurting and contamination by dust (to form MnO_2); the thermometer is placed in the neck of the funnel for stirring.

The temperature of the mixture is maintained in the range of 120–140°C until the purple color has changed to a pure deep green, as judged by drawing a drop up the side of the dish with the thermometer; the reaction requires 10–15 minutes. During the heating, the product separates as a black, coarse solid; the careful addition of a few milliliters of water may be required within the reaction period if evaporation has been excessive.

The contents of the beaker are cooled and a cold solution of 10g of potassium hydroxide in 10ml of water is stirred in; then the mixture is cooled thoroughly in an ice-salt bath to 0°C. After standing for 15 minutes, the product is filtered off through a hardened paper, a sintered glass funnel, or a Gooch crucible with asbestos mat. The crystals are thoroughly drained free of mother liquor and then spread on a porous plate in a vacuum desiccator over solid alkali to dry. The material, which is deliquescent, should be preserved in a tightly sealed vessel.

$$\text{Yield} = 12g$$

References:
1. RETGERS, Z. physik. Chem., 8:6 (1891).
2. AUGER, Compt. rend., 151:69 (1910).
3. P:485.
4. SHOLDER AND WATERSTRADT, Z. anorg. Chem., 277:172 (1954).

30 b. Sodium Manganate (V) X-hydrate ***

$$2KMnO_4 + 2Na_2SO_3 + 4NaOH \longrightarrow 2Na_3MnO_4 + Na_2SO_4 + K_2SO_4 + 2H_2O$$

Two grams of very finely powdered potassium permanganate are added to 50ml of a 30% (by weight) solution of sodium hydroxide at 0°C. Three and one-half grams of finely divided sodium sulfite 7-hydrate (or 1.8g of the anhydrous salt) are stirred in and the mixture agitated at 0°C for 10 minutes. The purple liquid turns blue and the similarly colored product separates during this time. The crystals are suction-filtered and washed with 15ml of 30% of ice-cold sodium hydroxide, then dried rapidly on a porous plate *in vacuo* over alkali. It is best to store the material in a dry, well-sealed, non-vitreous vessel, out of contact with heat and moisture. Nevertheless, decomposition sets in after a short time, especially if traces of water are present, according to the following disproportionation:

$$2Na_3MnO_4 + 2H_2O \longrightarrow Na_2MnO_4 + MnO_2 + 4NaOH$$

References:
1. LUX, Z. Naturforsch., 1:281 (1946).
2. SHOLDER et al., Z. anorg. Chem., 277:236 (1954).

30 c. Ammonium Permanganate *

$$KMnO_4 + NH_4Cl \longrightarrow NH_4MnO_4 + KCl$$

A solution of 16g of potassium permanganate and 44g of ammonium chloride in 300ml of water at 70°C is filtered through asbestos to remove traces of manganese (IV) oxide and evaporated on the steam bath to a volume of 200ml. The hot solution is re-filtered as before and cooled to 5°C in an ice bath.

The felted needles of product are drained thoroughly in a sintered-glass suction funnel and dried *in vacuo*.

$$Yield = 11g$$

The crude product may be recrystallized from water at 60–70°C.

31. Barium Sulfamate 2-Hydrate *

$$Ba(OH)_2 + 2H_2NSO_3H \longrightarrow Ba(O_3SNH_2)_2 + 2H_2O$$

To 33.2g of pure (recrystallized) sulfamic acid (No. 92) in 250ml of water are added 54.0g of pure barium hydroxide 8-hydrate. When all the solids have dissolved, any precipitate of barium sulfate is filtered off and the clear filtrate evaporated *in vacuo* at room temperature with the water pump. Successive crops of crystals are isolated, washed with 95% alcohol and the mother liquor with rinsings is further evaporated. Depending on the completeness of the water removal, yields of over 90% are readily attained.

$$(Theoretical\ Yield = 62g)$$

COGNATE PREPARATIONS

31 a. Cobalt Sulfamate 2-Hydrate *

Ten grams of sulfamic acid are dissolved in 100ml of warm water and cobalt carbonate is added in small portions until no more dissolves with evolution of carbon dioxide. The solution is filtered by suction, two crystals of the acid are added, and the mixture is evaporated to a pink oil on the steam bath. After cooling, the residue is triturated with acetone until solid.

Yield theoretical (based on the acid)

Both the **copper** and **nickel sulfamates** (2-hydrates) are obtained by similar procedures and in comparable yield. The only losses are mechanical. The salts are respectively blue and green in color. Both the cobalt and the nickel salts dissolve in 95% alcohol but the copper compound does not.

Reference: P:145.

32. Barium Trithiocarbonate *

$$Ba(OH)_2 + 2H_2S \longrightarrow Ba(HS)_2 + 2H_2O$$
$$Ba(HS)_2 + Ba(OH)_2 \longrightarrow 2BaS + 2H_2O$$
$$BaS + CS_2 \longrightarrow BaCS_3$$

Sixteen grams of barium hydroxide 8-hydrate are dissolved in 50ml of hot water and *saturated* with hydrogen sulfide. The pH of the resulting solution should be about 8 and the odor of the gas should persist even after it is well shaken. A clear solution of 16g more of baryta solution is mixed with the first and cooled to give normal barium sulfide. Eight grams of carbon disulfide are added, the flask is stoppered, and then shaken for at least one-half hour. The yellow product is filtered by suction and washed, first with a 50% solution and then with 95% alcohol. The alcoholic washings precipitate more product from the filtrate. The material is dried in warm air.

Yield $= 12$–15g

Acid decomposes the thiocarbonate to give unstable oily trithiocarbonic acid which dissociates into carbon disulfide and hydrogen sulfide.

$$2H^+ + CS_3 = \longrightarrow H_2CS_3 \longrightarrow H_2S + CS_2$$

References:
1. B:137; J:361.
2. Yeoman, *J. Chem. Soc.*, 119:38 (1921).

33. Basic Beryllium Acetate *

$$4BeCO_3 + 6HC_2H_3O_2 \longrightarrow Be_4O(C_2H_3O_2)_6 + 4CO_2 + 3H_2O$$

Eight grams of basic beryllium carbonate (of analyzed beryllium content) are stirred with 16ml of glacial acetic acid on a hot plate or steam bath until carbon dioxide is no longer evolved. The solution is cooled and the product is filtered off by suction and air-dried. The crude material is stirred with 20ml of dry chloroform and insoluble impurities are removed by filtration. The chloroform solution is evaporated to dryness on the steam bath and the colorless crystals of the product (m.p. 285–286°C) are dried *in vacuo* to remove residual solvent.

Yield = 65% (about 5.5g) based on beryllium content of the starting material.

COGNATE PREPARATION

33 a. Basic Beryllium Propionate *

Five grams of basic carbonate and 25ml of propionic acid are used. The solution is evaporated at 130–140°C to crystallization, cooled, and the product is ground to a fine powder. The latter is treated with 60ml of hot petroleum ether (b.p. 80–100°C), filtered, and the filtrate is cooled in ice overnight. The product is suction-filtered and dried in air.

Yield = 85% (about 9g) based on the content of beryllium in the basic carbonate.

For a fairly complete discussion of basic beryllium derivatives of organic acids, see reference 2.

For the preparation of basic zinc acetate, $Zn_4O(C_2H_3O_2)_6$, see reference 3. The zinc compound is more readily hydrolyzed than the beryllium analogue.

References:
1. B:222; vol. I, 3:9–10.
2. I, vol. 3:4–9.
3. AUGUR AND ROBIN, *Compt. rend.*, 178:1546 (1924).

34. Boron Phosphate *

$$H_3BO_3 + H_3PO_4 \longrightarrow BPO_4 + 3H_2O$$

Twelve grams of boric acid are heated on the steam bath with 20ml of sirupy phosphoric acid (85%) in an evaporating dish. The mixture gradually thickens to a stiff paste and a spatula should be used to keep it from adhering to the sides of the vessel. When the reaction mass has become sufficiently hard and dry, it is ground to a coarse powder in a mortar and re-transferred to the basin. The latter is heated for about two hours on a sand bath with the full flame of a Tirrell burner. The material shrinks considerably in volume due to loss of water and becomes a fine dry powder. The material is finally dehydrated by heating in a large crucible for one hour over a Meker burner. On cooling, the mass is readily separated from the crucible and reground. It is then boiled for 15 to 30 minutes with a mixture of 200ml of water and 5ml of concentrated hydrochloric acid to remove any excess of partially reacted starting material. After filtration by suction the white product is dried at 100°C.

Yield = 18g (87% based on the phosphoric acid)

Boron phosphate is vigorously decomposed by hot concentrated alkali to give sodium borate and phosphate. For the preparation of boron arsenate see references 4 and 5.

References:
1. P:210.
2. LEVI AND GILBERT, *J. Chem. Soc.*, 1927:2117.
3. MYLIUS AND MEUSSER, *Ber.*, 37:397 (1904).
4. GRUNER, *Z. anorg. Chem.*, 219:181 (1934).
5. SCHULZE, *Naturwiss.*, 21:512 (1933).
6. MEYER, *Ber.*, 22:2919 (1889).
7. SCHULZE, *Z. physik. Chem.*, (B) 24:216 (1934).

35. Chromium (II) Acetate Monohydrate ****

$$CrCl_3 + [H] \longrightarrow CrCl_2 + HCl$$
$$CrCl_2 + 2NaC_2H_3O_2 \longrightarrow Cr(C_2H_3O_2)_2 + 2NaCl$$

A 250ml Erlenmeyer flask is fitted with an inlet tube (A) and an outlet tube (B) for carbon dioxide or other inert gas. B is fitted with a stopcock (C) or with a pinch clamp. A third delivery tube (D), bent twice at right angles, is also attached to the flask. One leg of D runs almost to the bottom of the vessel.

Thirty grams of chromium (III) chloride 6-hydrate, dissolved in 35ml water, are placed in the flask together with 15g of zinc (preferably in the form of large lumps or rods). Thirty-five ml of concentrated hydrochloric acid are added and the clamp on B is opened. A steady stream of carbon dioxide is admitted through A, which is adjusted to about one inch from the surface of the reaction mixture. During the reduction the flask is kept immersed in a cold water bath.

In the meantime, a sintered glass funnel, 2–3 inches in diameter, is fitted with an inlet and exit tube for CO_2 and with a 60ml dropping funnel, preferably long-stemmed. The funnel is fitted into a 500-ml suction flask.

When the reduction is complete, as evidenced by a pure blue color with no trace of green in the reaction mixture, the clamp on B is closed (carbon dioxide flow is maintained) and the solution forced, under pressure of inert gas, through D *below* the surface of a solution of 84g of sodium acetate 3-hydrate in 100ml of cold, freshly boiled, distilled water.

NOTE: The following operations must be carried out expeditiously in order to obtain a good yield of pure product. At no time during the washing of the acetate on the filter (except after the last washing with ether) should the material be without a small layer of wash liquid on its surface, or the flow of gas interrupted.

The reaction mixture is now suction-filtered under a good flow of carbon dioxide, the funnel being uncapped briefly to add the remainder of the solution and precipitate.

The funnel is now stoppered again and the reddish precipitate is washed with 50ml of freshly boiled distilled water, in small portions from the dropping funnel, and then in similar fashion with three 30ml portions of absolute alcohol, and finally with the same quantity of absolute ether.

After the washing, the bright red product is dried under gentle suction for about half an hour in a strong current of carbon dioxide, and then quickly transferred to a tightly stoppered tared bottle under an inert atmosphere.

Yield = 15–17g (77–87% based on the hydrated chromic chloride)

References:
1. I, vol. 1:122; *Ibid.*, vol. 3:148.
2. J:364; P:382, 419.

36. Cobalt Thiocyanate 3-Hydrate *

$$Pb^{++} + 2SCN^- \longrightarrow Pb(SCN)_2$$
$$CoSO_4 + Pb(SCN)_2 \longrightarrow Co(SCN)_2 + PbSO_4$$

Eighty-two grams of lead nitrate in 300ml of distilled water are mixed with a solution of 49g of potassium thiocyanate (or 41g of the sodium salt) in 100ml water and cooled in ice. The resulting lead thiocyanate is filtered off and washed with 50ml of ice-cold water in portions and then with 100ml of 95% alcohol. It is dried in warm air in the dark.

Yield about 75g

A solution of 56g of cobalt sulfate 7-hydrate in 300ml of water is heated to boiling and 65g of lead thiocyanate is stirred in. When the lead sulfate is well settled, the mixture is cooled and filtered. The residue is washed with two 25ml portions of cold water; the washings are added to the main filtrate which is then evaporated to dryness on the steam bath. The product is finally dehydrated at 105°–120°C for 2–3 hours.

Yield = 32g (crude)

If desired, the thiocyanate may be purified by dissolving it in ethyl acetate, filtering it, and then evaporating the solvent.

The color of the material is violet-brown. It is soluble in alcohol, ether, and acetone as well as esters to give a blue solution in each case—probably an auto-complex $Co[Co(SCN)_4]$. In concentrated aqueous medium it is blue, but on dilution the color changes to the pink of hydrated cobalt (II) ions (dissociation of complex).

Reference: I, vol. 1:85.

37. Cobalt Thiosulfate (Hydrated) **

$$Ba^{++} + S_2O_3^= \longrightarrow BaS_2O_3$$
$$CoSO_4 + BaS_2O_3 \longrightarrow CoS_2O_3 + BaSO_4$$

To a solution of 35.0g of barium chloride 2-hydrate in 100ml of distilled water are added 35.5g of solid sodium thiosulfate 5-hydrate. The mixture is stirred until the latter dissolves. The barium thiosulfate 1-hydrate is filtered by suction, washed with three 20-ml portions of ice-cold water, and then with a similar quantity of 95% alcohol. It is dried in air.

Yield = 36.5g (95% based on barium chloride)

To a solution of 70.0g of cobalt (II) sulfate 7-hydrate in 200 ml of water warmed to 50°C are added 67.0g of barium thiosulfate 1-hydrate. The mixture is stirred at 50°C until the barium sulfate settles out completely and it is then filtered.

Acetone (about 500ml) is now added to the clear filtrate in a one-liter beaker until the deposition of a reddish oil is complete and the supernatant liquid is almost colorless. The oil is repeatedly stirred with fresh 75–100ml portions of acetone until it starts to solidify, whereupon it is transferred to a large mortar and further triturated with acetone until it is thoroughly granular. The reddish-brown residue is collected on a filter and dried in air.

Yield = 45g (Crude; contains sulfate)

A sample of about 1.2g, when dissolved in water and titrated with iodine, gave 35.8% thiosulfate; or 54.7% cobalt thiosulfate which corresponds to an 8-hydrate (54.3% CoS_2O_3). The product prepared as described decomposes slowly in boiling water to give cobalt sulfide. The color in a cold concentrated aqueous medium is deep blue— possibly $Co(Co(S_2O_3)_4)$.

COGNATE PREPARATION

37 a. Nickel Thiosulfate *

This compound may be prepared in solution by dissolving 4.5g of nickel sulfate 7-hydrate in 25ml of water and adding 5g of barium thiosulfate monohydrate.

The filtrate is sulfate-free but all attempts to isolate any solid product result in decomposition to nickel sulfide.

38. Copper (II) Aminomethanesulfonate **

$$CuSO_4 + 2NaOH \xrightarrow{\text{cold}} Cu(OH)_2(gel) + Na_2SO_4$$
$$Cu(OH)_2 + 2H_2NCH_2SO_3H \longrightarrow Cu(H_2NCH_2SO_3)_2 + 2H_2O$$

NOTE: Crystalline cupric hydroxide, precipitated by alkali at room temperature or above, is virtually unattacked by aminomethanesulfonic acid. The gel, produced at temperatures around 0°C in a far more reactive form, is relatively unstable because of conversion into the crystalline form and slow spontaneous dehydration in the presence of alkali finally to yield black cupric oxide. For good results therefore, the gel must be kept below normal temperatures and worked with as rapidly as possible until it has been dissolved in the acid.

A quantity of 2.5g of sodium hydroxide is dissolved in 50ml of water, a few small pieces of ice are added, and the vessel containing the solution is immersed in an ice bath. With continuous stirring (preferably mechanical), a solution of 5g of copper sulfate 5-hydrate in 50ml water is added—drop by drop from a tap-funnel or burette. After the addition is complete stirring is continued for five minutes longer and the mixture is then filtered on a large (5–6 inch) suction funnel with only moderate suction to avoid compacting the gel of cupric hydroxide. Before the latter has been completely drained, it is washed with 400ml of ice water in portions. The gel is not allowed to dry out until the washing operation has been completed. The hydroxide is ejected by gas pressure through the stem of the suction funnel into a small cooled dish, and added quickly—in small portions with vigorous shaking—to an ice-cold solution of 5g of aminomethanesulfonic acid (No. 85) with 200ml of ice water in a 500ml flask. The flask and contents are kept cold during the reaction. When no more of the gel seems to dissolve after continued agitation (10–15 minutes), the blue solution is filtered through a pleated paper and 100ml of methanol is added to the filtrate. After standing in ice overnight, the deep blue deposited crystals are suction-filtered, washed first with 50% ethanol, then with acetone, and finally dried in air.

Yield = 3.5g

After isolation, the compound is insoluble in water and in common organic solvents. Aqueous ammonia and acid decompose the salt, yielding the free amino acid; hot water converts the copper aminomethanesulfonate into an insoluble basic green salt. Because of its insolubility and its color, a chelate ring structure has been proposed similar to that of the alpha-amino acids with copper.

COGNATE PREPARATIONS

Solutions of **cobalt** and **nickel aminomethanesulfonates** may be prepared by using precisely the same technique as for the preceding. As starting materials, 5.6g of cobalt or nickel sulfate 7-hydrate, 2.5g of sodium hydroxide, and 5g of the amino acid are used. As they are soluble, neither product (light pink for cobalt and pale green for nickel) can be precipitated by alcohol.

References:
1. P:121, 141.
2. MEYER AND TAUBE, Z. anorg. Chem., 227:425 (1936).

39. Mercury (II) Cyanide *

$$HgO + 2KCN + H_2O \longrightarrow Hg(CN)_2 + 2KOH$$
$$2KOH + H_2SO_4 \longrightarrow K_2SO_4 + 2H_2O$$

To a solution of 7.3g of pure potassium cyanide in 100ml of water is added, in small portions, and with good stirring, 14.4g of mercuric oxide. When all but a small amount of the oxide remains undissolved, the solution is filtered. To the clear filtrate, immersed in ice water, one or two drops of phenolphthalein indicator are added and then 3M sulfuric acid is added by drops from a burette until the alkali is *just* neutralized. About 22ml of the acid should be required. The mixture is evaporated to dryness on the water bath in the hood, and the residue of product and potassium sulfate is treated with hot absolute methanol in three portions of 50, 30, and 30ml respectively. The filtered methanolic extracts are combined and evaporated to dryness on the steam bath.

Yield = 14–16g

Mercuric cyanide, when heated strongly in the absence of air, yields cyanogen $(CN)_2$ and mercury. The salt is only slightly dissociated in water and yields no precipitate of mercury salt with any reagent except hydrogen sulfide.

Reference: B:92.

40. Potassium Cyanate **

$$K_2CO_3 + 2(NH_2)_2CO \longrightarrow 2KCNO + CO_2 + 2NH_3 + H_2O$$

Seventy grams of anhydrous potassium carbonate and 80g of urea are *thoroughly* ground together in a mortar. The mixture should be handled with the minimum of delay because the carbonate is somewhat deliquescent. The mixed powder is now heated [hood] in a dish over a Tirrell burner with slowly increasing flame. It is tamped down from time to time but not stirred, because a lower yield would result. The material melts partially and a large volume of ammonia escapes. It then re-solidifies and finally melts to a clear liquid almost free of bubbles. The flame is lowered somewhat and one g of urea is stirred in quickly. When the evolution of gas stops, the molten fusion is at once poured into a large dry mortar and ground while hot during the process of solidification.

$$\text{Yield} = 70\text{--}74g$$

If desired, moisture-stable potassium bicarbonate may be substituted in the procedure described. One hundred grams are required.

$$2KHCO_3 \longrightarrow K_2CO_3 + CO_2 + H_2O$$

The crude cyanate that results is satisfactory for most purposes but it must be kept in tightly-stopped containers to prevent any access of atmospheric moisture, which would cause hydrolysis to carbonate.

$$2KCNO + 4H_2O \longrightarrow K_2CO_3 + (NH_4)_2CO_3$$

Recrystallization is accompanied by a 20% loss and, if temperature limits are exceeded, the final product may be less pure than the starting material.

COGNATE PREPARATION

40 a. Sodium Cyanate **

26.5g of pure anhydrous sodium carbonate and 35g of urea are used. As the melting point of sodium cyanate is higher than that of the potassium compound, two Meker burners and a tall porcelain crucible (for localization of heat) are used in the fusion. About 0.5g of additional urea is employed, but the final product still contains small amounts of carbonate.

$$Yield = 28–32g$$

Recrystallization incurs large (66%) losses but yields a pure product.

References:

1. I, vol. 2:88–89; B:241.
2. KLOEPFER, *Chem. Abstracts*, 27:4354 (1933).
3. PAULING AND HENDRICKS, *J. Am. Chem. Soc.*, 47:2904 (1925).

41. Potassium Perchlorate *

$$4KClO_3 \longrightarrow 3KClO_4 + KCl$$

NOTE: The success of this preparation depends entirely on careful temperature control of the high-temperature fusion. It is advisable, but not essential, to keep a *clean* clamped thermometer (range to 500°C) immersed in the reaction mixture during the experiment. Bear in mind that metallic catalysts and especially organic substances such as dust, paper, or cloth may cause violent and even explosive decomposition of the molten potassium chlorate. The crucible or dish used for the fusion should therefore be scrupulously clean and preferably new.

Fifty grams of pure dry potassium chlorate are heated in an *undamaged* and *clean* 100ml porcelain crucible or evaporating dish over a Tirrell burner until the salt *just* melts. By carefully adjusting the flame, the temperature of the melt should be maintained as uniform as possible (about 400°C) so that very little oxygen is evolved and the fusion mixture gradually becomes more viscous and pasty. After one-quarter hour, when the mass has become semi-solid, it is cooled *thoroughly* and covered with 50ml of *cold* water. After the melt disintegrates, the mixture is kept cool in running water and then filtered. The residual product is recrystallized from 200ml of boiling water and the mixture is allowed to stand in ice (preferably overnight) until no more of the salt settles out. The potassium perchlorate is washed on the filter with 30–50ml of ice water and dried in air. The purified material should show a negative or very faint test for chloride ion with silver nitrate.

Potassium perchlorate may also be obtained by the anodic oxidation of the chlorate at low temperatures.

$$ClO_3^- + H_2O \longrightarrow ClO_4^- + 2H^+ + 2e$$

Reference: B:118; J:362; P:468.

42. Potassium Periodate (meta-) **

(I)

$$2KClO_3 + I_2 \longrightarrow 2KIO_3 + Cl_2$$
$$2KIO_3 + 2Cl_2 + 6KOH \longrightarrow K_4I_2O_9 + 4KCl + 3H_2O$$
$$K_4I_2O_9 + 2H^\oplus \longrightarrow 2KIO_4 + 2K^\oplus + H_2O$$

In a 500ml flask 13.5g of potassium chlorate are dissolved in 50ml of water at 45°C containing a few drops of concentrated nitric acid. Ten grams of iodine are added and the mixture is cautiously warmed until a reaction just begins (hood). The mouth of the flask is loosely covered with an inverted beaker to prevent loss of iodine and a bath of cold water is provided in case the reaction becomes too vigorous. The reaction is complete in about 15 minutes, as shown by the disappearance of the iodine.

To the solution of potassium iodate obtained (or to 16.8g of potassium iodate in 50ml of hot water) are added 23g of 85% solid potassium hydroxide and 15ml of hot water. When solution is complete, a steady stream of chlorine is led in through a wide glass tube (at least 10mm in diameter) which is used as a hand stirrer. Best yields are obtained if the solution is boiled and stirred vigorously during this step. When chlorine is no longer absorbed (10–15 minutes) and the solution has become *acid* (test with litmus) the reaction is over. Some periodate may crystallize from the hot liquid towards the end of the chlorination. The mixture is cooled well in ice and filtered.

Yield = 16–18g (over 99% pure)

(II)

$$2KIO_3 + 2K_2S_2O_8 + 6KOH \longrightarrow K_4I_2O_9 + 4K_2SO_4 + 3H_2O$$
$$K_4I_2O_9 + 2HNO_3 \longrightarrow 2KIO_4 + 2KNO_3 + H_2O$$

A solution of potassium iodate in 50ml water is prepared from 10g of iodine according to (I), or 16.8g of the salt may be used. Fifteen grams of potassium hydroxide are added to the iodate in 50ml of water and the solution is heated to the boiling point. Twenty-three grams of potassium persulfate (fresh and active material must be used) are dissolved in the hot liquid and after five minutes 15g more of potassium hydroxide are added in small portions as solution takes place rather violently. After heating the mixture for 30 minutes on the steam bath to complete the reaction, about 150ml of hot water are added to dissolve precipitated potassium sulfate, and then the solution is cooled under running water. An equivolume mixture of concentrated nitric acid and water is added from a burette to the cooled liquid with agitation until it is acid to methyl orange, then 2ml of acid are added in excess. The product, which precipitates during the acidification, is to be well cooled, filtered off, then washed thoroughly with about 25ml of ice water and dried in air.

Yield = 12.5g

COGNATE PREPARATIONS

42 a. Sodium Paraperiodate **

($Na_3H_2IO_6$) is prepared in about 22g yield by the procedure given in (I) for the potassium salt (97–98% pure), by use of 12.5g of sodium chlorate and 14g of solid sodium hydroxide. Chlorine is passed in until the solution has become approximately neutral and the gas is no longer absorbed.

The *para*-salt obtained here may be converted to the *meta*-compound by acidifying with nitric acid.

$$Na_3H_2IO_6 + 2HNO_3 \longrightarrow NaIO_4 + 2NaNO_3 + 2H_2O$$

Twenty grams of sodium paraperiodate are dissolved in 40ml water and 11ml of concentrated nitric acid is added drop by drop with stirring and cooling. The solution is filtered if necessary and evaporated on the steam bath to crystallization. After cooling to 20°C (no lower), the mixture is filtered, washed with 10ml ice water, pressed well, and dried at 100°C.

$$Yield = 12g$$

About one gram of extra product, as the potassium salt, may be obtained from the mother liquor and washings by adding a few grams of solid potassium nitrate in concentrated aqueous solution.

(II)

A solution of sodium iodate, prepared from 10g of iodine according to (I), is diluted to 120ml with water and 4g of sodium hydroxide are added. Twenty-two grams of potassium persulfate are used as in (II) and then a second portion of 17g sodium hydroxide is added. The mixture is boiled for 15 minutes longer, then cooled to 40°C, and the liquid is decanted. The solid is brought on to the filter with about 25ml of ice water, pressed dry, and then heated at 110°C for one or two hours.

$$Yield = 22.5g, \text{ containing sulfate } (94-97\% \text{ pure})$$

To prepare the *meta*-salt the moist product obtained here is treated with nitric acid as under (I).

$$Yield = 13.5g$$

(III)

$$NaI + 4Br_2 + 10NaOH \longrightarrow Na_3H_2IO_6 + 8NaBr + 4H_2O$$

Ten grams of sodium iodide and 53g of sodium hydroxide are dissolved in 400ml of water. The solution is heated to 80°C and stirred continuously while 16ml of bromine are slowly added through a long-stemmed dropping funnel with the delivery spout under the surface of the hot liquid. The temperature is maintained during the reaction and the product precipitates during the oxidation. When all the

bromine has been added the mixture is cooled, the product
filtered by suction, and washed four times with 10ml portions of ice water. Each portion of wash water should remain in contact with the solid on the filter for at least five
minutes. The product is dried in air and may be converted
to the *meta*-salt as described under (II).

Yield of paraperiodate = 16–18g

About 10g of sodium metaperiodate are obtained.

References:

1. I, vol. I:168; *Ibid.*, vol. 2:212; P:273–4.
2. MÜLLER AND JACOB, *Z. anorg. Chem.*, 82:308 (1913).
3. LANGE AND PARIS, *J. pharm. Chim.*, 21:403 (1935).

43. Potassium Peroxylamine Disulfonate *

(I)

$$NaNO_2 + HC_2H_3O_2 + 2NaHSO_3 \longrightarrow (NaO_3S)_2NOH + NaC_2H_3O_2 + H_2O$$
$$6(NaO_3S)_2NOH + 2KMnO_4 \longrightarrow 3[(NaO_3S)_2NO]_2 + 2MnO_2 + 2KOH + 2H_2O$$
$$[(NaO_3S)_2NO]_2 + 4KCl \longrightarrow [(KO_3S)_2NO]_2 + 4NaCl$$

Thirty-five grams of sodium nitrite are dissolved in 100ml
of water and 200g of ice are added. While stirring this mixture, 50g of sodium bisulfite in 100ml water are added
slowly from a dropping funnel and finally, 20ml of glacial
acetic acid are added in the same manner. After five minutes a small sample of the solution is tested by adding a
drop of dilute iodine solution. If the reaction is complete
this should produce a blue color; if it does not, the reaction
mixture should stand until a later test is positive.

Fourteen ml of concentrated aqueous ammonia is now
added and the solution is continuously stirred while 12.6g
of potassium permanganate in 400ml of water are added
slowly. Five grams of Celite or Filter-Cel are stirred in and
the precipitated manganese dioxide is immediately filtered
by suction. To the clear violet-colored filtrate 500ml of a
saturated (33g/100ml) solution of potassium chloride are
added and crystallization is induced by scratching the walls
of the vessel. During this time the latter is kept well cooled
in an ice bath. When the orange precipitate has settled it is
filtered by suction, washed *carefully* three times with 20ml

of ice-cold 5% potassium hydroxide solution, and drained well. It is then rinsed successively with 50ml of 95% alcohol and a like amount of acetone or ether, and dried *in vacuo*. As soon as the product is dry it is stored in a clean tightly stoppered bottle, preferably out of the light.

Yield = 23g

Material prepared in this manner has retained a bright orange color for over one year of storage without access of air. The stability of the product appears to depend on the washing of the crystals on the filter. Potassium peroxylamine disulfonate is dimeric in the solid state but is dissociated into the monomeric form in solution. In this, it bears a close structural relationship to nitrogen (IV) oxide.

(II)

This method is similar to the preceding except that the bisulfite solution is prepared somewhat differently and lead dioxide is used as the oxidizing agent.

Forty-two grams of sodium bicarbonate and 35g of sodium nitrite are dissolved in 250ml of water, and 500g of ice are then added. While cooling and agitating the mixture at 0°C in a one-liter filter flask fitted for gas absorption, sulfur dioxide is passed in fairly rapidly for 40 minutes. The color of the mixture becomes orange-brown; the pH should be about 2. After standing for ten minutes longer with occasional shaking, clean air is bubbled through the liquid for five minutes. Saturated sodium carbonate solution is added until the pH becomes 9; about 65ml will be required. When the sodium bisulfite solution has stood for 90 minutes, 500ml of water and 180g of lead dioxide are added, and the mixture is stirred at 30°C for one-half hour. The violet liquid is filtered off and treated with carbon dioxide to pH 7. Any lead carbonate that forms is removed, 15ml of saturated sodium carbonate solution is added, and then 250g of potassium nitrate. After the latter has dissolved, the orange product is isolated as directed in (I). The yield is similar.

References:
1. P:263, 281.
2. HANTZSCH AND SEMPLE, *Ber.*, 28:2744 (1895).
3. HAGA, *J. Chem. Soc.*, 85:78 (1904).
4. TEUBER AND JELLINEK, *Ber.*, 85:95 (1952).
5. HARVEY AND HOLLINGSHEAD, *Chem. and Ind.*, 1953:249.
6. CRAM AND REEVES, *J. Am. Chem. Soc.*, 80:3094 (1958).

44. Rubidium Tetrachloroiodate (III) *

$$2RbCl + I_2 + 3Cl_2 \longrightarrow 2RbICl_4$$

Two and one-half grams of rubidium chloride are dissolved in 7–8ml water and 2.7g of iodine are suspended in the solution. If the chloride is not available it may be prepared by dissolving 2.4g of rubidium carbonate in the minimum of $6M$ hydrochloric acid and evaporating the neutral or slightly acid solution to dryness on the steam bath.

The mixture of rubidium chloride and iodine is cooled in ice and a slow stream of chlorine (2 bubbles/sec) is led in until the iodine has dissolved (about 5min). Orange-red crystals of the product may separate during the oxidation, and crystallization is complete after the reaction mixture has stood several hours in ice. The product is suction-filtered without washing and dried *in vacuo* for one hour. Longer drying times cause slow decomposition. The compound is stored in a tightly stoppered all-glass bottle.

Yield = 5g

The corresponding **potassium** salt, which is considerably less stable, may be prepared by triturating 2g of potassium iodate in a mortar with the addition of 10ml of concentrated hydrochloric acid in drops from a burette.

$$KIO_3 + 6HCl \longrightarrow KICl_4 + Cl_2 + 3H_2O$$

When the evolution of chlorine has ceased, the yellowish crystalline paste is filtered, dried, and stored as described.

Yield about 2g

Ether dissolves iodine trichloride out of this material, leaving potassium chloride as the residue.

Reference: B:111.

45. Silver Hypophosphate **

$$2P(red) + 2Ca(OCl)_2 + 2H_2O \longrightarrow Ca_2P_2O_6 + 4HCl$$
$$Ca_2P_2O_6 + 4HNO_3 \longrightarrow H_4P_2O_6 + 2Ca(NO_3)_2$$
$$4AgNO_3 + H_4P_2O_6 \longrightarrow Ag_4P_2O_6 + 4HNO_3$$

Shake 50g of *good* quality bleaching powder with a high content of available chlorine (preferably Perchloron or H.T.H.) together with 400ml water until no more dissolves. The insoluble residue is removed by suction-filtration and the filtrate cooled to 15–20°C by means of a little added ice. One-half gram of technical red phosphorus is now added to the mechanically stirred liquid and then a 1:4 solution of glacial acetic acid and water is added in dropwise from a burette. A turbidity, followed by the appearance of a white precipitate, indicates the onset of oxidation of the phosphorus. About 10ml of the acid mixture will usually be needed.

The vessel containing the reaction mixture is now surrounded by an ice bath in order to maintain a temperature range of 15–25°C throughout the oxidation. Stirring is continued while 5g more of the phosphorus is added in 0.5g portions at such intervals that the solution stays within the temperature limits prescribed. Care should be taken to add each amount of the phosphorus quickly so that the chance of ignition due to escaping chlorine is minimized. The initial precipitate of calcium hypophosphate redissolves during the reaction as the solution becomes increasingly acidic. When all the phosphorus has been added an inert violet residue remains in suspension through the stirred liquid, and this is agitated for ten minutes more.

The mixture is suction-filtered, warmed to 40°C, and again repeatedly stirred while solid sodium carbonate is added in small portions until the liquid is neutral to litmus paper. About 18g of carbonate should be required. A heavy white precipitate of calcium hypophosphate, orthophosphate, and carbonate forms during the neutralization. The whole mixture is stirred for 30 minutes just below the boiling point and then suction-filtered. The residue is washed free of chloride ion with water, rinsed with acetone, and dried at 100°C.

Yield about 15g (containing about 15% of
calcium hypophosphate)

The mixed calcium salt is dissolved in $3N$ nitric acid, using 15ml of the latter for every 2g of the material. The clear solution is diluted to double its volume with distilled water and 5g of silver nitrate (for each 2g portion of calcium salt) is dissolved in the liquid. The mixture is stirred until the beige precipitate settles out. This is filtered, the silver hypophosphate rinsed with acetone, and the product is dried in warm air. It is only slightly photosensitive and may be stored in clear bottles in artificial light for extended periods of time.

The yield is about 1g for every 2g of starting material. From this result the actual hypophosphate content of the calcium salts obtained may be estimated, as the formation of the silver salt is quantitative in terms of the hypophosphate actually present in the intermediate material.

References:
1. I, vol. 4:68; P:308.
2. PROBST, *Z. anorg. allgem. Chem.*, 179:155 (1929).
3. SALZER, *Ann.*, 187:322 (1877); 194:28 (1878); 211:1 (1882); 232:114 (1886).
4. PHILIPP, *Ber.*, 16:749 (1883).
5. SPETER, *Rec. trav. chim.*, 46:588 (1927).
6. KOLITOWSKA, *Z. anorg. allgem. Chem.*, 230:310 (1936).

46. Sodium Bicarbonate by the Solvay Process

$$NH_3 + H_2O + CO_2 \longrightarrow NH_4HCO_3$$
$$NH_4HCO_3 + Na^+ \longrightarrow NaHCO_3 + NH_4^+$$

Sixty grams of powdered sodium chloride are added to 180g of a 10% aqueous solution of ammonia and the mixture is allowed to stand, with occasional swirling, until almost all the salt has dissolved. The filtered solution is placed in a 1-liter flask fitted with a gas delivery tube leading almost to the bottom of the vessel and an exit tube of narrowbore glass (3mm inner diameter). A steady stream of carbon dioxide (about 3 bubbles/sec) is led into the flask, which is swirled from time to time. After some time, when the saturation point of sodium bicarbonate has been exceeded (see table), the product suddenly precipitates. The carbonation is continued for four hours, the mixture is then cooled in running water and filtered by suction. The product is pressed down well, washed with 25ml of ice water and dried in air.

Yield = 55–58g

The Solvay process depends on the fact that of all the possible combinations of ions present in the aqueous reaction mixture (NH_4^+, Na^+, Cl^-, HCO_3^-) sodium bicarbonate is the least soluble and hence precipitates out first under the proper concentration conditions. The facts are summarized in the following table, which shows percentage concentrations of the salts in 100g of a saturated aqueous solution.

Concentration in % Saturated Aqueous Solution

Compound	15°C	30°C
Sodium chloride	26.4	26.5
Sodium bicarbonate	8.1	9.9
Ammonium chloride	26.1	29.3
Ammonium bicarbonate	15.7	21.3

References:
1. B:134.
2. BODLANDER AND BREULL, Z. angew. Chem., 14:381, 405 (1901).
3. FEDOTIEFF, Z. physik. Chem., 49:162 (1904).

47. Sodium Dithionate 2-Hydrate *

(I)

$$Na_2SO_3 + 2AgNO_3 \longrightarrow Ag_2SO_3 + 2NaNO_3$$
$$Ag_2SO_3 + Na_2SO_3 \longrightarrow Na_2S_2O_6 + 2Ag$$

Two hundred grams of sodium sulfite 7-hydrate (or 100g of the anhydrous salt) are dissolved in one liter of water and the solution stirred mechanically while a solution of 130g of silver nitrate in 150ml water is added. The temperature of the agitated mixture is slowly raised to the boiling point over a flame. In the course of 20–30 minutes the white precipitate of silver sulfite disappears and a greyish mass of crystalline silver settles sharply at the bottom of the reaction vessel. The hot solution is filtered through a large suction funnel and the silver residue washed twice with 50ml of boiling water. The combined filtrate and washings are concentrated with continual stirring over a free flame to a volume of about 300ml. During the evaporation any small amounts of colloidal silver that settle out are filtered off. The solution is cooled in running water and crystallization is induced by scratching the walls of the vessel. The precipitated crystals are filtered on a large funnel and allowed to remain there without washing. The filtrate is heated to 80°C and 300ml of boiling 95% alcohol is added. The solution is cooled as above and the deposited solid is added to the first batch on the filter. The combined product is pressed well, washed first with 100ml of 95% alcohol and then with 50ml of acetone, and dried in air.

$$Yield = 80–86g$$

If desired, this preparation may be carried out on ½ or even 1/10 scale with proportionate yields. The product above is suitable for most purposes.

Recrystallization with a loss of about 10% may be effected from 1:1 alcohol-water at 80°C, using 30ml of this mixture for every 10g of the crude salt.

(II)

$$MnO_2 + 2SO_2 \longrightarrow MnS_2O_6$$
$$MnS_2O_6 + Na_2CO_3 \longrightarrow MnCO_3 + Na_2S_2O_6$$

Place 50g of highest quality (85–95%) finely powdered pyrolusite (native manganese dioxide) in a 500ml suction flask with 250ml of water. The flask is fitted with an inlet tube leading almost to the bottom of the vessel. The mixture is cooled in an ice-water bath and a stream of sulfur dioxide is led in (3 bubbles/sec) for a period of about two hours, during which time the flask is frequently swirled and good cooling maintained. The black dioxide disappears gradually in the course of the reaction, leaving a light brown slurry.

The crude manganese dithionate solution is heated to boiling and small portions of powdered barium hydroxide are added until a sample of the mixture, when filtered and acidified slightly with hydrochloric acid, gives no more test for sulfate ion with dilute barium chloride solution. (Sulfate is formed as a by-product in the oxidation of the sulfur dioxide by pyrolusite. Low temperatures of reaction minimize the formation of it). An excess of barium hydroxide does no harm as it is removed later.

The sulfate-free mixture is kept hot and stirred while about 40g of anhydrous sodium carbonate is added in 2g portions until the liquid is *just* alkaline (pale blue) to red litmus paper. The hot slurry is suction-filtered and the residue is stirred up with 200ml of hot water and refiltered. The combined washings and main filtrate must be slightly alkaline; otherwise a little more sodium carbonate is added and the solution refiltered through a clean paper.

The sodium dithionate is recovered by evaporation on the steam bath to a final volume of about 10ml. Successive crops of crystals are isolated by cooling and filtering without washing. Any insoluble material that forms during the initial concentration is filtered off.

Total Yield = 85–90% based on the MnO_2 content
of the pyrolusite used (about 100g)

COGNATE PREPARATIONS

47 a. Potassium Dithionate 2-Hydrate *

The potassium analogue can be prepared by both methods.

(I)

[To prepare the necessary potassium sulfite: Dissolve 44g of potassium metabisulfite in a solution of 100g of potassium hydroxide in one liter of water, add 5 drops of phenolphthalein indicator and then more of the 10% potash solution until a pink color *just* forms. Add the latter solution drop by drop from a separatory funnel. $KHSO_3 + KOH \longrightarrow K_2SO_3 + H_2O$]

Use 65g of silver nitrate as in (I) for the sodium salt and carry out the evaporation in a large, previously weighed basin until the weight of the concentrated solution is 450g. The *volume* should be 350–400ml at this point. Add 100ml of alcohol to the hot (75°C) solution and cool the entire mixture to room temperature (not lower) with cold water. Allow to stand for ½–1 hour to complete crystallization, filter and wash the crystals with 50ml of a 1:1 water-alcohol mixture. Dry in air.

Yield about 40g

(II)

The **potassium** compound (**) may also be prepared by the alternate method, in like yield, by substituting about 52g of anhydrous potassium carbonate for the sodium salt.

47 b. Calcium Dithionate 4-Hydrate **

The crude manganese dithionate slurry (II) is heated to boiling and stirred while 50g of calcium hydroxide is added in small portions. The liquid with the precipitate must be strongly alkaline to litmus paper. An excess of slaked lime does no harm, as it is removed in the next step. The entire mixture is diluted to about one liter with boiling water and a rapid stream of carbon dioxide is passed into the boiling mixture for 15–30 minutes. After cooling to about 50°C the slurry is filtered, washed with 150ml of boiling water, and the combined filtrates are evaporated on the steam bath to a volume of about 30ml. Several crops of crystals are isolated and filtered without washing. The remaining calcium salt in the final mother liquor is precipitated with 50ml of alcohol. The material is dried in air.

Total yield 85–90% (about 120g)

47 c. Barium Dithionate 2-Hydrate **

The procedure to be followed is the same as for the calcium salt except that about 160g of barium hydroxide 8-hydrate is employed, instead of the slaked lime. As the former is more soluble, some care should be exercised not to add too great an excess because the quantity of slurry formed would be very large. As barium dithionate tends to form supersaturated solutions crystallization is best encouraged by scratching the sides of the containing vessel.

$$\text{Yield} = 70\text{--}75\% \text{ of the MnO}_2 \text{ ore content}$$

References:
1. B:131; I, vol. 2:167; J:360; P:361ff.
2. BAUBIGNY, *Ann. chim. phys.*, 20:5 (1910).
3. VON HAUER, *J. prakt. Chem.*, 80:229 (1860).
4. MEYER, *Ber.*, 34:3606 (1901).
5. SPRING AND BOURGEOIS, *Bull. soc. chim.*, 46:151 (1885).

48. Sodium Monothioarsenate (V) 12-Hydrate *

$$As_2O_3 + 6NaOH \longrightarrow 2Na_3AsO_3 + 3H_2O$$
$$Na_3AsO_3 + S \longrightarrow Na_3AsSO_3$$

Twenty grams of arsenic trioxide are dissolved in a solution of 24g of sodium hydroxide in 100ml of water. Six and one-half grams of finely powdered roll sulfur are added and the mixture is boiled gently under reflux (or in an open vessel if water is added from time to time to replace that lost by evaporation) until virtually all the sulfur has dissolved (about 2½ hours). The clear filtered solution is evaporated on the steam bath to crystallization and several batches of crystals are isolated by cooling and filtering without washing. The yield of product depends entirely on the extent of the evaporation and may be almost quantitative. The product is colorless, but turns pale yellow on standing. It melts at 46°C and is somewhat efflorescent.

Reference: J:361.

COGNATE PREPARATION

48 a. Sodium Monothiophosphate 12-Hydrate **

(I)

$$PSCl_3 + 6NaOH \longrightarrow Na_3PO_3S + 3NaCl + 3H_2O$$

a) A one liter three-neck flask is fitted with a dropping funnel, a thermometer, and a mechanical stirrer. One hundred and twenty grams of sodium hydroxide (calculated as the 100% salt) and 400ml of water are placed in the flask and 70g of phosphorus (V) sulfochloride are added to the well-stirred alkali. The mixture is heated under stirred reflux until the layer of sulfochloride has disappeared; this requires about 30 minutes. The reaction mixture is gradually cooled in an ice bath and 100ml of alcohol are slowly added through the dropping funnel. When the contents of the flask have cooled to 5°C or below, the cold slurry is filtered, and the crude product, contaminated with sodium chloride, is filtered off and drained well.

Yield about 125g

The solid obtained here is dissolved in 90ml of water below 50°C and the solution is cooled rapidly in ice to 0°C. An analytically-pure material is obtained by filtering and draining the solid without washing.

Yield = 100g; m.p. 60°C

b) The same apparatus as in a) is used with 40g of 100% sodium hydroxide in 300ml of water and 17.5ml of phosphorus (V) sulfochloride. After heating at 103–109°C for 15–20 minutes, the reaction is complete. The crude material is redissolved in the minimum of water at 40–45°C and the crystalline product is precipitated by the addition of 185ml of anhydrous methanol for every 100ml of solution. The 12-hydrate is filtered off after cooling and the procedure of precipitating crystals is repeated. The isolated salt is then dehydrated by stirring it for one hour with 200ml of anhydrous methanol. After filtering, the material is dried at 100°C for one hour and stored in a well-sealed vessel. The anhydrous compound decomposes at 120–125°C.

Yield = 16–17g

(II)

$$P_2S_5 + 6NaOH \longrightarrow 2Na_3PO_3S + 3H_2S$$

[CAUTION: Because of the evolution of H_2S, all operations in this entire procedure should be performed in the hood.]

Fifty grams of sodium hydroxide are dissolved in 250ml of water and 50g of technical phosphorus (V) sulfide (No.

80) are added in portions at such a rate that the temperature remains below 50°C. This is accomplished by cooling with water. The yellow solution is cooled in ice and 100ml of alcohol are added. After remaining in the cold for 2–3 hours, the precipitated salt is filtered and washed with 75ml of cold 50% alcohol, then with the same volume of pure alcohol, and finally dried in air.

Yield about 110g

This salt is dissolved in 350ml of water and warmed to 70°C on the steam bath until a vigorous evolution of hydrogen sulfide starts. The solution is immediately cooled to 60° and held at this temperature for 10–15 minutes. After rapid cooling in ice, 100ml of alcohol are added and the product is isolated by filtering without washing. The material is recrystallized by dissolving it in the minimum of water at 45°C, cooling, and then precipitating the 12-hydrate by adding one-fifth the volume of alcohol.

Yield, variable

References:
(I) 1. I, vol. 5:102.
    2. WURTZ, *Ann. chim. et phys.* (3), 20:472 (1847).
(II) 3. KUBIERSCHKY, *J. prakt. Chem.* (2), 31:93 (1885).

49. Sodium Pyroantimonate (V) *

$$2Sb^{+++} + 3H_2S \longrightarrow Sb_2S_3 + 6H^+$$
$$Sb_2S_3 + 6NaOH \longrightarrow Na_3SbS_3 + Na_3SbO_3 + 3H_2O$$
$$Na_3SbS_3 + 4NaOH + H_2O_2 \longrightarrow NaSb(OH)_6 + 3Na_2S$$
$$Na_3SbO_3 + H_2O_2 + 3H_2O \longrightarrow NaSb(OH)_6 + 2NaOH$$

Three and four-tenths grams of antimony trisulfide is prepared by passing hydrogen sulfide into a solution of 6.6g potassium antimonyl tartrate (4.5g of the trichloride or 2.9g of the trioxide may be used instead) in 2N hydrochloric acid until precipitation is complete.

The moist precipitate thus obtained, after being suction-filtered and pressed down well, is carefully separated from the adhering filter paper by peeling the latter away cleanly and then stirred with 20ml of a 35% solution of sodium hydroxide (1 part solid alkali to 2 parts of water) until only a very small yellow residue remains. Slight warming aids the dissolution of the antimony trisulfide. The clear liquid (decanted from any residue) is diluted with water to 150ml and heated to 70–80°C. This temperature range is maintained while 50ml of 6% hydrogen peroxide is slowly added to the well-stirred liquid from a dropping funnel. The pale yellow color of the reaction mixture disappears towards the end of the oxidation while the sparingly soluble antimonate crystallizes out continuously. The sodium sulfide formed in the reaction is oxidized to sodium sulfate.

$$Na_2S + 4H_2O_2 \longrightarrow Na_2SO_4 + 4H_2O$$

The solution and precipitate are allowed to cool spontaneously to room temperature and the supernatant liquid is decanted. The solid is brought on to the filter with about 50ml of an equivolume water-alcohol mixture, washed twice with 20ml portions of the same solvent, then with absolute alcohol and finally dried in air.

$$Yield = 4g$$

The white salt dissolves in boiling water to the extent of 2.5g/liter.

References:
1. KNORRE AND OLSCHEWSKI, Ber., 18:2359 (1885).
2. JANDER AND BRANDT, Z. anorg. Chem., 147:5 (1925).

50. Sodium Tetrathionate 2-Hydrate *

(I)

$$2Na_2S_2O_3 + I_2 \longrightarrow Na_2S_4O_6 + 2NaI$$

One hundred grams of sodium thiosulfate 5-hydrate are ground in a large mortar with 52g of iodine and 10ml water until a smooth *light* yellow-brown paste results. The mass is allowed to stand for 15 minutes, then rinsed with 100ml of alcohol into a flask which is to be stoppered. When the mixture has stood for 2–3 hours, the residue of product is filtered off and washed with 25ml portions of alcohol until the rinsings are virtually colorless.

The crude product is dissolved in 40ml of water at 40°C, then cooled in ice while a total of 100ml of alcohol is added in 20ml portions with good swirling. The flask containing the reaction mixture is stoppered and allowed to stand overnight in the refrigerator (room temperature may be used, but the yield is slightly lower). The well-formed crystals are filtered off, washed with 50ml of alcohol, and dried *in vacuo*.

$$\text{Yield} = 38\text{--}40\text{g}$$

The **potassium** salt may be prepared [4] in the same way if potassium thiosulfate is available. Otherwise, potassium tetrathionate (anhydrous) is formed by dissolving the sodium salt in its own weight of water at 40°C, adding 200% of the calculated amount of potassium acetate, and 1–2 volumes of alcohol.

(II) **

$$S_2Cl_2 + 2SO_2 + 2H_2O \longrightarrow H_2S_4O_6 + 2HCl$$
$$H_2S_4O_6 + 2HCl + 4NaOH \longrightarrow Na_2S_4O_6 + 2NaCl + 4H_2O$$

One hundred milliliters of water are placed in a 500ml suction flask fitted with a stopper and a delivery tube leading to the bottom of the flask. The latter is cooled in an ice bath to 0°C and a stream of sulfur dioxide is passed in (hood) at this temperature until the water has been saturated with the gas. Saturation is indicated when, on interrupting the gas flow, the liquid no longer rises to an appreciable extent in the delivery tube. The latter is now replaced by a dropping funnel fitted with a drying tube. A solution of 10g (6ml) of freshly distilled sulfur chloride (b.p. 138°C) in 70ml of petroleum ether (60–80°C fraction) is placed in the funnel. The temperature of the aqueous sulfur dioxide solution is maintained at 0°C or below, while the sulfur chloride-petroleum ether mixture is added from the funnel in approximately 10ml portions. After each addition, the flask is shaken in the cooling bath until all the yellow color has disappeared from the layer of organic solvent. As the exhausted solvent accumulates in the reaction mixture, it dilutes the fresh incoming sulfur chloride solution and therefore the coloration of the petroleum ether persists somewhat longer during the shaking toward the close of the reaction.

The contents of the flask may now be allowed to warm up to room temperature and the organic layer is separted from the aqueous mixture of hydrochloric and tetrathionic acids in a funnel. The water layer is returned to the original filter flask with a stopper and a glass tube ending in a coarse capillary (1mm diameter) which leads well under the surface of the liquid. The flask is attached to the water pump and all the excess sulfur dioxide is removed by partial evacuation over a period of about two hours, until the residual liquid has practically no odor of the dissolved gas. A brisk stream of air may now be passed through the solution for about one hour to ensure removal of the sulfur dioxide.

During the process of evacuation, a solution of 15g of sodium hydroxide pellets in 10ml of warm water is prepared and mixed with 50ml of 95% alcohol. 120ml more of 95% alcohol are added, the entire solution is filtered if necessary and cooled in ice. The cold alkaline solution is now run slowly from a funnel into the acid mixture which is also immersed in an ice bath. Good swirling is essential during the neutralization. The mixture is allowed to stand in a stoppered vessel overnight (preferably at 5–10°C), the product is then filtered by suction, washed with 95% alcohol, and dried *in vacuo*. It is recrystallized if desired, as described in (I).

Yield = 80–85% of theory (crude)

NOTE: If crystallization of the crude product occurs at temperatures below 5°C, sodium chloride may contaminate the material.

COGNATE PREPARATION

50 a. Potassium Tetrathionate **

Twenty-five grams of solid potassium hydroxide are used instead of the sodium hydroxide. Ten grams of crude product are dissolved in 13ml of water at 70°C, filtered if necessary, then cooled quickly to 0°C. The pure product is filtered, washed with alcohol, and dried in air. Recrystallization involves a 25% loss.

References:
1. B:132; P:377.
2. STAMM, GOEHRING, AND FELDMAN, *Z. anorg. Chem.*, 250:226 (1942).
3. KURTENACKER AND FRITSCH, *Ibid.*, 121:335 (1922).
4. MARTIN AND METZ, *Ibid.*, 127:83 (1923).
5. SANDER, *Z. angew. Chem.*, 28:273 (1915).

51. Sodium Thioantimonate (V) 9-Hydrate *

$$Sb_2O_3 + 6HCl \longrightarrow 2SbCl_3 + 3H_2O$$
$$2SbCl_3 + 3H_2S \longrightarrow Sb_2S_3 + 6HCl$$
$$Sb_2S_3 + 3Na_2S + 2S \longrightarrow 2Na_3SbS_4$$

Thirty-four grams of antimony trisulfide are dissolved in 100ml of an aqueous solution containing 72g of sodium sulfide 9-hydrate; 6.4g of sulfur in finely powdered form are added and the mixture gently refluxed until all the sulfur has dissolved. The solution is evaporated on the steam bath to crystallization and crystal crops isolated without washing. The final mother liquor is heated to dryness on the water bath, and the entire crude product is recrystallized from an equal weight of boiling water containing a little (about 0.5g) sodium hydroxide. More product is isolated from the filtrate by the addition of alcohol and the material is dried *in vacuo* over lime. Pale yellow crystals.

Total Yield about 90g

The antimony sulfide required as starting material is easily made by dissolving either 46g of antimony trichloride or 29g of the trioxide in 2*N* hydrochloric acid and precipitating the trisulfide with hydrogen sulfide. The moist product may be used directly.

The sodium sulfide solution can be prepared by dissolving 12g of sodium hydroxide in 50ml of water, *saturating* (*p*H 8) with hydrogen sulfide, and mixing the resulting sodium hydrogen sulfide solution with a second portion of 12g of alkali in 50ml water.

(II)

(Procedure of Schlippe)

$$Na_2SO_4 + 2C \longrightarrow Na_2S + 2CO_2$$
$$3Na_2S + Sb_2S_3 \longrightarrow 2Na_3SbS_3$$
$$Na_3SbS_3 + S \longrightarrow Na_3SbS_4$$

Thirty-six grams of powdered stibnite (Sb_2S_3) are ground thoroughly in a mortar with 43g of anhydrous sodium sulfate and 16g of charcoal. The mixture is placed in a large clay crucible (the latter should be about half-filled), covered with a thin layer (about ⅛ inch) of charcoal and heated over a Meker burner to a state of quiet fusion, then ten minutes longer. The melt is poured into an iron dish, allowed to cool and then powdered. The material is then boiled under reflux with 7g of sulfur powder in 300ml of water, suction-filtered, and the product is isolated as described in (I).

Yield = 75g

COGNATE PREPARATION

51 a. Sodium Thioarsenate (V) 8-Hydrate *

This compound may be prepared by the same procedure just described except that either 24.5g of arsenic trisulfide or 20g of the trioxide is used. The solution is not evaporated to dryness, neither is the salt subjected to recrystallization, because of accompanying decomposition. The yield, which depends on the extent of evaporation, is usually about 60g.

References:

1. B:138; J:360.
2. VON SCHLIPPE, *Schweigger's J. Chemie u. Physik*, 33:320 (1821).

51 b. Sodium Tetrathiophosphate 8-Hydrate **

$$P_2S_5 + 3Na_2S \longrightarrow 2Na_3PS_4$$

Eighty grams of sodium sulfide 9-hydrate are melted in a suitable evaporating dish over a *small* flame. Under constant stirring, 8g of powdered phosphorus pentasulfide are sifted into the molten salt under the hood. After 10–20 minutes, during which the dark grey-brown fusion is continuously stirred and *gently* heated, the pentasulfide has dissolved. Eighty milliliters of water at 70–80°C are added and the hot solution is rapidly filtered by suction through a steam-jacketed Buchner funnel. The filtrate is allowed to stand in a stoppered flask cooled in ice for 30–45 minutes and the crude crystalline product is filtered off.

If desired, the salt may be purified as follows: The solid is rapidly dissolved below 10°C in five times its weight of 2% aqueous sodium sulfide containing 1ml of 2N sodium hydroxide. The crystals are washed with 100ml of ice-cold 1:1 alcohol-water, followed by 95% alcohol and by acetone; the product is briefly air-dried. An equal volume of ice-cold 95% alcohol is added during the cooling. After standing in ice until precipitation is complete (about 10 minutes), the salt is *immediately* suction-filtered and washed, first with cold 50% alcohol, then with 95% alcohol, followed by ether. The colorless crystals are dried briefly in air and preserved in a tightly stoppered bottle to prevent hydrolysis due to atmospheric moisture.

Yield = 50% of theory (unrecrystallized salt)

References:
1. GLATZEL, *Z. anorg. Chem.*, 44:65 (1905).
2. KLEMENT, *Ibid.*, 253:246 (1947).

52. Sodium Trithionate 3-Hydrate **

(I)

$$2Na_2S_2O_3 + 4H_2O_2 \longrightarrow Na_2S_3O_6 + Na_2SO_4 + 4H_2O$$

Sixty-two grams of sodium thiosulfate 5-hydrate are dissolved in 50ml of water and cooled to 0°–10°C. The solution is stirred mechanically and the temperature range maintained while 52ml of fresh 30% hydrogen peroxide are added by drops from a burette or separatory funnel. Sodium sulfate precipitates during the reaction and is almost completely (about 1–2g remain in solution) removed by cooling the oxidized solution to −10°C and filtering quickly by suction through a previously cooled fritted glass or Büchner funnel.

The hydrated product is obtained by evaporating the filtrate to a sirupy consistency *in vacuo* and scratching the walls of the vessel. The material is filtered off without washing and the mother liquor may be concentrated further. If the evaporation is carried too far, however, appreciable amounts of sodium sulfate will contaminate the product. The yield depends on the extent of evaporation, but about 70% of the theoretical amount may be expected.

Anhydrous sodium trithionate is formed in about 80–85% yield when the sulfate-free oxidized filtrate is run slowly into 150ml of alcohol. The precipitated crystalline salt is washed on the filter with about 50ml of alcohol and dried in air.

COGNATE PREPARATION

52 a. Potassium Trithionate **

The potassium analogue (anhydrous) may be prepared by the preceding method if the sulfate-free filtrate is mixed with 35g of potassium acetate, stirred until the latter has dissolved, and kept in ice for about one hour until crystallization is complete. The product is filtered off, washed twice with 30ml portions of 95% alcohol, and dried in air.

Yield = 80–85% of theory

References:
1. STAMM, GOEHRING, AND FELDMAN, *Z. anorg. Chem.*, 250:226 (1942).
2. MARTIN AND METZ, *Ibid.*, 127:83 (1923).
3. RIESENFELD *et al.*, *Ibid.*, 126:281 (1923).
4. HERTLEIN, *Z. physik. Chem.*, 19:287 (1896).

(II)

$$Na_2S_2O_3 + 2NaHSO_3 + 2SO_2 \longrightarrow 2Na_2S_3O_6 + H_2O$$

Twenty-one grams of sodium bisulfite and 0.5g of sodium arsenite are dissolved in a small volume of water and then made up to a volume of 40ml in a 125ml filter flask. Twenty-five grams of finely powdered sodium thiosulfate 5-hydrate are dissolved in the solution and the flask is fitted with a stopper and a delivery tube leading almost to the bottom of the vessel. The flask (with stopper and tube) and contents are now weighed to 0.1g on a pan balance.

Sulfur dioxide is passed into the liquid to the saturation point and the reaction mixture is allowed to stand for about 15 minutes. The solution now takes up more of the gas and, by repeating this saturating and standing several times during a period of about four hours, a total of 10–11g of sulfur dioxide will have been absorbed. Any crystalline precipitate that forms during the early part of the reaction may be ignored, as it dissolves later on.

The reaction mixture is allowed to stand at room temperature overnight and the next day treatment with sulfur dioxide is continued until a total of 13–14g (theory = 12.8g) of the gas has been absorbed. After standing for another 24 hours the reaction has been completed.

Hydrated sodium trithionate may be isolated by evaporating the liquid (plus any deposited crystals of product) *in vacuo*, and isolating the salt as described in (I). The yield is about the same.

The anhydrous product is formed when the liquid (warmed slightly to 30–35°C to redissolve any crystals) is poured slowly with good stirring into 75ml of 95% alcohol. Method of isolation and yield as in (I).

COGNATE PREPARATION

The **potassium** salt is prepared by dissolving 25g of potassium acetate in the reaction mixture and cooling it in ice. Isolation and yield are the same as described in (I).

Reference: J:360; P:370.

53. Zinc Dithionite ***

$$Zn + 2SO_2 \longrightarrow ZnS_2O_4$$

Ten grams of pure zinc powder (a grade of at least 100 mesh should be used; zinc "dust" is not suitable because of its high content of oxide) is added to 150ml of absolute alcohol contained in a 250ml filter flask fitted with a stopper and gas inlet tube leading to about one-half inch from the bottom of the flask. The mixture is saturated with sulfur dioxide at 0°C and allowed to stand at room temperature with occasional gentle swirling for about three days. By this time the solid in the flask should be pure white in color and no visible trace of zinc should remain.

The slurry is filtered under an inert atmosphere, in an apparatus similar to that described for chromium (II) acetate (No. 35), washed three or four times with 50ml of absolute alcohol, and then with two similar portions of absolute ether. During the filtration and washings the same precautions are observed as for the chromium salt. The material is dried in a desiccator filled with an inert gas and stored in tightly stoppered bottles under an indifferent atmosphere.

Yield is almost quantitative

Reference: German Patent 218192 (1907); to Badische Anilin-und-Sodafabrik.

COGNATE PREPARATION

53 a. Sodium Dithionite 2-Hydrate ***

Ten grams of zinc of similar quality as in the process just described are employed in 100ml of water. Sulfur dioxide is passed in at 0°C until all the zinc has dissolved. The reddish solution is filtered under inert atmosphere, in the apparatus described previously, and 75g of sodium acetate 3-hydrate are dissolved in the cold filtrate. The reaction mixture is stored in the refrigerator under nitrogen in a tightly stoppered bottle. Crystallization is aided by shaking and is complete after about 3 days. The crystalline product is filtered by suction under nitrogen and drained well. It is then washed thoroughly with 150ml of warm (50°C) absolute alcohol, dried, and stored as the zinc salt.

Yield about 25g

References:
1. HENDERSON AND FERNELIUS, *Inorganic Preparations*, McGraw-Hill Co., New York, 1935.
2. JELLINEK, *Z. anorg. Chem.*, 70:93 (1911).

C. COMPOUND CATION

54. Hydrazonium Hydrogen Sulfate *

(I)

$$2NaOH + Cl_2 \longrightarrow NaOCl + NaCl + H_2O$$
$$NH_3 + NaOCl \longrightarrow NH_2Cl + NaOH$$
$$NH_2Cl + NH_3 \longrightarrow N_2H_4 \cdot HCl$$
$$N_2H_4 \cdot HCl + H_2SO_4 \longrightarrow N_2H_6SO_4 + HCl$$

Eight grams of sodium hydroxide pellets are dissolved in 50ml of water and 50g of crushed ice are added when the solution has cooled. The alkaline liquid is poured into a 250ml suction flask fitted with a stopper and a gas inlet tube leading well into the mixture. A good current of chlorine is passed in while the flask is cooled in ice until the gain in weight is 6g. As no excess of chlorine must be present this weight of chlorine is somewhat less than the theoretical amount required.

Two grams of gelatin U.S.P. are dissolved in 15ml of hot water, diluted with cold water to 50ml and mixed with 165ml of concentrated aqueous ammonia contained in a one-liter Erlenmeyer flask. The prepared sodium hypochlorite solution is now added; the slight evolution of nitrogen soon ceases. The entire reaction mixture is immediately heated to the boiling point and then evaporated rapidly in a smaller vessel over a free flame until the volume is about 90ml. The solution is cooled in ice while concentrated sulfuric acid is added dropwise from a separatory funnel until no more product crystallizes out. About 25ml of acid are required. The mixture is allowed to stand in the cooling bath until the material has settled well (about 15 minutes), then suction-filtered, pressed well, washed first with 15ml of 2M sulfuric acid and then with 25ml of alcohol. It is dried in air.

Yield = 5–6g

NOTE: One hundred milliliters of *fresh* Clorox may be substituted for the prepared hypochlorite, but only one-half of the reagent quantities should be used. The yield is proportional (2.5–3g).

(II) ***

$$KCN + H_2O \rightleftharpoons HCN + KOH$$
$$HCN + 2KHSO_3 \longrightarrow HC(NH_2)(SO_3K)_2$$
$$HC(NH_2)(SO_3K)_2 + HCl \longrightarrow HC(NH_2)(SO_3K)SO_3H + KCl$$
$$HC(NH_2)(SO_3K)SO_3H + KNO_2 \longrightarrow (KSO_3)_2CN_2 + 2H_2O$$
$$(KSO_3)_2CN_2 + 2H_2SO_4 + Na_2SO_3 + H_2O \longrightarrow$$
$$N_2H_6SO_4 + K_2SO_4 + Na_2SO_4 + 2SO_2 + CO_2$$

Seventy-five grams of potassium hydroxide are dissolved in 300ml of water and cooled in ice while sulfur dioxide is passed in until no more is absorbed. Fifty grams of pure potassium cyanide are now dissolved in the liquid and the solution is heated with mechanical stirring on the steam bath *in the hood*. As soon as the hot liquid has become alkaline to red litmus paper, concentrated hydrochloric acid is added dropwise from a burette until the reaction mixture is *just* acid. This acidifying procedure is repeated over a period of 1.5 to 2 hours until the solution has become permanently acid. About 30ml of concentrated HCl are required. Then 150ml more of the latter acid are added and the mixture is allowed to stand in ice (preferably overnight). The acid potassium aminomethanedisulfonate produced is filtered off, pressed down well, washed with 50ml of ice water and dried *in vacuo*.

Yield = 60–80g

Twenty-three grams of the salt just prepared are stirred to a paste with 34ml of water and mixed with a solution of 10g of potassium nitrite in 6ml of water. The mixture warms up to 40–50°C and within 10 to 15 minutes all the solid material has dissolved. The solution is made alkaline to litmus with 6N potassium hydroxide solution and cooled in ice. The orange-yellow crystals of potassium diazomethanedisulfonate are filtered off without washing.

This moist product is dissolved in a solution of 18g of sodium sulfite 7-hydrate in 12ml of water, and the solution is made alkaline if necessary with dilute aqueous sodium carbonate, then warmed gently on the steam bath until the yellow color has disappeared. Ninety grams of 20% sulfuric acid are now added [Caution: *foaming!*] to the warm liquid and the reaction mixture is heated until the odor of sulfur dioxide has gone. On cooling in ice, the hydrazine sulfate crystallizes out and is isolated as described in (I). The mother-liquor may be concentrated to yield further product.

Total yield from 23g of acid potassium aminomethanedisulfonate is about 7g; m.p. 254°C.

References:

1. B:158–160; J:366.
2. RASCHIG, *Ber.*, 40:4586 (1907).
3. JOYNER, *J. Chem. Soc.*, 123:1114 (1923).

55. Hydroxylammonium Chloride **

$$KNO_2 + HC_2H_3O_2 \longrightarrow HNO_2 + KC_2H_3O_2$$
$$HNO_2 + 2KHSO_3 \longrightarrow (KSO_3)_2NOH + H_2O$$
$$2(KSO_3)_2NOH + 4H_2O \longrightarrow (NH_3OH)_2SO_4 + 2K_2SO_4 + H_2SO_4$$
$$(NH_3OH)_2SO_4 + BaCl_2 \longrightarrow 2(NH_3OH)Cl + BaSO_4$$

Forty grams of potassium nitrite and 50g of potassium acetate are dissolved in 100ml of ice-cold water and placed in a one-liter filter flask fitted for the introduction of sulfur dioxide through a delivery tube that leads well into the liquid. Seven hundred and fifty grams of crushed ice are added and sulfur dioxide is passed rapidly into the agitated mixture until absorption is complete. (This is indicated by the fact that the odor of the gas persists after shaking.) The temperature must not rise above 0°C and a small amount of ice should still be present in the reaction mixture when saturation is reached at the end of about one-half hour.

The precipitated potassium hydroxylamine disulfonate is expeditely filtered from the cold liquid, and the moist salt is dissolved in 500ml of N/2 hydrochloric acid. The solution is heated on the water bath for two hours and then well cooled in ice while 59g of potassium bicarbonate is added in small portions (*foaming!*) to the liquid in order to neutralize the free acid formed in the hydrolysis. The final solution should be adjusted to a faint acid reaction with hydrochloric acid. Sixty milliliters of alcohol are added to the mixture with good cooling below 10°C, the precipitated potassium sulfate is filtered off and washed with 75ml of an equivolume mixture of 95% alcohol and water. The washings are combined with the main filtrate, which is now heated to boiling while a solution of 40g of barium chloride 2-hydrate in about 125ml of hot water is added. The solution containing precipitated barium sulfate is digested on the steam bath for one hour and then filtered with the aid of 5–10g of Celite or Filter-Cel. The residue is washed with 50ml of boiling water which is run into the main filtrate.

The combined solution is evaporated to dryness, at first over a free flame, and then on the steam bath. The residue is extracted three times with respectively 200-, 100-, and 50ml portions of 95% alcohol, and the alcoholic extract is evaporated (or distilled) to dryness on the water bath. The product remains behind as white crystals.

$$\text{Yield} = 13\text{–}16\text{g}$$

COGNATE PREPARATION

55 a. Hydroxylammonium Phosphate *

This compound may be used to form oximes of aldehydes and ketones without alkali because the aqueous solution has a pH of about 5 at which the maximum rate of formation of oximes occurs. It is prepared conveniently from the chloride as follows:

Twenty-one grams of hydroxylammonium chloride are dissolved in 20ml of water at 40°C and constantly stirred while 12g of 85% phosphoric acid are added in one portion. An ice-cold solution of 12g of sodium hydroxide in 40ml of water is rapidly added dropwise from a separatory funnel while stirring is maintained. To avoid decomposition during the addition of the alkali, the temperature should not rise above 70°C; if necessary, the reaction mixture should be temporarily cooled in cold water. When all of the sodium hydroxide has been added, the crystalline slurry is cooled to 15°C, suction-filtered, and washed carefully three times with 10-ml portions of ice water.

The product is dried *in vacuo.*

$$Yield = 16–18g \quad (95\% \text{ purity})$$

Free hydroxylamine is produced when this compound is distilled *in vacuo;* see reference 4.

References:
1. B:157; J:366; P:279.
2. ROLLEFSON AND OLDERSHAW, *J. Am. Chem. Soc.*, 54:977 (1932).
3. I, vol 3:81.
4. UHLENHUTH, *Ann.*, 311:117 (1900).

D. COORDINATION ANION

56. Ammonium Hexachloroplumbate (IV) **

(I)

$$PbCl_2 + 2HCl + Cl_2 \longrightarrow H_2PbCl_6$$
$$H_2PbCl_6 + 2NH_4Cl \longrightarrow (NH_4)_2PbCl_6 + 2HCl$$

[If lead chloride is not available, it may be prepared as follows: Fifteen grams of neutral lead acetate 3-hydrate are dissolved in 100ml of water and the solution made faintly acid to litmus with glacial acetic acid added dropwise. Filter if necessary and mix with a solution of 3.5g of sodium chloride in 25ml of water. The precipitation must be performed in the *cold* due to the solubility of the precipitated lead chloride in hot water. When the product has settled well, suction filter and wash the material thoroughly with alcohol (three 20-ml portions to facilitate drying) after draining off the mother liquor completely. Dry in air. Yield = 10g]

[CAUTION: Use the hood and wear rubber gloves during the following step.]

Ten grams of lead chloride are triturated in a mortar with 20ml of concentrated hydrochloric acid for about two minutes. The almost clear supernatant liquid is decanted into a 500-ml suction flask carrying a stopper with an inlet tube leading to within one-half inch of the bottom of the vessel. The trituration operation is repeated until the lead chloride is in solution (or extremely fine suspension) in 200ml of the acid.

The flask and reaction mixture are cooled in ice and a

steady stream of chlorine is introduced (2 bubbles/sec). The liquid soon turns yellow and after 2–5 hours all of the lead chloride has dissolved. The flask and contents should be shaken occasionally during the chlorination. If the final mixture is not completely clear, it should be filtered through an asbestos or glass filter. A solution of 8g of ammonium chloride in 80ml of ice-cold water is now added and the precipitate is allowed to settle for three hours in the ice bath. The yellow crystalline product is collected rapidly on a hardened filter or sintered glass funnel, drained well by suction, and washed with two 25ml portions each of cold alcohol and acetone. The material is dried *in vacuo*.

$$Yield = 20g$$

Good yields are obtained *only* if the oxidation of the divalent lead to the tetravalent stage is complete. To test for plumbous lead, add ten drops of the reaction mixture to five milliliters of water and boil gently for a few minutes to hydrolyze all the tetravalent lead to lead dioxide. When the latter settles, filter the hot mixture, cool under the tap, and add several drops of saturated potassium iodide. A yellow precipitate of lead iodide constitutes a positive test.

The complex salt hydrolyzes to lead dioxide on treatment with water or on prolonged standing in moist air. It should be preserved in tightly stoppered bottles.

COGNATE PREPARATION

Pyridinium hexachloroplumbate (IV), which is more resistant to heat and moisture than the ammonium salt (larger, less polarized cation) may be prepared by substituting a solution of 12g of pyridine in 80ml of 3M hydrochloric acid for the ammonium chloride solution used above.

$$Yield\ about\ 25g$$

Similar results are obtained with quinoline.

(II)

$$Pb(C_2H_3O_2)_4 + 6HCl \longrightarrow H_2PbCl_6 + 4HC_2H_3O_2$$
$$2NH_4Cl + H_2PbCl_6 \longrightarrow (NH_4)_2PbCl_6 + 2HCl$$

Twenty-five grams of lead tetraacetate (No. 78) are dissolved in 20ml of concentrated hydrochloric acid cooled to 0°C. A cold solution of 8g of ammonium chloride in 80ml of water is added slowly to the yellow liquid with stirring and continued cooling in ice. The complex ammonium salt is isolated by a similar procedure, in a yield comparable to that from (I). Care should be taken to allow for complete crystallization.

References:

1. B:143; J:377; P:248.
2. GUTBIER AND WISSMULLER, *J. prakt. Chem.*, 90:491 (1914).
3. FRIEDRICH, *Ber.*, 26:1434 (1893).

57. Ammonium Hexachlorostannate (IV) **

(I)

$$SnCl_2 + Cl_2 \longrightarrow SnCl_4$$
$$2NH_4Cl + SnCl_4 \longrightarrow (NH_4)_2SnCl_6$$

Twelve grams of stannous chloride 2-hydrate are dissolved in 75ml of $3M$ hydrochloric acid contained in a 250ml suction flask fitted with a stopper and gas delivery tube leading well under the surface of the solution. The flask and contents are immersed in an ice bath and chlorine is passed in (2–3 bubbles/sec) until oxidation is complete. This is indicated by a persistent yellow color in the reaction mixture due to excess chlorine. The chlorination will take 15 to 30 minutes at the above rate of introducing the gas. The solution of hexachlorostannic (IV) acid is now warmed to 50°C and a solution of 6g of ammonium chloride in 25ml of $3M$ hydrochloric acid at the same temperature are mixed together. The warm solution is evaporated to crystallization on the steam bath, cooled, filtered by suction, and drained well. The complex salt is dried *in vacuo* over solid alkali. The mother liquor is worked up for further batches of crystals.

Total Yield about 16g

(II)

$$SnCl_4 + 2HCl \longrightarrow H_2SnCl_6$$
$$2NH_4Cl + H_2SnCl_6 \longrightarrow (NH_4)_2SnCl_6 + 2HCl$$

Thirteen grams of stannic chloride (No. 84; CAUTION: Fuming corrosive liquid—hood!) are weighed into a small stoppered flask and then poured slowly with good stirring into 75ml of 3M hydrochloric acid cooled in ice. The clear solution of hexachlorostannic (IV) acid is treated with ammonium chloride at 50°C as described in (I) and the complex salt is isolated in similar yield.

References:
1. J:377.
2. DICKINSON, *J. Am. Chem. Soc.*, 44:276 (1922).
3. BOLLEY, *Liebig's Ann.*, 39:100 (1841).

58. Cobalt Tetrakis(thiocyanato)mercurate (II) *

$$Co(NO_3)_2 + 4KSCN + HgCl_2 \longrightarrow Co[Hg(SCN)_4] + 2KCl + 2KNO_3$$

Thirty grams of mercuric chloride and 44.5g of potassium thiocyanate are dissolved in 500ml of water and mixed with a solution of 20g of cobalt nitrate 6-hydrate in 50ml of water. A shower of small deep blue crystals of the difficultly soluble complex salt begins to form almost immediately. The mixture is allowed to stand for twelve hours to complete the precipitation and then suction-filtered. The product is washed with three 30ml portions of cold water, drained well, and then rinsed with two 25ml volumes of 95% alcohol to aid in drying. The material is dried in air or in the oven at 100°C.

Yield = 34g (quantitative)

If the solid obtained here is allowed to stand in contact with a little concentrated sodium carbonate solution for several hours, the cobalt is converted to reddish cobalt carbonate and the colorless supernatant liquid contains sodium tetrakis(thiocyanato)mercurate (II).

The formation of the blue complex cobalt salt serves as a sensitive test for the detection of either cobaltous or mercuric ions with a sensitivity of 1γ Co or 10γ of Hg in solution. Depending on the cation to be tested for, the test reagent consists of a concentrated solution of either mercuric chloride or cobaltous acetate containing alkali thiocyanate. The test may be carried out in one drop of liquid on a slide under a microscope (50–100X). Agitation of the drop with a platinum wire will often hasten the formation of the characteristic dark blue needles, which often occur in concentric aggregates.

Reference: B:147; J:179.

59. Potassium Hexacyanochromate (III) **

$$Cr_2O_7^{--} + 3SO_2 + 2H^+ \longrightarrow 2Cr^{+++} + 3SO_4^{--} + H_2O$$
$$Cr^{+++} + 3OH^- \longrightarrow Cr(OH)_3$$
$$Cr(OH)_3 + 3HC_2H_3O_2 \longrightarrow Cr(C_2H_3O_2)_3 + 3H_2O$$
$$Cr^{+++} + 6KCN \longrightarrow K_3[Cr(CN)_6] + 3K^+$$

[CAUTION: Extreme care must be exercised when working with cyanide compounds. It is recommended that the worker wear gloves and perform all operations in a hood to minimize the escape of deadly hydrogen cyanide fumes into the laboratory. Cyanide residues should be rinsed down the drain with *plenty* of water immediately after use.]

a) Preparation of Chromium (III) Acetate

If this salt (as the 1-hydrate) is available, this section of the experiment may be omitted and the procedure begun with part *b*).

Twenty-five grams of potassium dichromate (or 17g of chromium (VI) oxide) are dissolved in 500ml of water. Sulfur dioxide is bubbled into the solution until reduction to the trivalent state is complete, as indicated by the pure green color of the liquid with no trace of yellow. The solution is then boiled to remove excess sulfur dioxide.

Alternatively, the reduction may be carried out by adding the chromium (VI) compound to a mixture of 420ml of water and 80ml of concentrated hydrochloric acid and then adding 35ml of ethyl alcohol. The reduced solution is boiled as directed to remove excess alcohol and acetaldehyde (oxidation product). Either reduction procedure should be carried out in a hood.

The solution of chromic salt is heated to boiling and stirred continuously while concentrated ammonia water is added slowly from a tap funnel or burette. About 40ml are required to give a slight excess of the reagent. Avoid adding too much ammonia because chromium tends to form complex ammines.

The precipitated chromium (III) hydroxide is suction-filtered on a large Büchner funnel and washed thoroughly with three 100ml portions of boiling water. It is then transferred, while still moist, to an evaporating basin and dissolved in about 100ml of glacial acetic acid. The solution is evaporated (hood) *almost* to dryness over a very small flame, care being taken to stir the mass frequently towards the end of the operation. The tacky paste of chromium (III) acetate is now dissolved in 180ml of water.

b) As starting materials for the reaction with potassium cyanide, either the acetate solution prepared in the preceding step, or 42g of commercially available chromium (III) acetate 1-hydrate dissolved in 180ml of water, may be used.

If desired, the chloride, sulfate, or nitrate (0.17 mole of any hydrate) may also be employed, but the potassium salts that contaminate the final chromicyanide are not so readily removed from the product; potassium acetate is freely soluble in alcohol, but KCl, K_2SO_4, and KNO_3 are not.

The solution of the chromium (III) salt is poured into a boiling solution of 75g of potassium cyanide in about 300ml of water. Two grams of activated charcoal are added, and after stirring the hot mixture for several minutes it is filtered and evaporated to 300ml on a steam bath in an evaporating dish. The hot solution is treated with charcoal as before and filtered while hot. On cooling in ice, the product crystallizes out as pale-yellow needles. The material is suction filtered and pressed well. The mother liquor is further evaporated to obtain two or three more crops of product. After draining off the main aqueous liquor, each batch of crystals is thoroughly washed with two 25ml portions of 95% alcohol, and dried in a desiccator away from light. To obtain a pure product (the crude material is satisfactory for most purposes) two or three crystallizations from water (not over 60°C) are necessary. Precipitation from aqueous solution by alcohol is somewhat less satisfactory.

Total crude yield about 35 grams

The solubility of the complex salt in water is about 31g/100ml at 20°C.

References:
1. I, vol. 2:203.
2. CRUSER AND MILLER, J. Am. Chem. Soc., 28:1132 (1906).
3. CHRISTENSEN, J. prakt. Chem. (2) 31:163 (1885).

60. Potassium Hexacyanocobaltate (III) *

(I)

$$CoCl_2 + 2KCN \longrightarrow Co(CN)_2 + 2KCl$$
$$Co(CN)_2 + 4KCN \longrightarrow K_4[Co(CN)_6]$$
$$2K_4[Co(CN)_6] + 2H_2O \longrightarrow 2K_3[Co(CN)_6] + 2KOH + H_2$$

A solution of 30g of potassium cyanide in 200 ml of water is added slowly from a separatory funnel to a well-stirred boiling solution of 48g of cobalt chloride 6-hydrate in 500ml of water. The buff-violet precipitate of cobalt cyanide (hydrated) is filtered by suction and washed with two 50-ml portions of cold water. The moist salt is transferred to a 600-ml beaker containing a solution of 60g of potassium cyanide in 175ml of water and stirred until solution is complete. A slight excess of alkali cyanide is used to prevent precipitation of green $K_2Co[Co(CN)_6]$ on standing; this occurs if not enough cyanide is present. The dark red solution of potassium hexacyanocobaltate (II) is heated to boiling over a *small* flame and maintained at this temperature for 10–15 minutes. The color of the liquid changes to pale yellow with evolution of hydrogen during this time. The solution is filtered while hot if necessary and cooled in ice. Very light yellow crystals of product separate, which are filtered off, and drained well. Two or three more crops of material can be isolated from the mother liquor by evaporating it on the steam bath, and then filtering and cooling it. If desired, the complex salt may be purified by recrystallization from water.

Crude yield about 60g (90%)

The product, if pure, will give little or no precipitate when boiled with a little dilute acetic acid. Losses incurred during recrystallization may be minimized by evaporating the solvent on a steam bath in order to recover a part of the large quantity of product that remains in solution.

(II)

$$4CoCO_3 + 24KCN + 2H_2O + O_2 \longrightarrow 4K_3[Co(CN)_6] + 4K_2CO_3 + 4KOH$$
$$K_2CO_3 + KOH + 3HC_2H_3O_2 \longrightarrow 3KC_2H_3O_2 + CO_2 + 2H_2O$$

Thirty grams of cobalt carbonate are triturated to a paste in a mortar with 20ml of water and then washed into a beaker with 80ml of water. A solution of 110g of potassium cyanide in 400ml of water is now added and the mixture stirred until the cobalt carbonate has dissolved. The solution is poured into a one-liter suction flask fitted with a stopper and inlet tube leading almost to the bottom of the vessel. The side arm of the flask is connected to the water pump and a vigorous stream of air is drawn through the liquid for one hour. The dark yellow oxidized solution is filtered and treated with 40ml of glacial acetic acid.

[CAUTION: Foaming! This operation, as well as the rest of the experiment, MUST be carried out in a well-ventilated hood because vapors of hydrogen cyanide (from the excess of the potassium salt used) are liberated by the acid.]

The acidified mixture is evaporated to crystallization on the steam bath, filtered, and cooled in ice. The product is then suction-filtered off and rinsed free of adhering potassium acetate with a 2:1 alcohol-water mixture (three 25ml portions). The mother liquor (without the washings) is evaporated further and several more crops of product are isolated as described. Finally, when the volume of residual liquid has reached 100ml, the rest of the complex salt is precipitated out by the addition of 200 ml of 95% ethyl alcohol. The combined product may be purified further by precipitation with 2–3 volumes of 95% alcohol from a saturated aqueous solution or by recrystallization from water as in (I).

Yield about 60g

60 a. Hexacyanocobaltic (III) Acid 5-Hydrate **

$$H_3[Co(CN)_6] \cdot 5H_2O$$

This compound may be prepared from its potassium salt as follows:

A saturated aqueous solution containing 10g of the latter salt is placed in a 50ml suction flask fitted with a stopper and delivery tube at least 10mm wide. The vessel is cooled in tap water while a steady stream of hydrogen chloride is introduced. [CAUTION: Use an empty trap in the apparatus to avoid suck-back.]

When precipitation appears complete the flow of gas is stopped and the white solid, consisting of potassium chloride and the complex acid, is filtered off and thoroughly drained on the filter. The residue is treated in a stoppered flask with two 20ml portions of absolute alcohol and refiltered. The potassium chloride remains behind whereas the acid passes into solution and is recovered as colorless glistening needles by evaporating the alcohol at room temperature with a stream of *dry* air or nitrogen. The material should be stored in tightly stoppered all-glass bottles out of the light.

Yield about 8g

The free acid is completely ionized in aqueous solution and may be used to prepare cobalticyanides of other cations by the usual acid-base reactions.

References:

1. I, vol. 2:225.
2. Benedetti-Pichler, *Z. anal. Chem.*, 70:258 (1927).
3. GRUBE, *Z. Elektrochem.*, 32:561 (1926).
4. Zwenger, *Ann.*, 62:163 (1847).

61. Potassium Hexacyanomanganate (III) *

$$3Mn(NO_3)_2 + 3H_3PO_4 \longrightarrow 3MnPO_4 + NO + 5HNO_3 + 2H_2O$$
$$MnPO_4 + 6KCN \longrightarrow K_3[Mn(CN)_6] + K_3PO_4$$

Fourteen grams of concentrated nitric acid are mixed with 42g of 85% phosphoric acid contained in an evaporating dish. Ninety milliliters of a 50% (by weight) solution of manganese (II) nitrate are stirred in, the dish is covered with a close-fitting watch glass and heated on the steam bath, preferably in the hood. The color of the solution soon changes to amethyst, and oxides of nitrogen are evolved. The olive-green product settles out on the bottom of the vessel and some of it adheres tenaciously to the sides of the dish. When considerable material has formed, the mixture is suction-filtered and washed carefully with two 20ml portions of water, allowing the washings to run into the mother liquor. The filtrate is further heated on the steam bath and the residue on the filter is rinsed with 20ml of acetone to facilitate drying. The reaction mixture is worked over three or four more times in this manner and finally evaporated to a heavy sludge which is treated as described to isolate more of the product. The material is dried in air.

Total Yield = 65g (1-hydrate)

This yield is quantitative based on the phosphoric acid. The product should be acid-free for further use; otherwise it must be washed with water and acetone until the rinsings are neutral to litmus.

Thirty-nine grams of manganese (III) phosphate monohydrate are added in 5g portions with stirring to a solution of 150g of potassium cyanide in 400ml of water at 75°C. The latter solution is prepared by stirring the cyanide into the water previously heated to 95°C. The strong endothermic heat of solution reduces the temperature to about 75°C. As the phosphate is added to the cyanide the heat of the reaction maintains the temperature between 75–80°C. A deep red liquid forms and a fresh portion of phosphate is added only when the previous one has completely dissolved. At no time should the temperature exceed 80°C; otherwise manganese (III) oxide is precipitated, causing a loss in yield. The solution is filtered by suction while hot, if necessary, using one gram of Celite as a filter aid, and then allowed to stand under a hood in a large open evaporating dish. The brick-red product that forms is filtered off daily over a period of about one week. Any crystalline crusts which form on the surface of the liquid are broken up to facilitate evaporation. When the volume of the mother liquor has reached 300ml and the color has become a very pale orange, the isolation of product is complete. Dry *in vacuo.*

Total Yield = 70g or 92% based on manganese (III) phosphate

The salt dissolves in cold water but hydrolyzes after some time to yield dark brown $Mn(OH)_3$. It forms insoluble precipitates with many coordinated cations, e.g., [Co-$(NH_3)_6]^{+++}$ and $(Cren_3)^{+++}$.

For the preparation of the complex cyanide from potassium pentafluoroaquomanganate (III), $K_2[MnF_5(H_2O)]$, see Palmer, pp. 479, 481. The advantage of this method is that it can be carried out at room temperature, thus avoiding the possible decomposition of the product.

References:

1. I, vol. 2:213.
2. CHRISTENSEN, *J. prakt. Chem.* (2), 28:20 (1883); *Ibid.*, (2), 31:167 (1885).
3. MEYER, *Z. anorg. Chem.*, 81:390 (1913).

62. Potassium Hexafluoromanganate (IV) **

$$4KMnO_4 + 20HF + 4KF + 3C_4H_{10}O \longrightarrow 4K_2MnF_6 + 3C_4H_8O_2 + 13H_2O$$

[CAUTION: Plastic beakers and stirring rods are required for this preparation. An apron, goggles, and rubber gloves must be worn at all times when handling hydrofluoric acid.]

Eighty-nine grams of 48% hydrofluoric acid are mixed with 11ml of water in a 150ml plastic beaker and 8.9g of anhydrous potassium carbonate are added in portions with stirring. When the effervescence has subsided, the solution of potassium hydrogen fluoride, KHF_2, is cooled thoroughly in an ice bath and 8g of powdered potassium permanganate are stirred in. Without delay, absolute ether (*free* from alcohol and peroxides), is added dropwise, with good stirring, from a medicine dropper or a small burette. To avoid any possible reaction with the non-vitreous material, the ether should be run into the center of the solution and not onto the walls of the plastic vessel. About 2ml of ether are required for the complete discharge of the characteristic purple color of the permanaganate. A brown liquid and yellow crystals of product remain at the end of the reaction; the mixture is left for 20 minutes in the ice bath and then the clear liquid is decanted into a second plastic beaker as completely as possible in order to avoid etching the filter flask subsequently. The brown mother liquor is reserved for the isolation of $K_3(MnF_6)$. The crystals of product are transferred to the suction filter with about 25–30 ml of glacial acetic acid, pressed dry, washed twice more with 20ml portions of acid, and finally with a similar quantity of acetone. The complex fluoride is dried *in vacuo* on *filter paper*.

$$Yield = 7.5–8.0g$$

The product must be stored out of contact with moist air in plastic or paraffin coated vials because water causes instant hydrolysis to MnO_2, and the fluoride, itself, etches glass with the formation of a brown deposit.

Most of the ethyl ether used in the reduction is oxidized to ethyl acetate, and about one-half of the manganese is further reduced to the trivalent stage and remains in solution.

When 4g of potassium hydrogen fluoride are dissolved in the clear brown liquid (reserved as directed) and the mixture is allowed to stand in ice overnight, crystals of red-brown **potassium hexafluoromanganate** (III) can be isolated from the solution by the method just outlined for the tetravalent complex fluoride.

References:
1. P:484.
2. WEINLAND AND LAUENSTEIN, *Z. anorg. Chem.*, 20:40 (1899).

63. Potassium Hexathiocyanatochromate (III) *

(I)

$$KCr(SO_4)_2 + 6KSCN \longrightarrow K_3Cr(SCN)_6 + 2K_2SO_4$$

Twelve grams of potassium thiocyanate are heated *very* gently in an evaporating dish until the salt just begins to melt, around 170°C. Gentle heating is continued while 10g of finely powdered potassium chrome alum is sifted onto the fused salt in about 1-gram portions from a spatula. The mixture is stirred well after each addition and the evolution of steam is allowed to subside before more alum is added. The reddish-violet reaction mixture, which is almost solid towards the end of the fusion, is finally allowed to cool in a desiccator to avoid deliquescence. The cold melt is quickly scraped into 75ml of 95% ethanol contained in a mortar, and thoroughly triturated with the liquid. The residue of potassium sulfate is removed by suction-filtration and washed with 10ml of alcohol. The combined filtrate and washing are evaporated on the steam bath almost to dryness and the semi-solid residue is dried *in vacuo*. The crude material is recrystallized by dissolving it in the minimum of absolute methanol (filtering if necessary), and allowing the solution to evaporate spontaneously at atmospheric pressure over concentrated sulfuric acid. The purple-red product (4-hydrate) is stored in dark-colored, tightly sealed vessels because it is very deliquescent and photo-sensitive, especially when hydrated.

$$\text{Yield} = 8\text{g} \quad (96\% \text{ based on the alum})$$

(II)

$$Cr(NO_3)_3 + 6KSCN \longrightarrow K_3Cr(SCN)_6 + 3KNO_3$$

Twenty grams of chromium nitrate 9-hydrate, or 0.05 moles of the hydrated sulfate or chloride, are fused with 30g of potassium thiocyanate as in (I), and the melt allowed to cool in a desiccator and then triturated with 25ml portions of ethyl acetate until no more material dissolves. The violet liquid is filtered; a small green residue remains behind together with the potassium nitrate, sulfate, or chloride. The ethyl acetate extract is evaporated to dryness on the steam bath and the violet residue is further dried *in vacuo*. The anhydrous salt is violet.

$$\text{Yield (based on the chromium salt)} = 22\text{g}$$
$$(\text{Theory} = 26\text{g})$$

The product should be stored out of light. Cold aqueous solutions of pure potassium hexathiocyanatochromate (III), when freshly prepared, give no color with ferric salts. In very dilute or hot solution, however, the complex anion is dissociated.

Many salts with large cations, e.g. pyridine, quinoline, hexamminecobalt (III), yield relatively stable and insoluble products with the complex salt by simple metathetical reactions.

COGNATE PREAPARATIONS

63 a. Pyridinium Hexathiocyanatochromate (III) 1-Hydrate *

Two milliliters of pure pyridine are dissolved in 20ml of $1.5N$ hydrochloric acid and mixed with a solution of 3.5g of the hydrated potassium salt in 15ml of water. The red-violet pyridine salt precipitates quantitatively at once, leaving an almost colorless supernatant liquid. The salt is filtered off and washed with 10ml of water containing five drops of pyridine, and then dried in the dark in warm air. The product is soluble in polar organic solvents, as is the potassium salt. As all thiocyanatochromates are fairly photosensitive they must be kept away from direct light.

63 b. Ammonium Hexathiocyanatochromate (III) 4-Hydrate

This analogue is easily prepared by evaporating the equivalent quantities of chromium chloride 6-hydrate and ammonium thiocyanate in aqueous solution to dryness on the steam bath and extracting the residue with absolute alcohol. Evaporation of the alcoholic extract yields the red salt.

References:

1. P:391.
2. ROESLER, *Ann.*, 141:185 (1867).
3. BJERRUM, *Z. anorg. Chem.*, 118:131 (1921); 119:39, 179 (1921).

64. Potassium Octacyanomolybdate (IV) 2-Hydrate ***

$$K_2MoO_4 + 2HCl \longrightarrow H_2MoO_4 + 2KCl$$

$$(MoO_3 \cdot H_2O)H_2MoO_4 \xrightarrow{KSCN} MoO_2(SCN)_3 \xrightarrow{C_5H_5N}$$

$$MoO_2(SCN)_3 \cdot 2C_5H_5N \xrightarrow{KCN} K_4Mo(CN)_8$$

Eighty-three grams of potassium molybdate are dissolved in 100ml of water; or 50g of pure molybdenum (VI) oxide are treated with a solution of 40g of potassium hydroxide in 100ml of water. Two hundred and fifty milliliters of concentrated hydrochloric acid are now added slowly from a dropping funnel with constant stirring and the entire mixture is heated on the steam bath while a solution of 150g of potassium thiocyanate in 150ml water is slowly stirred into the hot liquid. The resulting blood-red solution is now heated on the steam bath in the hood for two hours with frequent stirring.

The liquid is filtered by suction while hot to remove a black by-product and cooled in an ice bath while 70ml of pyridine are added slowly (with good stirring) from a separatory funnel. A red oily layer precipitates which soon becomes very viscous in the ice bath. The supernatant liquid, which is still pale red in color, is decanted and the oil is rinsed twice with two 50ml portions of ice-cold water.

A solution of 200g of potassium cyanide in 300ml of water is added to the oil obtained in the preceding step. As poisonous cyanotic gases are evolved, this must be done in a well-ventilated hood. The oil dissolves rapidly to give first a green and then a yellow-brown solution which is heated on a steam bath for one-half an hour with occasional stirring. It is then suction-filtered (hood) to remove a black material. The filtrate is evaporated on the water bath to one-half its original volume, cooled in ice, and filtered. The *filtrate* may be reserved for further treatment by purification (b) ; otherwise it is discarded.

Purification of Product

a) The yellowish-black crystalline solid obtained in the preceding step is dissolved in the minimum amount of boiling water needed; a black impurity remains behind. Five grams of decolorizing charcoal are stirred in for about five minutes and the hot material is suction-filtered and cooled in ice.

About two volumes of ethanol are added and crystallization is completed by allowing the mixture to stand in ice for about thirty minutes. The golden-yellow crystals are fil-

tered off, washed with two 50ml portions of alcohol and a
similar quantity of ether, and dried in air.

Yield about 80g

b) The crude residue is treated with boiling water and
charcoal, as in *a*), and the filtrate is reheated gently to
boiling and continuously stirred while a faintly acid solution of 140g of cadmium chloride 2½-hydrate in 200ml of
water is added slowly. When no more yellow cadmium octacyanomolybdate (IV) 8-hydrate settles out, the addition is
discontinued. The solid is filtered off, washed with about
100ml of hot water, rinsed with the same amount of alcohol,
and then dried in warm air.

After the crude product is separated the *filtrate* obtained
from the cyanide treatment previously described is diluted
to about 500ml with water, boiled for five minutes with
approximately 5g of charcoal, and filtered while hot. The
boiling filtrate is treated with aqueous cadmium chloride,
as described, to remove the remaining octacyanomolybdate
from the excess thiocyanate present. Although this batch of
cadmium salt is not so pure as the material obtained the
first time, further purification is not necessary for the decomposition step that follows.

Total yield of cadmium salt, about 125g

The cadmium salt is mixed with 175ml of concentrated
aqueous ammonia and warmed gently until solution is complete, adding a little more ammonia if necessary. The warm
liquid is added slowly to a boiling solution of 100g of anhydrous potassium carbonate in 1500ml of water and stirred
continuously on the steam bath for about 30 minutes. The
precipitated cadmium carbonate is filtered off and washed
with 50ml of hot water. The filtrate is evaporated until the
ammonia has been driven off and it is then refiltered to remove further amounts of cadmium carbonate. Finally the
liquid is concentrated to a volume of about 200ml, filtered
hot, if necessary, and cooled in ice while 300–400ml of alcohol are added. The mixture is cooled and stirred until the
precipitated product is solid. The material is filtered and
the residue is triturated in a large mortar with a solution

of 10ml of glacial acetic acid in 150ml of alcohol, to remove adherent potassium carbonate. The crystals are refiltered and washed carefully with three 50ml portions of alcohol until acid-free and then are dried in air.

$$Yield = 90-100g$$

The compound loses its water of hydration at 110°C. Aqueous solutions are photosensitive and as they are eventually decomposed by sunlight, with evolution of hydrogen cyanide, the color of the liquid changes first to red and then to pale green.

References:

1. I, vol. 3:160; P:410.
2. WILLARD AND THIELKE, *J. Am. Chem. Soc.*, 57:2609 (1935).
3. ROSENHEIM AND KOSS, *Z. anorg. Chem.*, 49:148 (1906).
4. ROSENHEIM, *Ibid.*, 54:97 (1907).
5. ROSENHEIM, GARFUNKEL AND KOHN, *Ibid.*, 65:166 (1910).
6. BUCKNALL AND WARDLAW, *J. Chem. Soc.*, 1927:2983.
7. SAND AND BURGER, *Ber.*, 38:3384 (1905).
8. JAKOB AND TURKIEWICZ, *Chem. Abstracts*, 26:2933 (1932).
9. FIESER, *J. Am. Chem. Soc.*, 52:5226 (1930).

65. Potassium Pentanitromercurate (II) 1-Hydrate *

$$HgO + 5KNO_2 + 2HC_2H_3O_2 \longrightarrow K_3[Hg(NO_2)_5] + 2KC_2H_3O_2 + H_2O$$

Seventy-five grams of pure potassium nitrite are dissolved in 240g of 10% acetic acid, and 21.5g of yellow or red mercuric oxide are added. The mixture is agitated until all the oxide has dissolved; gentle heating aids in the solution of the last traces. The yellow liquid is evaporated on the steam bath to a volume of about 50ml and cooled in ice. The product is filtered off and washed with three 30ml portions of alcohol which are allowed to run into the mother liquor. A further crop of crystals can be isolated by working up the combined filtrate through evaporation. The residual liquid is thoroughly triturated with about 30ml of 95% alcohol to obtain more product; the potassium acetate is readily soluble in alcohol. Yields of 90% and over can easily be obtained.

An aqueous solution of the very pale yellow product gives no precipitate with urea or with cold sodium bicarbonate solution saturated with carbon dioxide. Alkali, in the form of sodium hydroxide or carbonate, precipitates yellow mercuric oxide. These reactions indicate that the degree of dissociation of the complex anion is about the same as that of mercuric chloride.

Reference: B:140.

66. Potassium Tetracyanonickelate (II) 1-Hydrate *

$$Ni^{++} + 2CN^- \longrightarrow Ni(CN)_2$$
$$Ni(CN)_2 + 2KCN \longrightarrow K_2[Ni(CN)_4]$$

Six one-hundredths of a mole of any soluble nickel salt (16g of the sulfate, 14.5g chloride, or 17.5g nitrate—all 6-hydrate) is dissolved in 100ml of boiling water and a solution of 7g of pure potassium cyanide in 100ml water is slowly added dropwise with stirring. The liquid and its gray-green precipitate of hydrated nickel cyanide are digested for one hour on the steam bath (optional) to render the solid more easily filterable. The precipitate is collected on a Büchner funnel, washed with three 20ml portions of hot water, and pressed down well.

The moist cake of residue and paper is transferred to a small dish and the filter paper is peeled clean from the solid, which is then re-moistened with about 10ml of water. On addition of a solution of 7g more of potassium cyanide in 15ml of water, the nickel cyanide dissolves with the formation of an orange-red solution. The clear liquid is evaporated to crystallization on the steam bath, cooled in ice, suction-filtered, and dried in air.

$$\text{Yield} = 12\text{--}13g$$

Addition of potassium cyanide to aqueous solutions of the salt causes a marked deepening of the color, probably due to the formation of the unstable hexacyanonickelate (II) ion. Mineral acids decompose the complex salt to form nickel cyanide; alkaline oxidants destroy the material with the production of black hydrated nickel (III) oxide.

References:
  1. I, vol. 2:227; P:558
  2. CORBET, J. Chem. Soc., 1926:3190.

67. Potassium Tetraiodomercurate (II) 2-Hydrate *

$$HgCl_2 + 2KI \longrightarrow HgI_2 + 2KCl$$
$$HgI_2 + 2KI \longrightarrow K_2[HgI_4]$$

A solution of 13.5g of mercuric chloride in 200ml of water is mixed with 16.6g of potassium iodide in 150ml of water and the red precipitate of mercuric iodide is filtered off, washed with two 25ml portions of water, and drained dry. It is then dissolved in a hot solution of 16g more of potassium iodide in 10ml of water, the yellow supernatant liquid is decanted from the small residue of undissolved mercuric iodide, and allowed to crystallize *in vacuo* over concentrated *sulphuric acid*. The crystalline crusts on the surface should be broken up from time to time. The final paste of light-yellow crystals is completely dried in an ordinary desiccator. Based on the mercuric chloride taken, the yield is almost quantitative. The product is deliquescent and should be stored in tightly stoppered vessels to avoid absorption of moisture from the air.

The well known Nessler's reagent for ammonia is a solution of mercuric oxide in aqueous potassium iodide.

$$HgO + 4KI + H_2O \longrightarrow K_2HgI_4 + 2KOH$$

The copper (I) and silver salts of tetraiodomercuric (II) acid, $H_2[HgI_4]$, exhibit color changes with variations in temperature which are reversible in nature.

COGNATE PREPARATIONS

67 a. Copper (I) Tetraiodomercurate *

Mercuric iodide is precipitated by mixing solutions containing 6.8g of mercuric chloride and 8.3g of potassium iodide. The washed material is dissolved in 50ml of water containing a similar quantity of potassium iodide, and mixed with a saturated aqueous solution of 12g of copper sulfate 5-hydrate. A stream of sulfur dioxide is passed into the mixture until precipitation is complete and the supernatant liquid is very faintly colored.

$$2Cu^{++} + SO_2 + 2H_2O \longrightarrow 2Cu^+ + SO_4^= + 4H^+$$

The deep red salt is filtered off, washed with water, and irrigated with 50ml of acetone to facilitate drying in warm air. Yield about 20g.

By means of a melting point capillary and a water bath, the transition point from red to black is easily observed. The procedure may be hastened by pre-heating the bath to about 65°C.

67 b. Silver Tetraiodomercurate (II) *

A solution of the potassium salt is prepared in 50ml of water (using the directions given for the cuprous compound) and mixed with 8.5g of silver nitrate in 150ml of water. The bright yellow precipitate is isolated as in the previous procedure. Yield, quantitative.

Determine the range of temperature for the transition point of this salt as described for the preceding. The color changes from yellow through orange to red.

Both the copper (I) and the silver salts may be prepared more simply by merely boiling together aqueous suspensions of the stoichiometrically correct quantities of the iodides for 30 minutes in aqueous suspension.

$$2CuI + HgI_2 \longrightarrow Cu_2[HgI_4] \quad 2AgI + HgI_2 \longrightarrow Ag_2[HgI_4]$$

References:

1. B:37, 145; J:377; P:191.
2. STEGER, Z. physikal. Chem., 43:595 (1903).
3. KOCH AND WAGNER, Ibid. [B], 34:317 (1936).
4. TAMMAN AND VESZI, Z. anorg. Chem., 168:46 (1927).
5. PERNOT, Ann. Chim. [10], 15:1 (1931).
6. MEUSEL, Ber., 3:123 (1870).

68. Potassium Tetrakis(thiocyanato)cobaltate (II) *

$$Co(NO_3)_2 + 4KSCN \longrightarrow K_2[Co(SCN)_4] + 2KNO_3$$

A mixture of 0.05 mole of a cobalt salt (14.5g of the nitrate or 12g of the chloride—both 6-hydrate) and 21g of potassium thiocyanate are heated in 30ml of water until solution is complete. The dark blue liquid is cooled in ice until crystallization of potassium nitrate or chloride is complete and then suction-filtered. The residue is washed repeatedly with 10ml portions of ethyl acetate until it is almost colorless. The aqueous filtrate is combined with the organic solvent, transferred to a separatory funnel, and then thoroughly shaken. The two layers, both of which are strongly colored, must be separated by strong transmitted light to distinguish the liquid interface. The bottom (aqueous) layer is extracted twice more with 25ml portions of the ester and it should then be virtually colorless. The combined organic extracts are freed mechanically from remaining drops of aqueous solution by pouring the liquid cautiously into a clean dry evaporating dish. The solvent is completely removed on the steam bath and the slightly tacky blue residual product is dried *in vacuo*. The yield is almost quantitative, based on the cobalt salt taken.

In concentrated aqueous solution the product has a blue color which turns pink on dilution because of the dissociation of the complex; and it reverts to blue on addition of solid potassium thiocyanate.

$$[Co(SCN)_4]^{--} \rightleftharpoons Co^{++} + 4SCN^-$$

In this respect, the potassium salt behaves exactly similarly to the cobalt compound (see No. 36).

Reference: B:147.

69. Potassium Trioxalatoaluminate (III) 3-Hydrate *

(I)

$$Al_2(SO_4)_3 + 6NaOH \longrightarrow 2Al(OH)_3 + 3Na_2SO_4$$
$$2Al(OH)_3 + 3K_2C_2O_4 + 3H_2C_2O_4 \longrightarrow 2K_3[Al(C_2O_4)_3] + 6H_2O$$

A hot solution of 67g of aluminum sulfate 18-hydrate in 300ml water is treated with 24g of sodium hydroxide in 300ml of water, and the resulting mixture is digested on the steam bath for one hour. The gelatinous aluminum hydroxide is suction-filtered on a large funnel, washed three times with 50ml of hot water, and then pressed down well. The moist filter cake is transferred to a beaker and the paper peeled off clean. The gel is then gently boiled with 55.2g of potassium oxalate monohydrate and 37.8g of oxalic acid 2-hydrate in 400ml of water until no more of the hydrous oxide dissolves. This is filtered hot and the filtrate is evaporated to crystallization on the steam bath. The white product is removed without washing and successive crops of crystals are isolated. The final residual mother liquor is treated with one to two volumes of 95% alcohol to precipitate the remaining salt. The yield is almost quantitative, based on the aluminum salt.

In this procedure 0.1 mole of any soluble aluminum salt may be used; and 40ml of concentrated aqueous ammonia in 300ml of water can be substituted for the alkali in the precipitation step.

(II)

$$2Al + 2KOH + 6H_2O \longrightarrow 2KAl(OH)_4 + 3H_2$$
$$KAl(OH)_4 + K_2C_2O_4 + 2H_2C_2O_4 \longrightarrow K_3[Al(C_2O_4)_3] + 4H_2O$$

One gram of pure aluminum turnings is placed in a 200-ml beaker and covered with 10ml of hot water. A solution of 6g of potassium hydroxide in 30ml of water is added in small portions to regulate the vigorous evolution of hydrogen. Finally, the liquid is heated almost to boiling in order to dissolve any residual metal. Heating is maintained while first 10ml of water are added, and then 14g of oxalic acid 2-hydrate in small portions. During the neutralization hydrated alumina precipitates, but it redissolves at the end of the addition after further gentle boiling. The solution is filtered, if necessary, and cooled under the tap to room temperature while 50ml of 95% alcohol is added. The mixture is further cooled in ice until crystallization is complete. Any oily material which may separate at first soon solidifies with vigorous stirring and cooling; scratching the walls of the vessel with the stirring rod is also effective. The complex salt is washed on the filter with a 20ml portion of cold 1:1 alcohol-water, and finally with a similar quantity of pure alcohol. It is dried in the air.

Yield = 11g

This material has been resolved into its two optically active mirror images; as produced here it is a racemic mixture of the d and l forms.

References: I, vol. 1:36; P:213.

70. Potassium Trioxalatochromate (III) 3-Hydrate *

$$K_2Cr_2O_7 + 7H\ C_2O_4 + 2K_2C_2O_4 \longrightarrow 2K_3[Cr(C_2O_4)_3] + 6CO_2 + 7H_2O$$

One hundred and ten grams of oxalic acid 2-hydrate are suspended in 200ml of cold water in a one liter beaker and 36g of potassium dichromate are stirred in. The orange mixture soon warms up spontaneously almost to the boiling point as the vigorous evolution of gas starts. When the reaction is over, 42g of potassium oxalate monohydrate are dissolved in the hot liquid, which has become green-black in color. The fairly viscous reaction mixture is transferred to a smaller vessel and cooled in ice. About 1ml of the solution is mixed with 5ml of 95% alcohol and the pasty precipitated solid is used for seeding as directed below. Sixty milliliters of 95% alcohol are stirred into the main solution and cooling is continued while the solid for seeding is introduced. The whole liquid soon thickens with crystals which are filtered off after standing in ice for 15–30 minutes. Addition of 40ml of 95% alcohol to the filtrate yields 3g more of product. The blue-green crystals are washed on the filter with three 30ml portions of cold 1:1 alcohol-water, and then with 50ml of 95% ethanol. The product is dried in air.

Yield = 88g

If only 50ml of alcohol are used in the precipitation the yield is decreased to 83g; and the use of 250ml of water for the reaction drops the yield to 77g. The reaction may be readily scaled down to give proportionate yields.

Addition of aqueous barium chloride to the potassium salt yields the bluish insoluble barium trioxalatochromate (III). Many other heavy metal ions and coordination cations give insoluble chromioxalates which are interesting from the standpoint of inorganic isomerism.

The product, which is a racemic mixture of d and l forms, has been resolved into its enantiomers by Werner.

References:

1. J:379; I, vol. 1:37; P:386.
2. GRAHAM, Ann., 29:9 (1839).
3. WERNER, Ber., 45:3061 (1912).

71. Potassium Trioxalatocobaltate (III) 3-Hydrate **

$$CoCO_3 + H_2C_2O_4 + K_2C_2O_4 \longrightarrow K_2[Co(C_2O_4)_2] + CO_2 + H_2O$$
$$2K_2[Co(C_2O_4)_2] + 2K_2C_2O_4 + PbO_2 + 4HC_2H_3O_2 \longrightarrow$$
$$2K_3[Co(C_2O_4)_3] + Pb(C_2H_3O_2)_2 + 2KC_2H_3O_2 + 2H_2O$$

Thirty-seven grams of potassium oxalate monohydrate and 12.5g of oxalic acid 2-hydrate are dissolved in 250ml of boiling water and 12g of cobalt carbonate are added in small portions to avoid excessive effervescence. When the reaction is over, the deep purple solution containing potassium dioxalatocobaltate (II) is cooled to 40°C and stirred mechanically. It is advisable, though not necessary, to surround the reaction vessel with a water bath maintained around 35°C, as the ensuing oxidation proceeds relatively slowly at temperatures below 30°C. Twelve grams of powdered lead dioxide are added in portions to the briskly stirred liquid, followed by 12–13ml of glacial acetic acid added in drops from a burette over a period of 15–30 minutes. As the oxidation to the trivalent state of cobalt takes place only during and after the addition of the acid, the mixture must be stirred at 30–40°C for one hour longer, whereupon the color of the liquid changes to dark green. The unused lead dioxide is then filtered off by suction, the filtrate is cooled in ice and stirred while 250ml of 95% alcohol are slowly added from a separatory funnel. The precipitated green needles of product are filtered off and washed with 25ml of cold 1:1 alcohol-water and then with 25ml of alcohol. The product must be dried in a dark place which is not too warm, because decomposition by heat and light cause a pink layer of cobaltous oxalate to form on the surface.

Yield = 25–35g

The final operations of the preparation should be conducted without interruption because aqueous solutions of the complex salt are unstable, especially to light, and deposit insoluble cobalt (II) oxalate on standing. If decomposition of the preparation is suspected, the mother liquor from the alcohol precipitation should be decanted from the product, carrying with it the finely divided cobaltous oxalate. The product that remains may then be brought onto the filter with about 50ml of a cold equivolume mixture of alcohol and water.

The racemic complex oxalate has been resolved by the fractional crystallization of the cations of optically active bases. As the product itself is "self-resolving," it may be separated into its d and l forms by simply crystallizing above the transition temperature of 13.2°C; the two isomers settle out independently.

References:

1. I, vol. 1:37; P:550 (Salt listed as a 3½-hydrate).
2. SORENSEN, *Z. anorg. Chem.*, 11:2 (1896).

72. Potassium Trioxalatoferrate (III) 3-Hydrate *

(I)

$$BaCl_2 + C_2O_4^{--} \longrightarrow BaC_2O_4 + 2Cl^-$$
$$Fe_2(SO_4)_3 + 3BaC_2O_4 + 3K_2C_2O_4 \longrightarrow 2K_3Fe(C_2O_4)_3 + 3BaSO_4$$

Fifty grams of barium chloride 2-hydrate are dissolved in 250ml of water and mixed with a saturated solution of 29.3g of sodium oxalate in water at 70°C. (Forty grams of potassium oxalate monohydrate in 200ml of water may be substituted for the sodium salt.) The mixture is cooled and filtered, and the precipitate washed 3 times with 30ml of water. It is then suspended in 600ml of water containing 25g of ferric sulfate and 27.3g of potassium oxalate monohydrate and the entire mixture digested on the steam bath for about 3 hours with occasional stirring in the absence of direct light. The barium sulfate is filtered off and washed with 50ml of hot water; the filtrate and washing are then evaporated to 100ml on the steam bath in the dark and allowed to cool in ice. The yellow-green crystals that settle out are dried in the dark after filtering.

Yield almost quantitative (based on iron salt)

(II)

$$Fe(NH_4)_2(SO_4)_2 + H_2C_2O_4 \longrightarrow FeC_2O_4 + (NH_4)_2SO_4 + H_2SO_4$$
$$2FeC_2O_4 + 3K_2C_2O_4 + H_2C_2O_4 + H_2O_2 \longrightarrow 2K_3[Fe(C_2O_4)_3] + 2H_2O$$

Fifteen grams of Mohr's salt (ferrous ammonium sulfate 6-hydrate) are dissolved in 50ml of water containing one ml of 3*M* sulfuric acid. The solution is stirred well while it is mixed with 7.5g of oxalic acid 2-hydrate in 75ml of water. The mixture, which now contains a yellow precipitate of ferrous oxalate, is carefully [CAUTION: bumping!] heated to the boiling point, allowed to settle, and cooled somewhat. The supernatant liquid is decanted and the solid washed once by decantation with about 50ml of hot water.

The hydrated ferrous oxalate is suspended in a solution of 10g of potassium oxalate monohydrate in 30ml of water and the mixture is warmed to 40°C. Twenty-five milliliters of 6% hydrogen peroxide is then added dropwise from a burette with continuous agitation. The greenish liquid with a red-brown precipitate of ferric hydroxide is heated to boiling while a solution of 2.5g of oxalic acid 2-hydrate is added slowly with stirring. The hot liquid is filtered, if necessary, and cooled in ice while 30ml of 95% alcohol are stirred in. The product is filtered off and the mother liquor is evaporated on the steam bath to recover the remaining material.

The yield is over 95% based on 6.5g of ferrous oxalate monohydrate starting material.

(III)

$$Fe^{++} + HNO_3 + H^+ \longrightarrow Fe^{+++} + NO_2 + H_2O$$
$$Fe^{+++} + 3NH_4OH \longrightarrow Fe(OH)_3 + 3NH_4^+$$
$$2Fe(OH)_3 + 3K_2C_2O_4 + 3H_2C_2O_4 \longrightarrow 2K_3[Fe(C_2O_4)_3] + 6H_2O$$

A solution of 35g of ferrous sulfate 7-hydrate in 100ml of water is heated to boiling under the hood while 20ml of concentrated nitric acid are added in small portions to moderate the vigorous evolution of nitrogen dioxide. When the reaction is over, a test portion of the liquid should give, not a precipitate with potassium ferricyanide, but a greenish color, which indicates that oxidation to the ferric state is complete. As long as the test for ferrous ions is still positive, about 5ml more of nitric acid should be added and the boiling continued. The hot, fully oxidized liquid is diluted with water to about two liters and heated to boiling while

35ml of concentrated aqueous ammonia is added with stirring. When the hydrated ferric oxide settles well, most of the supernatant liquid is carefully decanted, and the precipitate is filtered off and washed several times with boiling water.

The moist gel is added to a mixture of 23.5g of oxalic acid 2-hydrate and 34.5g of potassium oxalate monohydrate in 100ml of hot water. The solution is filtered, if necessary, and evaporated to crystallization on the steam bath. The product is filtered off and dried in the dark. The mother liquor yields small additional amounts of product.

Yield over 95%

Both the dry complex oxalate and its aqueous solution are unstable to direct light and deposit yellow ferrous oxalate. This property was formerly utilized in platinotypes—a photographic process by which the FeC_2O_4 produced by illumination reduces a platinic salt to a black platinum image. The oxalate is a *d-l* mixture, which has been resolved into its mirror images.

For the preparation of the isomorphic trioxalatomanganate (III) (K salt, 3-hydrate) see reference 2.

References:

1. B:153; I, vol. 1:36; P:519, 521.
2. OBERHAUSER AND HENSINGER, *Ber.*, 61:530 (1928).

73. Sodium Hexanitrocobaltate (III) **

$$Co(NO_3)_2 + 5NaNO_2 + 2HNO_2 \longrightarrow Na_3[Co(NO_2)_6] + 2NaNO_3 + NO + H_2O$$

One hundred and twenty grams of pure potassium-free sodium nitrite are dissolved in 120ml of hot water. The solution is cooled to 50°C, and 40g of cobalt nitrate 6-hydrate are dissolved in the liquid. With continuous stirring, 40ml of 50% acetic acid are added dropwise from a burette and the dark brown solution is transferred to a filter flask fitted with a stopper and an inlet tube leading almost to the bottom of the vessel. A steady stream of air is drawn through the solution for 30 minutes to remove excess oxides of nitrogen; some product may crystallize out during the aeration. The liquid and any solid that has formed (the more vigorous the air current the more material tends to settle out) are now placed in a beaker and surrounded by an ice bath. From a dropping funnel 200–300ml of 95% alcohol are added slowly with agitation, and the mixture is then allowed to crystallize in the cold for one-half hour. The orange-brown product is filtered by suction and the mother liquor is set aside. The material is washed three times with 30ml of alcohol; the final washing should be almost colorless. The crystals are dried in air.

$$\text{Yield} = 52\text{--}55g$$

By diluting the reserved filtrate to 500ml with water, and adding a solution of 2g of potassium chloride in 20ml of water, the remainder of the complex ion may be precipitated as the insoluble potassium salt.

$$\text{Yield} = 2\text{--}3g$$

The hexanitrocobaltate ion is fairly stable in aqueous solution and gives insoluble metathetical products with numerous large-volume and heavy metal cations.

References:
1. B:149; P:549.
2. BILLMANN, Z. anal. Chem., 39:284 (1900).
3. CUNNINGHAM AND PERKIN, J. Chem. Soc., 95:1568 (1909).

74. Sodium Pentacyanonitrosylferrate (III) 2-Hydrate **

$$3K_4[Fe(CN)_6] + 4HNO_3 + 2NO \longrightarrow$$
$$3K_2[Fe(CN)_5NO] + 3KCN + 3KNO_3 + 2H_2O$$

Forty grams of finely powdered potassium ferrocyanide 3-hydrate are dissolved in 60ml of water in a 500ml beaker. In the hood, 64ml of 38% nitric acid are added. (The requisite concentration is obtained by mixing 55ml of the concentrated acid (68–70%) with 45ml of water.) As poisonous cyanotic fumes escape during this reaction the mixture should be heated in the steam bath under the hood. Completion of the reaction is indicated when a drop of the reaction mixture no longer yields a blue but a deep green precipitate with aqueous ferrous sulfate. The deep red solution is allowed to stand in the dark for 1–2 days and then *exactly* neutralized by the dropwise addition of a saturated solution of sodium carbonate. The liquid is heated to boiling, suction-filtered from black by-products while hot, and then rapidly evaporated over a free flame to a volume of 40–50ml, while a current of air is blown over the surface of the solution. The concentrated filtrate is cooled in ice and 50ml of 95% alcohol are added to precipitate the potassium nitrate that is filtered off. The ethanolic-aqueous extract of product is evaporated to crystallization on the steam bath in a current of air. After cooling and filtering, the mother liquor may be worked up for a further crop of product. The material is dried in the dark in air.

Yield $=60$–75% of theory

The ruby-red crystals are stable when stored in dark bottles, but under strong illumination of both the solid and its aqueous solution Prussian blue is soon formed.

(II)

$$K_4[Fe(CN)_6] + 4NaCl \longrightarrow Na_4[Fe(CN)_6] + 4KCl$$
$$2Na_4[Fe(CN)_6] + 2NaNO_2 + 3BaCl_2 + 3CO_2 + H_2O \longrightarrow$$
$$2Na_2[Fe(CN)_5NO] + 2HCN + 3BaCO_3 + 6NaCl$$

If sodium ferrocyanide 10-hydrate is not available, it may be prepared as follows from the potassium salt:

Forty grams of pure sodium chloride are dissolved in 105ml of boiling water and 25g of finely powdered potassium ferrocyanide 3-hydrate are added in portions to the boiling solution. When virtually all of the potassium salt has disappeared the liquid is filtered hot and the filtrate is cooled in ice. As the product tends to remain in the supersaturated state, crystallization is encouraged by stirring and by scratching the walls of the vessel. Allow the salt to crystallize for one hour, filter and drain the product well; wash it with two 25ml portions of alcohol, then dry it in air.

Yield $= 25$g

A 500ml filter flask is fitted with a stopper carrying a wide (10mm) inlet tube that reaches to about one inch from the bottom. Twenty-four and two tenths grams of sodium ferrocyanide 10-hydrate and 3.5g of sodium nitrite are dissolved in 150ml of hot water in the flask and a solution of 18.3g of barium chloride 2-hydrate in 50ml of water is added. The precipitate that forms (sodium barium ferrocyanide) is ignored as it disappears later in the reaction with conversion to barium carbonate. The flask is fitted with the inlet tube and clamped so that it is well immersed in a steam bath mounted under the hood. [CAUTION: Evolution of hydrogen cyanide!] A steady stream of about 2–3 bubbles/sec of carbon dioxide is passed in for 6–8 hours, or until a test portion of the mixture no longer gives a precipitate, but only a blue color with an aqueous ferric salt.

The synthesis requires little attention during this time except the occasional addition of water to maintain a constant volume. The color of the liquid in the flask changes slowly from pale yellow to ruby-red as the reaction proceeds. The precipitated barium carbonate is filtered off and the filtrate is rapidly concentrated to a volume of about 60ml on the water bath, avoiding direct illumination of the solution. The concentrated liquid is cooled in ice and 100ml of alcohol is added to precipitate the sodium chloride which is filtered off. The aqueous-alcoholic extract is then treated as in (I) for the isolation of the product.

Yield = 85–95% of theory based on sodium ferrocyanide.

Even small amounts of alkali convert the nitroprusside ion to pentacyanonitroferrate (II) which, in turn, is changed to ferrocyanide by the action of cyanide.

$$[Fe(CN)_5NO]^= + 2OH^- \longrightarrow [Fe(CN)_5NO_2]^{4-} + H_2O$$
$$[Fe(CN)_5NO_2]^{4-} + CN^- \longrightarrow [Fe(CN)_6]^{4-} + NO_2^-$$

The sensitivity of the product to hydroxyl ions is the reason for their being continuously removed by the barium as carbonate in the given procedure.

For the preparation of the interesting analogous **Potassium Pentacyanonitrosylmanganate** (III) from readily available starting materials, see—von Bemmelen and Klobbie, *J. prakt. Chem.* [2], 46:502 (1892).

References:
1. P:523.
2. RÜST, Z. Phys. Chem., 55:91 (1906).
3. CONROY, J. Soc. Chem. Ind., 1898:103.
4. SCHWARZKOPF, Chem. Zentr. (II):1536 (1912).

75. Sodium Tris(thiosulfato)plumbate (II) *

$$Pb(NO_3)_2 + Na_2S_2O_3 \longrightarrow PbS_2O_3 + 2NaNO_3$$
$$PbS_2O_3 + 2Na_2S_2O_3 \longrightarrow Na_4[Pb(S_2O_3)_3]$$

Twenty-one grams of lead nitrate are dissolved in 100ml of distilled water and mixed with 15.5g of sodium thiosulfate 5-hydrate in a similar volume of water. The white precipitate of lead thiosulfate is filtered off, washed with three 30ml portions of distilled water, and then twice with 20ml volumes of acetone to aid in drying. The material is dried in air.

Yield about 19g (95%)

Twenty-five grams of sodium thiosulfate 5-hydrate are suspended in 25ml of distilled water and the mixture is allowed to warm up to room temperature. Sixteen grams of lead thiosulfate are stirred in; the salt dissolves rapidly forming a colorless solution. The clear supernatant liquid is at once decanted or filtered from the slight residue of lead salt because the product tends to crystallize quickly from the highly concentrated solution. The decanted liquid is then concentrated in a vacuum desiccator virtually to dryness. A mass of colorless transparent needles remains. If it is desired to isolate the product more quickly, with an attendant loss of crystalline form, the aqueous solution or filtrate may be mixed with 100–150ml of 95% alcohol; the complex thiosulfate is precipitated as a white flocculent powder, which is filtered off, washed with 50ml of alcohol, and dried in air. The yield of product is almost quantitative (30g). When it is completely dry the material keeps well for a period of several years but eventually turns gray because of the formation of lead sulfide.

Chapter 4

COVALENT COMPOUNDS

76. Arsenic (III) Iodide *

(I)

$$2As + 3I_2 \longrightarrow 2AsI_3$$

Five grams of powdered arsenic are suspended in 200ml of carbon tetrachloride and 25g of dry iodine are added. The mixture is refluxed until the characteristic violet color of the iodine has completely disappeared. The organic solvent is distilled off on the steam bath and the residue treated repeatedly on a pleated filter paper in an ordinary glass funnel with 25 ml portions of carbon disulfide [CAUTION: Highly flammable!], until only a gray residue of arsenic remains. The red product is recovered in 80–90% yield by evaporating the solvent. It must be stored out of contact with moisture in a tightly sealed all-glass vessel.

Carbon tetrachloride is preferred as the reaction solvent because it is non-flammable, but, with due precautions, ether, carbon disulfide, chloroform, benzene, or toluene may be used instead. The same method may be used for SbI_3 also.

(II)

$$As_2O_3 + 6HCl \longrightarrow 2AsCl_3 + 3H_2O$$
$$AsCl_3 + 3KI(HI) \longrightarrow AsI_3 + 3KCl(HCl)$$

A solution of 7g of arsenic trioxide in 100ml of concentrated hydrochloric acid is mixed with a solution of 35g of potassium iodide in 35ml of water. After standing for 5 minutes the orange precipitate of product is filtered off, drained thoroughly, and dried *in vacuo* over solid alkali. The product is freed from adhering potassium chloride by

109

extraction with carbon disulfide as under (I) until a white residue remains. Evaporation of the solvent yields about 28g of product.

Both antimony and bismuth triodides may be prepared in this way but concentrated (57%) hydriodic acid (No. 89) should be used as precipitating reagent for the bismuth salt because the latter is not readily soluble in organic liquids; about 50g of acid are required.

(III)

$$2As_2O_3 + 3S + 6I_2 \longrightarrow 4AsI_3 + 3SO_2$$

Seven grams of arsenic trioxide are intimately ground with 1.6g of sulfur in a mortar and transferred to a 100-ml flask. Twenty-seven grams of iodine are added and mixed in well with a stirring rod. A 150mm air condenser is attached and (in the hood) the apparatus is heated gently in an oil bath until vapors of sulfur dioxide begin to evolve, as indicated by testing with moist blue litmus paper. Any iodine that sublimes into the condenser is periodically pushed back into the reaction mixture with a long glass rod. Heating is regulated over a period of 14 hours so that sulfur dioxide escapes steadily with the least possible vaporization of iodine. Towards the end of the reaction the temperature of the bath should be above the melting point of the product (142°C). The residue in the flask after cooling is repeatedly extracted with 50ml portions of boiling benzene until nothing more will dissolve; evaporation of the solvent yields 80–90% of product.

This procedure can also be used for arsenic tribromide; 17g of bromine and 7 hours heating are required until the the condensing vapors are colorless.

References:
1. I, vol. 1:103, 104; J:373, 374.
2. BILTZ AND SAPPER, Z. anorg. Chem., 203:282, 377 (1932).
3. ODDO AND GIACHERY, Gazz. Chim. ital., 53:56 (1923).

77. Antimony (V) Chloride **

$$SbCl_3 + Cl_2 \longrightarrow SbCl_5$$

a) Preparation of Antimony Trichloride

(I)

$$Sb_2S_3 + 6HCl \longrightarrow 2SbCl_3 + 3H_2S \text{ or}$$
$$Sb_2O_3 + 6HCl \longrightarrow 2SbCl_3 + 3H_2O$$

Twenty-five grams of antimony trisulfide ore (stibnite) or 21.5g of technical antimony trioxide are dissolved in 100ml of concentrated hydrochloric acid on the steam bath in the hood. When no more material dissolves, the residual gangue is filtered through a plug of glass wool and the filtrate is transferred to a distilling flask fitted with a fractionating column (6–8 inches), packed with glass or porcelain rings. Several boiling chips are added to prevent bumping. An all-glass apparatus is preferable but paraffin-coated stoppers can be used. The side-arm of the flask carries a short (about 150mm) air condenser and adapter leading to the receiver. The latter consists of another distilling flask with a drying tube on the side-arm; for the initial aqueous fractions a beaker or other vessel may be used to catch the distillate.

Fractions are collected as follows:

(1) Up to 120°C
(2) 120–215°C
(3) Above 215°C

As fraction (1) consists of water and hydrochloric acid it is discarded. Fraction (2) contains a mixture of acid and product together with possibly a trace of ferric chloride (yellow distillate); if this fraction is large it must be refractionated, and the portion boiling below 215°C discarded. Fraction (3) is antimony trichloride, which, at 73°C, becomes a soft mass of colorless crystals that are extremely sensitive to moisture.

Yield = 85% of theory; b.p. 223°C

A gram or two of antimony powder may be added to the solution before distillation to reduce any trivalent iron to the ferrous state.

To purify the product further, it may be redistilled and sublimed from a steam bath.

(II)

$$2Sb + 3Cl_2 \longrightarrow 2SbCl_3$$

Nine grams of antimony in the form of small lumps are placed in a 50ml distilling flask carrying a waxed stopper with 8mm glass tubing extending down to one-half inch from the surface of the metal, and carrying a drying tube filled with calcium chloride at the top. Chlorine, which has been dried with sulfuric acid and calcium chloride, is passed in steadily through the side-arm of the flask until the gain in weight (7–8g) of the flask and contents corresponds to the formation of the trichloride. There is no danger of the glass tubing becoming clogged because the excess chlorine passing through liquefies any solid $SbCl_3$ with the formation of the fluid pentachloride. When the uptake of chlorine is complete, a stream of any *dry* gas is used to displace the chlorine and the long glass tube is removed. About one gram of powdered metallic antimony is added to reduce any Sb(V) to Sb(III) and the product is purified by distillation as in (I).

Yield over 90% of theory

b) Chlorination of Antimony Trichloride

Seventeen grams of antimony trichloride are placed in the chlorinating apparatus (using a Claisen flask instead), as described in (I), and heated very gently to the melting point of the salt. A steady flow of dry chlorine is passed over the fused trichloride until the gain in weight (5g) indicates that the theoretical amount of chlorine has been absorbed. The glass tube is removed and substituted by a capillary connected with a drying tube and a thermometer inserted in the other neck of the flask. The product distills

over as a lemon-yellow liquid which fumes and hydrolyzes
in moist air; b.p. 68°C (14mm); 79°C (22mm).

$$\text{Yield} = 85\text{–}95\%$$

Antimony pentachloride forms the hexachloroantimonate
(V) ion with concentrated solutions of chlorides yielding
numerous stable double salts ($RCl\cdot SbCl_5$ or $RSbCl_6$) especially if the cation is large.

References:

1. B:77 H; J:372.
2. KENDALL AND CRITTENDEN, *J. Am. Chem. Soc.*, 45:967 (1923).
3. WERNER, *Z. anorg. Chem.*, 181:154 (1929).
4. HÖNIGSCHMID AND ZINTL, *Ibid.*, 136:270 (1924).
5. BILTZ AND JEEP, *Ibid.*, 162:33 (1927).
6. SEEL, *Ibid.*, 252:35 (1944).
7. RUFF, *Ber.*, 42:4026 (1909).
8. MOLES, *Z. phys. Chem.*, 90:87 (1915).

78. Lead (IV) Acetate *

$$Pb_3O_4 + 8HC_2H_3O_2 \longrightarrow Pb(C_2H_3O_2)_4 + 2Pb(C_2H_3O_2)_2 + 4H_2O$$
$$(C_2H_3O)_2O + H_2O \longrightarrow 2HC_2H_3O_2$$
$$2Pb(C_2H_3O_2)_2 + Cl_2 \longrightarrow Pb(C_2H_3O_4)_4 + PbCl_2$$

Twenty-four grams of pure red lead is thoroughly dried
for a day or two at 100–200°C and stored in a vacuum
desiccator until needed.

A mixture of 55ml of glacial acetic acid and 17ml of
acetic anhydride is placed in a 125ml Erlenmeyer flask,
loosely fitted with a stopper carrying a thermometer that
leads well down into the mixed liquid. The flask and contents are then gently warmed to 40°C and the minium is
added in 6g portions with swirling, maintaining the temperature below 65°C, and waiting until each portion of
oxide has dissolved before adding the next. Care must be
taken not to soil the neck of the flask with the red lead as
it may contaminate the product later on. If the temperature
rises too high, the flask should be cooled slightly in a dish
of cold water. Towards the end of the reaction the flask is
heated gently in order to keep the temperature of the reaction mixture at 60–65°C. When all the red lead has dissolved, the solution is cooled to 5°C in an ice bath; colorless

needles of the product crystallize in quantity and are filtered by suction, washed with 10ml of cold glacial acetic acid, and dried *in vacuo* for several days over solid alkali.

$$Yield = 12{-}15g; \; m.p. \; 175{-}180°C$$

About 10g more of the product may be obtained from the mother liquor by heating it to 80°C and passing in a stream of dry chlorine until no more lead chloride forms. The mixture is filtered while hot and the residue is washed with 5–10ml of hot glacial acetic acid. On cooling, the lead tetraacetate precipitates. It is contaminated with a small amount of lead chloride.

The synthesis may be effected without the acetic anhydride, but the temperature of the reaction must then be carefully held around 55°C in order to avoid hydrolysis of the product by the water formed in the reaction.

As water decomposes the material immediately with the formation of lead dioxide, it must be stored in tightly stoppered vessels. When absolutely dry, the salt keeps well for several months.

The product is moderately soluble in chloroform, carbon tetrachloride, and benzene; it may be recovered unchanged from the perfectly dry solvents.

References:
1. I, vol. 1:47.
2. CRIEGEE, *Angew. Chem.*, 53:266 (1940).

COGNATE PREPARATIONS

78 a. Silicon Tetraacetate **

$$SiCl_4 + 4(C_2H_3O)_2O \longrightarrow Si(C_2H_3O_2)_4 + 4CH_3COCl$$

Twenty-five grams of silicon tetrachloride (No. 84 c) are added dropwise from a separatory funnel, protected from atmospheric moisture, to 70g of acetic anhydride contained in a distilling flask. Precautions to exclude moisture must be taken throughout the procedure by means of drying tubes and thoroughly dry glassware. Heat is evolved during the addition and colorless crystals of product soon form. After standing for 2 or 3 days, the reaction mixture is cooled in a bath of dry ice and acetone and the cold liquid is decanted as completely as possible. The mother liquor should be discarded *carefully* because it reacts violently with water. The residual mass of crystals is covered with about 50ml of absolute ether and agitated with the solvent.

After re-cooling to −70°C with dry ice, the wash solvent is completely decanted and any residual adhering liquid is removed from the product by evacuating the flask for several hours, first at room temperature and then at 100°C.

Alternatively, the material can be purified by vacuum distillation directly from the flask after the washing with ether; b.p. (5–6mm) 148°C; m.p. 110°C.

Yield = 30g

The substance is a little discolored when distilled because of slight decomposition which becomes appreciable at 160°–170°C, with the evolution of acetic anhydride. Silicon tetraacetate is vigorously decomposed by water but it dissolves to a moderate extent in inert liquids such as acetone and benzene. With ethyl alcohol it forms ethyl acetate and silicon dioxide as products of alcoholysis.

References:

1. I, vol. 4:45.
2. GOUBEAU AND MUNDIEL, *Z. anorg. Chem.*, 272:313 (1953).
3. SCHMIDT, BLOHM AND JANDER, *Angew. Chem.*, 59:235 (1947).

78 b. Boron Acetate **

$$H_3BO_3 + 3(C_2H_3O)_2O \longrightarrow B(C_2H_3O_2)_3 + 3HC_2H_3O_2$$

Twenty grams of boric acid and 100g of acetic anhydride are cautiously warmed on the water bath in a flask fitted with a reflux condenser. Around 60°C a vigorous reaction sets in and the boric acid dissolves. The white needles of product crystallize out almost completely after being cooled in ice and they are worked up similarly to the silicon compound; m.p. 147–148°C.

Yield about 80% of theory

The product cannot be distilled, even *in vacuo*, without considerable decomposition into the starting materials. Contact with water causes immediate hydrolysis.

References:
1. PICTET AND GELEZNOFF, *Bull. soc. chim.*, 36:2219 (1903).
2. DIMROTH, *Ann.*, 446:109 (1925).
3. KAHOVEC, *Ber.*, 43:111 (1939).

78 c. Arsenic (III) Acetate **

$$As_2O_3 + 3(C_2H_3O)_2O \longrightarrow 2As(C_2H_3O_2)_3$$

Twenty grams of arsenic trioxide are heated in a Claisen flask with 30ml of acetic anhydride on the steam bath. When no more solid dissolves on further heating and swirling, 5ml more of the anhydride is added. This procedure is repeated until the oxide just dissolves to a clear liquid. A total of about 50ml of acid anhydride is required. The material is then fractionally distilled *in vacuo;* the product comes over after the excess acetic anhydride has distilled. It forms an oily liquid which sets to a white crystalline mass in the receiver; b.p. (31mm) 165–170°C.

Yield almost theoretical

Arsenic (III) acetate is very readily hydrolyzed by water. In other respects, also, it resembles the acetates of the non-metals described previously.

Reference: PICTET AND BON, *Ber.* (3), 33:1114 (1905).

79. Lead (IV) Chloride **

$$PbCl_6^= + H_2SO_4 \longrightarrow PbCl_4 + 2HCl + SO_4^=$$

[CAUTION: Lead tetrachloride decomposes with explosive violence when strongly heated. Quantities larger than that given here should not be made, and the compound should be used as soon as possible after it is prepared. Protective clothing should be worn.]

Twenty grams of ammonium hexachloroplumbate (IV), (or, preferably, 25g of the corresponding pyridinium salt) are prepared according to the directions in Experiment No. 56.

Six hundred grams of concentrated sulfuric acid are cooled to −10°C in an ice-salt bath and stirred mechanically while the dry chloroplumbate (IV) salt is added in small portions. Slow and steady agitation is continued for one hour after the temperature of the mixture has risen to 0°C; further rise of temperature is to be avoided. During this time, the product settles out on the bottom of the vessel as a clear yellow oil. The supernatant liquid is carefully decanted; it is slightly turbid with a fine white precipitate. The residual oil is quickly transferred to a small, dry—preferably pre-cooled—separatory funnel with the aid of 50ml of concentrated sulfuric acid (previously cooled to −10°C), and shaken well. As soon as the lower layer of lead tetrachloride has settled out sharply it is run into a small glass-stoppered amber bottle and stored in the freezing compartment of a refrigerator until needed.

$$\text{Yield} = 10\text{g } (66\%)$$

Prolonged contact of the material with sulfuric acid causes decomposition to lead sulfate and chlorine. The compound dissolves without decomposition in dry chloroform and carbon tetrachloride, and also in concentrated hydrochloric acid.

$$PbCl_4 + 2HCl \longrightarrow H_2PbCl_6$$

Decomposition is indicated when a fine precipitate of lead chloride begins to appear in the liquid.

$$PbCl_4 \longrightarrow PbCl_2 + Cl_2$$

References:
1. B:114.
2. BILTZ AND MEINECKE, *Z. anorg. Chem.*, 131:1 (1923).

80. Phosphorus (V) Sulfide **

$$2P + 5S \longrightarrow P_2S_5$$

Twelve and one-half grams of red phosphorus are stirred with about 100ml of hot water and suction-filtered. The material is washed freely, first with hot water, then with two 25ml portions of alcohol, and dried at 105–120°C for several hours.

The purified phosphorus is intimately mixed with 32g of pure flowers of sulfur and transferred to a Pyrex retort, or a distilling flask with a short wide side-arm. A 250ml Erlenmeyer flask is used as a receiver and fitted to the arm of the reaction vessel with a loose stopper of glass wool (see

No. 10). The retort or flask is filled with carbon dioxide using a brisk current of gas; it is then stoppered.

[CAUTION: As a safety measure, place a metal pan under the apparatus. If the glass vessel should crack during the experiment the molten mixture would catch fire on contact with the air; sand may be used to extinguish the fire.]

The upper edge of the phosphorus-sulfur mixture is heated with a *small* flame until a reaction begins which spreads throughout the contents of the vessel. The flame is removed after the onset of the reaction which causes melting of the mass.

When the decomposition is completed, the vessel is heated until the material just begins to reflux, and the molten product is then allowed to cool slightly in a vigorous current of carbon dioxide. The flow of gas is reduced and the grayish crude sulfide is distilled directly into the receiver where it collects as a light-yellow solid. The arm of the distilling vessel may occasionally be cleared of solidified product by fanning with a flame.

$$Yield = about\ 35g$$

The crude, somewhat hygroscopic, substance may be further purified by extraction with 200ml of carbon disulfide for about 24 hours in a Soxhlet apparatus on the *steam bath*. The pure material crystallizes out in the receiver as very pale-yellow crystals which are dried *in vacuo*.

$$Yield = 25–30g$$

Phosphorus pentasulfide decomposes with water or moist air to hydrogen sulfide and phosphoric acid and should therefore be preserved in tightly stoppered vessels, preferably under an inert gas or in a vacuum. With aqueous alkali, mixtures of thiophosphates, e.g. PO_3S^{---} and $PO_2S_2^{---}$, are formed. Heating with ammonia at 850°C produces the material P_3N_5.

The solubility of the compound in boiling carbon disulfide is one part in 197 parts of solvent.

References:
  1. B:86.
  2. STOCK AND HERSCOVICI, *Ber.*, 43:1223 (1910).

81. Sulfur Monochloride **

$$2S + Cl_2 \longrightarrow S_2Cl_2$$

A 250ml distilling flask is fitted with a stopper and an inlet tube which leads below the side-arm and is connected to a water-cooled condenser. A second distilling flask, attached with a stopper to the condenser, acts as a receiver; the side-arm carries a drying tube.

Fifty grams of powdered sulfur are introduced into the flask and heated to 150°C in an oil bath under the hood while a moderately rapid stream (about 5 bubbles/sec) of dry chlorine is led over the molten sulfur. The crude orange-red product distills rapidly into the receiver. The chlorination requires about two hours and is stopped when only a very small amount of sulfur remains in the reaction flask. About 5–8g of sulfur are added to the crude condensate to combine with the excess of dissolved chlorine; a redistillation yields over 90% of the dark yellow chloride boiling at 137–140°C. Large amounts of low-boiling materials must be distilled again from a little sulfur. To obtain a pure product, the material may be fractionated once more or distilled *in vacuo;* b.p. 29–30°C (12mm).

When pure, sulfur monochloride is a light yellow oily liquid with an unpleasant pungent odor, which fumes in moist air and hydrolyzes in water to give sulfur dioxide, hydrogen sulfide, and hydrochloric acid. The chloride is soluble in a variety of inert organic solvents and it finds wide commercial use in the rubber industry in the vulcanization process.

Reference: B:77E; J:371.

COGNATE PREPARATIONS

(I)

81 a. Sulfur Monobromide **

$$2S + Br_2 \longrightarrow S_2Br_2$$

Twenty-four grams of pure sulfur (recrystallized from carbon disulfide) are mixed in a pressure bottle with 19ml of dry bromine, and heated behind a safety screen for 2 hours on the steam bath. The deep-red liquid product is cooled in ice before the bottle is opened [CAUTION: Gloves and safety glasses!]. It is then distilled in high vacuum yielding about 80% of pure material; b.p. 57°C (0.22mm); 52.5°C (0.14mm); 46–48°C (0.1mm).

(II)

$$S_2Cl_2 + 2HBr \longrightarrow S_2Br_2 + 2HCl$$

A steady stream of hydrogen bromide (dried by passage through two calcium chloride towers) is passed into 30g of sulfur monochloride contained in a distilling flask fitted with a drying tube; the apparatus is mounted under the hood. After about 2 hours the reaction is completed, as shown by a negative qualitative test for chloride ion on a small portion of the liquid when decomposed in water. When the product is distilled as in (I) it gives over 95% of pure material.

Sulfur monobromide dissociates into its elements when heated to 100°C. Water reacts with the substance to form hydrogen bromide, sulfur dioxide, and elemental sulfur. It dissolves in many organic solvents such as carbon tetrachloride and benzene.

To prepare the series of compounds with the general formula $S_{(3-8)}Br_2$ see references 3 and 4. The apparatus described under (II) may be used.

References:
1. RUFF AND WINTERFELD, Ber., 36:2437 (1903).
2. FEHÉR AND KRAEMER, Z. anorg. Chem., 279:18 (1955).
3. FEHÉR AND REMPE, Ibid., 281:261 (1955).
4. FEHÉR AND RISTIC, Ibid., 293:311 (1958).

81 b. Sulfur Dichloride **

$$S_2Cl_2 + Cl_2 \longrightarrow 2SCl_2$$

Fifty grams of sulfur monochloride are placed in the distilling flask of the set-up outlined in the procedure for that substance (No. 81). About 0.1g of iron powder is added to the liquid as a halogen carrier and bone-dry chlorine is led in steadily (3–4 bubbles/sec) for one-half hour. The dark liquid that is produced is allowed to stand one hour and then one milliliter of phosphorus trichloride is added. The product is fractionated through a small column packed with glass and the portion that boils at 55–62°C is collected. This fraction is redistilled as before from a few drops of PCl₃ and the pure sulfur dichloride is collected at 59–61°C.

Yield about 55g

The deep-red material is stable for several days at room temperature in the presence of a trace of phosphorus trichloride; it then slowly decomposes into chlorine and sulfur monochloride and may be re-purified by distillation as described.

With water, the dichloride forms sulfuric acid, sulfur, and a mixture of thionic acids, $H_2S_xO_y$. It dissolves without reaction in hexane, carbon tetrachloride, carbon disulfide, and ethylene dichloride.

References:

1. FEHÉR AND MEYER, Z. Naturforsch., 11b:605 (1956).
2. FEHÉR AND NAUSED, Z. anorg. Chem., 290:303 (1957).
3. FEHÉR AND RISTIC, Ibid., 293:307 (1958).
4. BRAUER, Handbuch der Präparativen Anorganischen Chemie, 2nd ed., vol. 1, p. 336, Enke Verlag, Stuttgart, 1960.

These references also contain the procedures for preparing the series $S_{(3-8)}Cl_2$ by reaction of sulfur mono- and dichloride together with various hydrogen persulfides, H_2S_x, where $x = 1$–4.

82. Sulfuryl Chloride **

$$SO_2 + Cl_2 \longrightarrow SO_2Cl_2$$

(I)

a) With activated carbon as catalyst

A 5-, or 6-bulb Allihn condenser is plugged with glass wool at the delivery end and loosely filled with activated charcoal. The top of the condenser is fitted with a T-tube leading to sources of chlorine and sulfur dioxide; both gases pass through wash bottles filled with concentrated sulfuric acid before mixing at the T-tube. The condenser is mounted vertically on a 250ml suction flask fitted with a drying tube on the side-arm. The experiment is conducted in the hood to carry away excess gaseous materials.

As the gases combine with evolution of heat, a good flow of cold water should be passing continuously through the condenser; the chlorine and sulfur dioxide are led into the charcoal at a uniform rate (3–5 bubbles/sec). After 20–30 minutes the latter has become saturated with product and the sulfuryl chloride starts to drop into the receiving flask at the rate of about 150g an hour thereafter in over 95% yield. The crude material is colored yellow from free dissolved chlorine which may be removed by shaking with mercury, or by leading a dry nitrogen stream through the ice-cold chloride.

One fractional distillation suffices to produce a pure product; the fraction boiling at 68–70°C is collected; pure sulfuryl chloride boils at 69.1°C.

b) With camphor as catalyst

Fifty grams of coarsely powdered camphor are placed in a 250ml distilling flask fitted with a stopper that carries two gas-inlet tubes and that is protected from moisture with a drying tube on the side-arm. The inlets are connected to sources of the dry component gases as described in a). Sulfur dioxide is led in until the camphor has liquefied and become saturated with the gas; it will take up about 45g at 760mm pressure. Chlorine is passed into the liquid until the color just turns yellow, indicating an excess. From this point on, depending on the quantity of product desired, the synthesis may be interrupted and the crude product purified as in a); or equal volumes of the two gases may be then led in simultaneously so that there is a very slight constant excess of sulfur dioxide. The yield is over 90% of theory.

In both a) and b) the apparatus is easily modified so that up to several kilograms of material can be prepared without difficulty.

(II)

$$2HSO_3Cl \longrightarrow SO_2Cl_2 + H_2SO_4$$

One gram of mercury is added to 100g of chlorosulfonic

acid contained in an all-glass apparatus consisting of a flask, a short packed column, a water-cooled condenser, and a receiver protected from moisture. The mixture is gently refluxed for 1½–3 hours so that the temperature at the top of the column does not exceed 70°C. As indicated by the equation, the pure colorless product collects in the receiver in almost theoretical yield.

If decomposition of the acid is carried out for 20 hours at 200–210°C in a sealed tube without the catalyst, the yield drops to 40%.[5]

Sulfuryl chloride is slowly decomposed into the starting materials by direct sunlight. When mixed with cold water, the oily drops of chloride disappear slowly, with hydrolysis, to sulfuric and hydrochloric acids. By shaking the compound with water and ice, it forms a hydrate, which is stable at 0°C. Alkalies react violently with the material to form sulfates and chlorides. Sulfuryl chloride is soluble in numerous inert organic solvents.

References:

1. B:202; I, vol. I:114; J:368.
2. MEYER, Z. angew. Chem., 44:41 (1931).
3. DANNEEL, Ibid., 39:1553 (1926).
4. SCHULZE, J. prakt. Chem., 24:168 (1881).
5. BEHREND, Ibid., 15:23 (1877).

COGNATE PREPARATIONS
82 a. Pyrosulfuryl Chloride *

$$6HSO_3Cl + P_2O_5 \longrightarrow 3S_2O_5Cl_2 + 2H_3PO_4$$

Twenty grams of phosphorus (V) oxide are quickly introduced into an all-glass distilling apparatus fitted with an air condenser, and 30g of chlorosulfonic acid (No. 87) are then added. The mixture is heated *slowly* and the distillate is collected in a receiver protected from atmospheric moisture. The crude product is refractionated to yield 20–25g of the chloride, which boils at 146–153°C with slight decomposition.

The compound is decomposed by water to form sulfuric and hydrochloric acids. Very pure pyrosulfuryl chloride is obtained by distillation *in vacuo;* it boils at 152.5–153°C at 760mm.

References:

1. B:204; I, vol. 3:124.
2. SANGER AND RIEGEL, *Z. anorg. Chem.*, 76:79 (1912).
3. PRANDTL AND BORINSKI, *Ibid.*, 62:24 (1909).
4. ROSE, *Pogg. Ann.*, 44:291 (1838).

82 b. Thionyl Bromide **

(I)

$$SOCl_2 + 2HBr \longrightarrow SOBr_2 + 2HCl$$

A good current of hydrogen bromide (carefully dried with calcium chloride and phosphorus (V) oxide) is passed for 12 hours at 0°C through 50ml of thionyl chloride. The contents of the flask turn slowly to a reddish color as the reaction progresses. The crude product is distilled *in vacuo* in an all-glass apparatus to give about 50ml of an orange-red oil boiling at 69–70°C at 62mm. Refractionation at 20mm gives an almost theoretical yield of pure orange-yellow bromide boiling at 48°C.

(II)

$$PBr_5 + SO_2 \longrightarrow SOBr_2 + POBr_3$$

Fifty grams of phosphorus (V) bromide are first prepared, either by allowing 18.5g of bromine to drop slowly into 31.5g of ice-cold phosphorus tribromide, or by dropping 46.5g of bromine dropwise on 3.6g of dry red phosphorus. Either reaction is conducted in a stout pressure bottle of about 500ml capacity; moisture must be carefully excluded.

[CAUTION: The operator must wear protective clothing at all times when working with pressurized vessels.]

The bottle and contents are now cooled to −20°C in a bath of dry-ice and acetone and about 100ml of previously condensed sulfur dioxide [hood!] are rapidly introduced into the vessel. The bottle is sealed and placed behind a safety screen for about 3 days at 35°C. During this time the yellow crystals of phosphorus (V) bromide slowly dissolve completely in the excess sulfur dioxide to yield a red solution. When all the pentabromide has disappeared the bottle is recooled to −20°C and cautiously opened. A drying tube is inserted into the mouth of the bottle and the excess of sulfur dioxide is allowed to evaporate at room temperature. The residual deep-red oil is carefully fractionated *in vacuo* (using ground glass joints) to yield the product, which boils at 48°C (20mm).

$$\text{Yield} = 80\text{--}90\%$$

The residue in the distilling flask consists of phosphorus oxybromide (No. 82 c) which may be purified by distillation; b.p. 193–195°C. The almost-white solid melts at 56°C.

Thionyl bromide is very sensitive to moisture, heat, and direct light. It reacts with water to produce sulfur dioxide and hydrobromic acid; under illumination the liquid turns dark red, with the formation of SO_2, Br_2, and S_2Br_2 as decomposition products. Inert organic solvents readily dissolve the material.

(III)

$$PCl_3 + Br_2 \longrightarrow PCl_3Br_2$$
$$PCl_3Br_2 + SO_2 \longrightarrow SOBr_2 + POCl_3$$

Eighty grams of bromine are slowly added to 69g of phosphorus trichloride contained in a flask well protected from moisture. The reaction vessel is cooled in an ice-water bath while dry sulfur dioxide is passed into the mixture until the gain in weight is 32g, corresponding to the theoretical uptake of the gas. Careful fractionation as in methods (I) or (II) yields 85–90% of pure product. The by-product of phosphorus oxychloride, which distills over first, may be collected by cooling the distillation receiver to about −10°C or lower.

A method for making thionyl bromide using KBr and thionyl chloride in liquid sulfur dioxide in 50% yield is described in reference 5.

References:
1. I, vol. 1:113, *Ibid.*, vol. 2:151, 153 (preparation of PBr₅).
2. BESSON, *Compt. rend.*, 122:320; 123:884 (1896).
3. BEHNE, *Dissertation*, University of Greifswald, Germany, 1945; see Hecht, *Präparative Anorganische Chemie*, p. 96, Springer Verlag, Berlin, 1951.
4. German patent, DRP 665061 (I. G. Farben), 1936.
5. FRAZER AND GERRARD, *Chem. and Ind.*, 1954:280.

82 c. Phosphorus Oxybromide **

$$P_2O_5 + 3PBr_5 \longrightarrow 5POBr_3$$

One hundred grams of phosphorus (V) bromide are prepared by method (II) for thionyl bromide. A ground-glass distilling flask is used. With due precautions against moisture, 12g of fresh phosphorus (V) oxide, (preferably from a new bottle) are quickly added to the flask and the mixture is slowly heated on the steam bath for several hours until the material has completely liquefied; a drying tube is used to exclude water vapor. The liquid is now heated in an air bath for one hour just to the point of reflux and then distilled through an air condenser; the fraction boiling at 193–195°C (760mm) is collected in a moisture-protected receiver. The compound must be stored in *dry*, tightly sealed vessels.

Yield = 80% based on the PBr₅

Phosphorus oxybromide reacts slowly with water to yield orthophosphoric and hydrobromic acids. It dissolves readily in many organic solvents such as ether, benzene, and carbon tetrachloride. Because the bromide decomposes readily at high temperatures, it should always be melted in a hot water bath (m.p. 55–56°C), never with a flame. Prepared as described, the product contains traces of phosphorus tribromide which can be removed only by 6-fold high-vacuum distillation.

References:
1. I, vol. 2:152.
2. JOHNSON AND NUNN, *J. Am. Chem. Soc.*, 63:141 (1941).
3. BESSON, *Compt. rend.*, 111:972 (1890).

82 d. Chromyl Chloride **

$$K_2Cr_2O_7 + H_2SO_4 \longrightarrow 2CrO_3 + K_2SO_4 + H_2O$$
$$2NaCl + H_2SO_4 \longrightarrow 2HCl + Na_2SO_4$$
$$CrO_3 + 2HCl \longrightarrow CrO_2Cl_2 + H_2O$$

In the hood, a finely ground intimate mixture of 50g of sodium chloride and 80g of potassium dichromate is placed in a distilling flask fitted to a water-cooled condenser and a moisture-protected receiver cooled in ice. The flask and contents are kept cold (below 10°C) while 100ml of concentrated sulfuric acid are added dropwise through a separatory funnel mounted in the neck of the flask. A vigorous reaction ensues and the flask begins to fill with red fumes. After all the acid has been added the mixture is distilled and the product collected as a red fuming liquid; heating is continued until no more colored material passes over. The crude material is cooled to 0°C and a *dry* stream of air bubbled slowly through the liquid for about three hours to remove dissolved hydrogen chloride. Pure chromyl chloride is produced by a second distillation and collected at 115–118°C as a clear red oil which must be stored in the dark out of contact with moisture.

Yield = 65–75% based on the dichromate

The product slowly deposits solids on standing; the supernatant liquid, however, is still fairly pure. It reacts with cold water to form a mixture of hydrochloric and dichromic acids $H_2Cr_2O_7$ but dissolves without reaction in carbon tetrachloride.

References:
1. I, vol. 2:205.
2. MOLES AND GOMEZ, *Z. physik. Chem.*, 80:513 (1912).
3. ETARD, *Ann. chim. phys.* (5), 22:218 (1881).

83. Tin (IV) Sulfide (crystalline) *
(I)

$$Sn + 2S \longrightarrow SnS_2$$

Fourteen grams of finely granulated tin (20–30 mesh) are warmed *gently* with 6.5g of mercury in a porcelain basin under the hood. The mass is stirred with a glass rod until it is homogeneous and quickly poured into a mortar where it is ground to a fine powder as it cools. The cold pulverized amalgam is then intimately mixed with 8g of flowers of sulfur and 6.8g of ammonium chloride. The entire mixture is transferred to a loosely covered crucible which is embedded in a sand bath up to the level of the reaction mixture. The crucible is heated at 400°C *in the hood* until no more vapors escape; a Meker burner is suitable. The temperature is then gradually raised to a dull red heat, and *as soon* as sulfur vapors escape, or the brown mass turns black in spots, the crucible (covered) is allowed to cool. The cold reaction product is carefully picked apart for the gold-colored flakes of the sulfide. The best-crystallized portion is obtained as the uppermost layer in the crucible with poorer crystals below. The product is obtained pure by sublimation in a sandbath (see No. 19).

Yield about 50% (based on the tin)

When carried out with much larger amounts of materials, a lower yield of material is obtained because of the difficulty involved in heating the poorly-conducting contents of the crucible at a uniform temperature.

(II)

$$Sn + 2HCl \longrightarrow SnCl_2 + H_2$$
$$SnCl_2 + H_2S \longrightarrow SnS + 2HCl$$
$$SnS + S \longrightarrow SnS_2$$

Twelve grams of pure tin are dissolved in a mixture of 50g of concentrated hydrochloric acid and 2.5ml of $8M$ nitric acid. Alternatively, 23g of tin (II) chloride 2-hydrate may be used, omitting the nitric acid. The solution is diluted to 2 liters with boiling water and hydrogen sulfide passed in under the hood until the light-brown precipitate of stannous sulfide settles well. The solid is suction-filtered, washed with 100ml of hot water followed by 50ml of acetone, and dried at 100°C.

Yield quantitative (15g)

The tin (II) sulfide so obtained is ground with 7.5g of sulfur and 6g of ammonium chloride and heated in a sand bath under the hood at 400°C for about 2 hours. When the ammonium chloride and the excess of sulfur have completely volatilized the mass is cooled, removed mechanically and the impurities floated away by decantation with water. The sulfide ($D = 4.2g/cc$) remains behind. It is dried at 100°C and sublimed.

Yield, same as in (I)

Talc-like crystalline tin (IV) sulfide is also known as mosaic gold and used technically as a pigment.

References:

1. B:88
2. LAGUTT, Z. angew. Chem., 9:557 (1897).

COGNATE PREPARATION

83 a. Tin (II) Sulfide (crystalline) **

$$SnO_2 + 2KSCN \longrightarrow SnS + K_2S + 2CO + N_2$$

Pure, dry potassium thiocyanate is prepared by recrystallizing about 100g of the commercial product from alcohol, concentrating the mother liquor, and drying the material in an evacuated flask that is immersed in boiling water.

Eighty grams of the purified salt are heated to 400°C in a porcelain dish under the hood, using a high-temperature thermometer as a stirring rod. Eight grams of pure dry tin (IV) oxide are added in small portions; each addition is accompanied by vigorous frothing which is allowed to subside before more oxide is introduced into the melt. The temperature should not be allowed to rise appreciably during the fusion, otherwise loss of the sulfide to form K_2SnS_3 occurs. When all the oxide has been added the mixture is heated at 400°C for 15 minutes longer and then allowed to cool. After treating the melt by repeated decantation with warm water, the analytically-pure dark-gray crystalline product ($D = 5g/cc$) that remains behind is filtered, rinsed with a little acetone, and dried at 100°C.

$$Yield = 7g$$

Reference: MILBAUER, Z. anorg. Chem., 42:433 (1904).

84. Tin (IV) Chloride **

(I)

$$Sn + 2Cl_2 \longrightarrow SnCl_4$$

a) At elevated temperatures

Twenty grams of pure tin are placed in a retort or in the flask of a distilling apparatus with a water-cooled condenser; in either case, a second distilling flask serves as a receiver and this is protected from moisture with a drying tube. The tin is melted over a small flame and a steady stream of dry chlorine (dried with sulfuric acid and a calcium chloride tube) is passed over the surface of the metal. The tin burns with a pale blue flame and the product, colored yellow from excess chlorine, collects at a steady rate in the receiver in almost theoretical yield; the reaction is stopped as soon as the metal has disappeared from the reaction flask or retort. The crude distillate is allowed to stand with a little tin foil for a day or two and then distilled directly from the foil. The portion boiling at 110–115°C is collected and it should be colorless; if not, a second distillation over tin is required.

Yield about 40g

b) At room temperature

The apparatus described in a) is used except that the inlet tube for the chlorine should reach almost to the bottom of the distilling flask. A rapid stream (about 5 bubbles/sec) of dry chlorine is passed under the granulated tin and as the liquid product begins to form in the flask the gas inlet tube is progressively raised so that it is always about one-half inch below the surface of the liquid. From time to time particles of tin glow up in the fluid but this does not affect the preparation. When all the metal has disappeared, the crude chloride is purified as in a). The yield is similar to that in a).

These two procedures readily lend themselves to the production of kilograms of tin (IV) chloride; method b) is somewhat preferable because it is relatively inconvenient to keep large amounts of tin in the molten condition, as required in the high-temperature method.

(II)

$$Sn + 4HSO_3Cl \longrightarrow SnCl_4 + 2SO_2 + 2H_2SO_4$$

[CAUTION: This experiment must be performed in the hood because of the quantities of sulfur dioxide evolved.]

The distillation set-up described previously is used, but a moisture-protected dropping funnel filled with 60ml of chlorosulfonic acid (see No. 87) is substituted for the chlorine inlet tube. The acid is dropped very slowly at first onto 20g of coarsely granulated tin; the reaction is rather violent initially but it moderates somewhat after a few milliliters of acid have been added. The addition of the latter should be regulated so that the product distills into the receiver at the same rate. No heating of the flask is necessary; if the reaction becomes too violent, the chloro-acid is introduced more slowly. The crude product is then fractionated and the portion that boils at 105–115°C is collected; a few drops of material (largely sulfuryl chloride) are obtained below 105°C.

$$Yield = 35g$$

(III)

$$SnCl_4 \cdot 5H_2O + 5SOCl_2 \longrightarrow SnCl_4 + 5SO_2 + 10HCl$$

Fifty-five grams of tin (IV) chloride 5-hydrate are refluxed in an all-glass apparatus with 100g of thionyl chloride for 3–4 hours [hood]. Moisture is excluded during this operation; the reaction is over when no more acid vapors escape from the drying tube at the top of the condenser. The product is then fractionally distilled to remove the excess thionyl chloride which is collected up to 110°C; the material boiling at 110–115°C must be colorless, otherwise a redistillation is necessary.

Yield about 90% of theory

With small quantities of water tin (IV) chloride eventually forms a 5-hydrate, but when it is dissolved in large amounts it hydrolyzes with evolution of heat to form colloidal hydrated SnO_2. The product must be preserved in tightly stoppered vessels; corks used for the preparation or storage of the material must be coated with paraffin wax. It is freely soluble in numerous organic solvents.

References:
1. B:79; J:372; P:244.
2. DANNEEL, Z. angew. Chem., 39:1553 (1926).
3. LORENTZ, Z. anorg. Chem., 10:44 (1895).
4. HEUMANN AND KÖCHLIN, Ber., 15:419 (1885).
5. HECHT, Z. anorg. Chem., 254:37 (1947).

COGNATE PREPARATIONS

$$Sn + 2Br_2 \longrightarrow SnBr_4$$

84 a. Tin (IV) Bromide **

[Use a distilling apparatus with an air-cooled condenser; moisture must be excluded.]

Twenty grams of coarse lumps of tin are used and 54g of dry bromine are added from a long-stemmed dropping funnel whose delivery tip reaches to the end of the neck of the reaction flask. The bromine is introduced at such a rate that no brown vapors pass out of the flask; the reaction is very vigorous and the metal may burn in the halogen. At the end of the addition a thermometer is inserted and the liquid in the flask is heated just to reflux, in order to drive off any excess bromine. The almost colorless residual product is then distilled; the portion boiling at 200–205°C comprises the pure material, which sets eventually to a white crystalline mass (m.p. 33°C) in the receiver. If the tetrabromide is still colored it may be redistilled and preserved in a sealed container away from moisture.

Yield = 85–95% of theory

The product resembles the tetrachloride in chemical properties and solubility; it forms a 4-hydrate with small amounts of water.

Reference: LORENTZ, Z. anorg. Chem., 9:365 (1895).

84 b. Tin (IV) Iodide *

(I)

$$Sn + 2I_2 \longrightarrow SnI_4$$

Ten grams of finely granulated tin are heated gently with 40g of dry iodine and 75ml of carbon tetrachloride under reflux until a fairly vigorous reaction begins; the flame is then removed until the spontaneous ebullition has ceased. Heating is resumed until all the iodine has reacted, as shown by the color of the solution (orange-red) and the absence of violet condensate. The boiling solution is rapidly filtered from excess tin through a fluted filter and the residue is washed with 2-10ml portions of boiling carbon tetrachloride. The bulk of the orange product crystallizes out on cooling; more material may be isolated by concentrating the mother liquor with the exclusion of moisture.

Total yield about 90% (based on the iodine)

The iodide is hydrolyzed by moisture but dissolves unchanged in most organic solvents; m.p. 143°C. It can be sublimed at 200°C.

(II)

$$SnCl_2 + I_2 \longrightarrow SnCl_2I_2$$
$$2SnCl_2I_2 \longrightarrow SnI_4 + SnCl_4$$

Thirty grams of tin (II) chloride 2-hydrate in 125ml of glacial acetic acid and an equal volume of acetic anhydride are refluxed for 30 minutes. The solution and white precipitate of anhydrous tin (II) chloride are allowed to cool somewhat and the condenser is removed. Thirty-three grams of iodine are added in small portions; the whitish precipitate of tin (IV) iodochloride initially formed redissolves towards the end of the reaction. The mixture is finally boiled under reflux for 10 minutes and the solvents, together with the tin (IV) chloride, are distilled off at about 40mm. The residue is recrystallized from carbon tetrachloride as in method (I); a similar yield is obtained.

Reference: I, vol. 4:119; J:373; P:246.

84 c. Silicon Tetrachloride **

$$Si + 2Cl_2 \longrightarrow SiCl_4$$

The apparatus for method (I) under SnCl₄ (No. 84) is used with an ice-cooled receiver. Ten grams of commercial silicon (No. 2) in the form of powder or small lumps are employed; the element is heated to about 400°C after the air in the reaction flask has been displaced by *dry* chlorine. A steady flow of gas is maintained; the heat under the flask may be considerably reduced once the reaction (incandescence) has started. A slight residue of silicon dioxide finally remains behind and a trace of aluminum chloride (if aluminothermic Si was used) may sublime in the cooler part of the apparatus. The method of purifying the crude liquid product (which is colored yellow from dissolved chlorine) is the same as for the tin compound; b.p. 57–60°C.

$$Yield = 35–40g$$

The fluid material remaining in the distilling flask consists of higher homologous chlorides of silicon which may be collected as follows:

$$Si_2Cl_6 \ 145–147°C; \ Si_3Cl_8 \ 210–216°C.$$

Silicon tetrachloride fumes in air and is instantly hydrolyzed by moisture to hydrated silica. Other properties are similar to those of $SnCl_4$.

References:
1. B:80; I, vol. 1:42; J:370.
2. GATTERMAN, Ber., 22:187 (1889).

84 d. Silicon Tetrabromide ***

$$Si + 2Br_2 \longrightarrow SiBr_4$$

Ten grams of silicon are heated in bromine vapor generated by passing *dry* nitrogen or carbon dioxide through 150g of bromine in a flask or wash-bottle. A distillation apparatus with an air condenser is employed; the vapor inlet tube leads into the bulb of the reaction flask which is heated to about 600°C with the full flame of the Bunsen burner. The crude product in the receiver is purified by distillation over a few grams of powdered copper to remove any excess dissolved bromine; b.p. 153°C.

The bromide is a colorless liquid which is easily hydrolyzed. It reacts vigorously with metallic potassium (in contrast to $SiCl_4$) to produce elemental silicon.

$$SiBr_4 + 4K \longrightarrow Si + 4KBr$$

References:
1. I, vol. 1:38.
2. GATTERMAN, Ber., 22:189 (1889).

84 e. Silicon Tetraiodide ***

$$Si + 2I_2 \longrightarrow SiI_4$$

This compound is prepared from 3g of silicon and 50g of iodine in an apparatus silimar to that used for aluminum iodide (No. 10 b), at a temperature of 600–700°C. The crude colored product may be purified by distillation over finely granulated (*not* powdered) copper; m.p. 122°C; b.p. 288°C.

Yield = 70% (based on the iodine)

The iodide is a pure white crystalline solid which is sensitive to light and moisture. Heating it with silver powder *in vacuo* at 280°C produces Si_2I_6 and silver iodide. The compound dissolves without reaction in dry hydrocarbons.

References:
1. I, vol. 4:117.
2. GUICHARD, *Compt. rend.*, 145:808 (1907).
3. SCHWARTZ AND PFLUGMACHER, *Ber.*, 75, 1062 (1941).
4. WANNAGAT AND SCHWARTZ, *Z. anorg. Chem.*, 277:82 (1954).
5. LITTON AND ANDERSON, *J. Electrochem. Soc.*, 101:287 (1954).

Chapter 5

ACIDS

85. Aminomethanesulfonic Acid *

$$HCHO + NaHSO_3 \longrightarrow HOCH_2SO_3Na$$
$$HOCH_2SO_3Na + NH_3 \longrightarrow H_2NCH_2SO_3Na + H_2O$$
$$2H_2NCH_2SO_3Na + H_2SO_4 \longrightarrow 2H_2NCH_2SO_3H + Na_2SO_4$$

One hundred and twenty grams of sodium hydrogen sulfite * is slurried well with 120ml of water in a 500ml Erlenmeyer flask and 90ml of 40% aqueous formaldehyde is added with shaking. The temperature of the mixture rises slowly to 65–70°C and the aldehyde odor disappears completely. When this occurs the vessel and contents are cooled to 50°C under running water and 90ml of concentrated aqueous ammonia is stirred in. This causes a second rise in temperature to 65–70°C.

When the reaction mixture has cooled to 60°C, the loosely-stoppered flask is immersed in a water bath at 60°C for one hour with occasional swirling.

Alternatively, the flask may be allowed to cool spontaneously immediately after the addition of the ammonia and stand for one or two days at room temperature.

The solution is filtered by suction through a dense grade of paper to remove small amounts of residual material and impurities. A cold mixture of 33ml of concentrated sulfuric acid and 96ml of water is added fairly rapidly to the solution of sodium aminomethanesulfonate with good agitation. The acidified liquid is immediately cooled in an ice-water bath to 5–10°C. During this time the product continuously crystallizes out.

* Yields from products of good technical grade and of analytical reagent purity give almost identical yields.

136

The solid is filtered by suction, preferably in a sintered-glass funnel, and drained thoroughly. It is then washed carefully with 25ml of ice water, followed by two 50ml portions of cold 50% aqueous ethanol. Several final rinsings with 95% ethanol are used to remove all excess sulfuric acid.

The white crystalline material is dried *in vacuo*.

Yield = 60–64g (50–55% based on the formaldehyde)
Purity = 98+% m.p. 190°C (dec)

To obtain a perfectly pure product, the acid is recrystallized rapidly from eleven times its weight of water at 70°C, washed with a little ice-cold water, and dried *in vacuo*. The recovery is 70–75% using 50g of crude amino acid.

The product can be assayed by titrating a sample of 0.3–0.4g to a phenolphthalein end point with carbonate-free $N/10$ sodium or potassium hydroxide. The alkali should be added rather slowly towards the end-point as the neutralization is not quite instantaneous.

The calculated equivalent weight of aminomethanesulfonic acid is 111.1. For the recrystallized material, values of 99.9% to 100.2% purity were consistently obtained.

References:
1. P:359.
2. REINKING AND DEHNEL, *Ber.*, 38:1077 (1905).
3. RASCHIG AND PRAHL, *Ann.*, 448:265 (1926).
4. BACKER AND MULDER, *Rec. trav. chim.*, 52:454 (1933).

COGNATE PREPARATION

85 a. Aminoethanesulfonic Acid *

$$H_3CHC(NH_2)SO_3H$$

Seventeen grams of acetaldehyde are dissolved in 20ml of water and added dropwise to a suspension of 40g of sodium bisulfite in 30ml of water. The reaction mixture is kept cold in an ice bath to prevent loss of the aldehyde by volatilization; much heat is liberated by the formation of the bisulfite addition compound. The temperature of the solution is adjusted to 50°C and 17ml of 20% aqueous ammonia are added. The latter is prepared from 13ml of the concentrated base and 5ml of water. The contents of the reaction vessel rise to 55°C and are allowed to cool back slowly to room temperature. The solution is acidified as described previously, using 20ml of water mixed with 6ml of concentrated sulfuric acid. The white needle-like product settles out after standing in ice for a few hours and crystallization is completed by allowing the mixture to remain overnight in the refrigerator. The material is filtered and washed with 20ml of cold 50% alcohol and then with an equal volume of the pure solvent. The crystals are dried in air.

$$\text{Yield} = 11g \quad (23\% \text{ based on the aldehyde})$$

The product is more soluble in water than is its lower homologue; on boiling, sulfur dioxide and acetaldehyde are formed. When warmed with dilute sulfuric acid, the compound liberates SO_2. The acid is extremely soluble in aqueous sodium hydroxide because of the formation of the sodium salt, but almost insoluble in alcohol. On ignition a carbonaceous residue and an odor of burning hair are produced.

86. Arsenic (V) Acid ½-Hydrate *

$$As_2O_3 + 2HNO_3 + 2H_2O \longrightarrow 2H_3AsO_4 + N_2O_3$$

The residue from Experiment No. 9 may be used, or the compound may be prepared independently as follows:

Twenty grams of arsenic trioxide are treated dropwise with 20ml of concentrated nitric acid under the hood and the mixture is heated on the steam bath until the evolution of nitrogen oxides is complete. The liquid is decanted from any undissolved oxide and evaporated just to dryness over a very small flame. The residue is dissolved in 75ml of hot water and filtered by suction if necessary. A thermometer is placed in the filtrate and the latter is evaporated until the viscous liquid has reached a temperature of 130°C. The vessel and contents are transferred to a vacuum desiccator which is placed in the refrigerator; an almost solid mass of white crystalline product is obtained.

$$\text{Yield} = 25\text{--}30g$$

As the material is hygroscopic it must be stored in tightly closed vessels; m.p. 35°C.

If the aqueous solution obtained is evaporated to 175°C instead of 130°C, the compound $As_2O_5 \cdot \frac{5}{3}$-hydrate crystallizes out; at 250–300°C, anhydrous As_2O_5 is formed.

For the preparation of the various indefinite hydrates of antimony pentoxide see references 4, 5, 6.

References:
1. B:62, J:358.
2. SIMON AND THALER, Z. anorg. Chem., 161:143 (1927); 246:19 (1941).
3. GUÉRIN, Bull. soc. chim. (5), 22:1536 (1955).
4. JANDER, Kolloid Z., 23:130 (1918).
5. JANDER AND SIMON, Z. anorg. Chem., 127:71 (1923).
6. SIMON AND THALER, Ibid., 161, 116 (1927).

87. Chlorosulfonic Acid **

(I)

$$H_2SO_4 + PCl_5 \longrightarrow HSO_3Cl + POCl_3 + HCl$$
$$2H_2SO_4 + POCl_3 \longrightarrow 2HSO_3Cl + HPO_3 + HCl$$

Thirty milliliters of concentrated sulfuric acid are mixed with an equal volume of 15–20% oleum and 100g of the mixture is transferred to a 500ml round ground-glass flask under the hood. [CAUTION: The operator must wear gloves during this operation.] Seventy-five grams of phosphorus pentachloride are added in small portions from a porcelain or glass spatula; the reaction mixture warms up and large quantities of hydrogen chloride escape.

When all the solid has been added, the solution is *gently* heated until the evolution of hydrogen chloride has ceased; care must be taken not to overheat it; otherwise some product may be lost through volatilization. The material is then distilled, using an air condenser, until the temperature of the vapor reaches 165°C; the receiver consists of a 250-ml round flask protected from moisture. As the acid attacks cork and rubber readily an all-glass apparatus must be used. The crude product is redistilled from the receiver and the colorless liquid is collected at 149–154°C; pure chlorosulfonic acid boils at 153°C and must be kept in tightly sealed all-glass vessels.

$$\text{Yield} = 60\text{--}75\text{g}$$

(II)

$$SO_3 + HCl \longrightarrow HSO_3Cl$$

All operations are carried out in ground-glass equipment. One hundred and forty grams of 60% oleum (or 100g of the 80% acid) are placed in a gas-washing bottle and a slow (about 2 bubbles/sec) stream of thoroughly dried hydrogen chloride (use sulfuric acid and calcium chloride) is passed in until absorption of the gas is complete. The liquid is distilled and the fraction boiling at 145–165°C is collected. Refractionation yields the pure material at 150–155°C.

$$\text{Yield about 85g}$$

Water hydrolyzes the acid vigorously to HCl and H_2SO_4.

References:
1. B:203.
2. SANGER AND RIEGEL, *Z. anorg. Chem.*, 76:79 (1912).
3. SIMON AND KRATSCH, *Ibid.*, 242:369 (1939).
4. BECKURTS AND OTTO, *Ber.*, 11:2058 (1878).

COGNATE PREPARATION

87 a. Fluorosulfonic Acid **

$$2KHF_2 + 4SO_3 + H_2SO_4 \longrightarrow 4HSO_3F + K_2SO_4$$

Forty milliliters of 60% oleum are placed in a non-vitreous vessel and cooled to about −10°C in an ice-salt bath. Twenty grams of finely powdered and carefully dried potassium acid fluoride are added in small portions with stirring. A viscous mass is obtained which fumes slightly in air; heating slowly to 100°C (hood) drives off the excess sulfur trioxide and hydrogen fluoride.

The mixture is now distilled in an all-glass apparatus until the vapor temperature reaches 250°C. The distillate is then redistilled and the fraction boiling at 160–165°C is collected; b.p. 163°C.

$$\text{Yield} = 85\% \text{ (based on the potassium salt)}$$

Pure fluorosulfonic acid does not attack glass. It reacts explosively with water and fumes in air, and it rapidly destroys cork and rubber. It decomposes in the presence of benzene and chloroform, splitting off hydrogen fluoride; with ether, a strongly exothermic reaction causes the formation of ethyl acetate. The fluoro acid vapor itself is stable to about 900°C.

Reference: MEYER AND SCHRAMM, *Z. anorg. Chem.*, 206:25 (1932).

88. Hydrobromic Acid *

Of the six methods given here, the first three may be used for the production of gaseous hydrogen bromide as well as for aqueous solutions of the gas; IV, V, and VI can be employed only for making the constant-boiling acid.

(I)

$$H_2 + Br_2 \longrightarrow 2HBr$$

The following apparatus is assembled in order:

1. A gas-washing bottle filled with water.
2. A distilling flask filled with 50ml of bromine cooled in ice with the inlet tube leading almost to the bottom of the flask.
3. A Pyrex tube, 50cm long, packed with about 30cm of activated charcoal which is held in place with glass wool plugs.
4. A U-tube filled with glass beads or porcelain chips coated with moist red phosphorus.
5. Two wash bottles in series filled with 100ml and 50ml of water, respectively; if constant-boiling acid is desired, the second bottle should contain 100ml of water. Both bottles are surrounded by an ice-salt bath. The reaction train is set up in the hood.

A steady flow of hydrogen is started through the apparatus to displace the air. This operation requires about thirty minutes, during which time the bromine is kept in the cooling bath.

The furnace is now slowly warmed to 350–375°C and the flow of hydrogen is increased to a point where the bubbles are just too rapid to count. A bath of water at 40–45°C is now placed under the vessel containing the bromine; under these conditions, conversion to hydrogen bromide is complete in about 20 minutes. No vapors of bromine should be visible at the outlet of the reaction tube; otherwise the bromine must be cooled somewhat in water.

At the end of the experiment the two wash bottles are removed and the hydrobromic acid absorbed is determined from the gain in weight; if the smaller volume of water was used, the concentration of acid should be 60–65% by weight. If constant-boiling acid is desired, the solution should be distilled and the fraction boiling at 122–127°C collected as 47–48% hydrobromic acid. A rapid method for determining the concentration of the solution produced is by a rough determination of specific gravity. 65%, 1.78; 60%, 1.68; 55%, 1.60; 50%, 1.52; 45%, 1.44.

(II)

$$2P + 3Br_2 \longrightarrow 2PBr_3$$
$$PBr_3 + 3H_2O \longrightarrow 3HBr + H_3PO_3$$

In a distilling flask fitted with a dropping funnel are placed 25g of clean sand and, over this, a mixture of 25g of red phosphorus and 100g of sand. The mass is moistened with 40–45ml of water, and 50ml of bromine are introduced into the funnel. A U-tube and absorption bottles as described under (I) are connected to the flask. The reaction flask is cooled in ice while the bromine is added dropwise at a very slow rate; the phosphorus may glow with each addition of halogen. In order to avoid a suck-back of the water in the absorption flasks, it is advisable to place an empty safety trap between the U-tube and the water traps. As the reaction proceeds, the evolution of gas is more readily controlled and the cooling bath may be removed. When all the bromine has been added, the distilling flask is *gently* warmed to drive off the remaining acid vapors. The working-up of the hydrobromic acid solutions is the same as previously described.

Yield in I and II is over 90% of theory

(III)

$$C_{10}H_{12} + 4Br_2 \longrightarrow 4HBr + C_{10}H_8Br_4$$

If anhydrous hydrogen bromide is desired, the procedure is carried out in the absence of water, using *dry* reagents. The apparatus of method II is used.

Thirty-five grams of tetrahydronaphthalene are placed in the flask with either 150 or 200ml of water, depending on the desired concentration of the acid. At first the flask is cooled in ice while 50ml of bromine are slowly added dropwise; about one gram of iron filings catalyzes the bromination. As the reaction proceeds, the flask may be allowed to warm up to room temperature. After all the bromine has been added the flask should be shaken for some time; the aqueous layer should be colorless. The acid layer is then separated from the organic material and worked up as in I.

Yield about 90%

(IV)

$$H_2SO_4 + KBr \longrightarrow HBr + KHSO_4$$

A mixture of 120g of potassium bromide and 200ml of water is cooled in ice while 90ml of concentrated sulfuric acid is slowly added. The temperature must not rise over 75°C during this addition; otherwise free bromine may be formed, causing a loss in yield. The reaction mixture is cooled to room temperature and the potassium bisulfate is filtered off by suction through a fritted funnel or a hardened filter paper. The filtrate is then fractionated and the material boiling from 122–127°C is collected as constant-boiling acid.

Yield = 85%

In all cases where a mixture of sulfuric and hydrobromic acids is obtained, a redistillation is necessary to remove about 0.01% of sulfate in the first fractionation; only the acid with a steady boiling point is retained. This operation entails a loss of about 15% in yield.

(V)

$$Br_2 + SO_2 + 2H_2O \longrightarrow 2HBr + H_2SO_4$$

Fifty milliliters of bromine are covered with 200ml of water and sulfur dioxide is passed into the mixture, under the hood, until a straw-colored liquid results. Fractionation yields about 300g of 47–48% acid, which is an almost theoretical yield.

As this reaction proceeds, the bromine dissolves in the hydrobromic acid that is formed, yielding a homogeneous liquid into which the sulfur dioxide may be more rapidly introduced.

$$HBr + Br_2 \rightleftarrows HBr_3$$

(VI)

$$2S + Br_2 \longrightarrow S_2Br_2$$
$$S_2Br_2 + 5Br_2 + 8H_2O \longrightarrow 12HBr + 2H_2SO_4$$

One hundred and fifty grams of bromine are weighed into a glass-stoppered bottle in the hood and 10g of powdered sulfur are quickly introduced. The bottle is then agitated and the sulfur rapidly dissolves to yield a red oily liquid.

Two hundred grams of ice are placed in a 500ml glass-stoppered bottle and the vessel is immersed in ice. About one-third of the sulfur-bromine mixture is added; over the course of about one hour the red oil disappears. Cooling is maintained throughout the hydrolysis. The second third of the sulfur-bromine compound is now added, followed by the last portion about 30 minutes later. When all the material has dissolved and reacted, a pale yellow liquid remains which is fractionally distilled as usual; b.p. 122–127°C.

Yield about 300g of acid

Hydrobromic acid may be kept colorless for long periods of time by storage in a dark bottle in the refrigerator.

References:
    (I) 1. I, vol. 1:152.
    (II) 2. Fileti and Crosa, *Gazz. chim. ital.*, 21:64 (1891); B:71.
   (III) 3. I, vol. 1:151; footnote, p. 152.

(IV) 4. I, vol. 1:155.
 (V) 5. *Organic Syntheses,* Collective Vol. 1, p. 23, Wiley, 1935.
(VI) 6. FARKAS *et al., J. Soc. Chem. Ind.,* 66:115 (1947).
    7. P:464.

89. Hydriodic Acid *

(I)

$$H_2 + I_2 \longrightarrow 2HI$$

Rubber stoppers, as well as direct light, should be avoided in all operations with iodine and hydrogen iodide. This procedure and the one following may be used for the preparation of the anhydrous halogen acid using some modifications (see references).

Platinized asbestos is prepared by soaking 3g of asbestos in 7ml of 10% hexachloroplatinic (IV) acid, evaporating the mixture to dryness, and igniting the residue at red heat.

The following apparatus is connected in order:

1. A 250-ml distilling flask with a short side-arm at least 10mm wide. The flask is fitted with a gas inlet tube reaching just above the surface of 100g of pure iodine contained in the vessel.
2. A glass tube, 80–100cm in length and 2cm in diameter, which is packed with platinized asbestos for a distance of about 15cm, starting 5cm from the flask containing the iodine. A circular oven is arranged to heat only the forward portion of the tube.
3. A U-tube packed with glass or porcelain chips covered with a paste of moist red phosphorus.
4. A dry wash bottle to prevent suck-back.
5. An absorption vessel containing 50ml of water which is cooled in an ice-salt bath.

The air in the apparatus is displaced by a stream of dry nitrogen for 30 minutes; because if any oxygen is present when the hydrogen is introduced next, an explosion may result on contact with the catalyst.

Dry hydrogen is now introduced for about one-half hour in place of the nitrogen at a rate of about 5 bubbles per second. The circular oven is slowly heated to 500°C and the flask containing the iodine is immersed in an oil bath at 160°C. Only a slight purple color, due to uncombined iodine, should be visible in the cold part of the reaction tube; a series of loose asbestos plugs will serve to retain some of the iodine that condenses there. The blockage of the side-arm of the distilling flask by sublimed iodine may be prevented by gentle heating. Under the conditions described, about 3 hours will be needed to convert all the iodine; approximately 70ml of 57–59% hydriodic acid is formed in the absorption flask.

$$Yield = 80\%$$

If 135g of iodine are used instead in the preceding experiment, about 75ml of 65–68% acid are produced.

(II)

$$2P + 3I_2 \longrightarrow 2PI_3$$
$$PI_3 + 3H_2O \longrightarrow 3HI + H_3PO_3$$

The apparatus described under (II) for hydrobromic acid is used, except that an ordinary filter funnel replaces the dropping funnel; only 50ml of water are used for absorbing the hydrogen iodide. A glass rod fitting snugly into the neck of the funnel serves as a valve for the periodic introduction of material into the evolution flask.

The latter is filled with 100g of iodine and 10ml of water. A slurry of 5g of red phosphorus and 10ml of water is placed in the funnel. The reaction flask is cooled in water while the phosphorus slurry is *slowly added, dropwise,* to the iodine; evolution of gas proceeds smoothly. When all the phosphorus has been added, the flask is gently warmed to complete the reaction. If the residue in the flask is still iodine-colored, a little more phosphorus may be added.

Yield 90% (based on the iodine)

Great care must be taken to add the aqueous slurry of red phosphorus slowly, especially at the beginning of the reaction; otherwise the gas may be evolved with explosive violence.

(III)

$$H_2S + I_2 \longrightarrow 2HI + S$$

Two hundred and eighty-five grams of iodine are suspended in 250ml of water contained in a one-liter filter flask fitted with a wide gas inlet tube that reaches to about one-half inch from the bottom of the vessel. Under the hood, a stream of hydrogen sulfide is passed into the suspension as rapidly as it can be absorbed. Some heat is evolved and the flask may be cooled in a water bath. Frequent agitation is necessary to prevent a coating of sulfur from forming over the initially undissolved iodine; as the reaction progresses, the iodine dissolves in the hydriodic acid already formed.

$$I_2 + HI \rightleftarrows HI_3$$

The sulfur, which settles out as a spongy mass on the bottom of the flask, is separated from the pale brown liquid that is finally produced by decantation, and filtration through a plug of glass wool. The filtrate is refluxed to remove excess dissolved hydrogen sulfide, using boiling chips to prevent bumping. Five milliliters of 30% hypophosphorous acid are added, the mixture is fractionated through a short efficient column, and the portion boiling at 125–127°C (760mm) is collected.

$$\text{Yield} = 425\text{–}450g \text{ of } 57\% \text{ HI}$$

Hydriodic acid that is stored in a dark all-glass container in the refrigerator, preferably under an inert gas, remains colorless for 4–6 months. If the treatment with hypophosphorus acid is omitted, the resulting acid is straw-colored and it deteriorates more rapidly on standing; only distillation in hydrogen or carbon dioxide gives a colorless material.

For the production of gaseous hydrogen iodide by dehydration of concentrated aqueous solutions with phosphorus pentoxide see references 6 and 7.

References:
(I) 1. I, vol. 1:159.
2. BODENSTEIN AND LIENEWEG, Z. physik. Chem., 119:124 (1926).
3. OGG, J. Am. Chem. Soc., 56:526 (1934).
(II) 4. MEYER, Ber., 20:3381 (1887).
(III) 5. I, vol. 1:157; Ibid., vol. 2:210.
6. BONHOEFFER AND STEINER, Z. physik. Chem., 122:288 (1926).
7. ROLLEFSON AND BOOHER, J. Am. Chem. Soc., 53:1728 (1931).

90. Iodic Acid **

(I)

$$Ba(IO_3)_2 + H_2SO_4 \longrightarrow 2HIO_3 + BaSO_4$$

A solution of 12g of barium chloride 2-hydrate in 100ml of water is mixed with 22g of potassium iodate (or 20g of the sodium salt) in an equal volume of boiling water. The resulting mixture is cooled thoroughly in an ice bath and suction-filtered. The residue is washed twice with 25ml of cold water and dried in warm air.

Yield of barium iodate monohydrate = 24g

The material may also be produced directly from iodine and chlorate as follows:

$$2KClO_3 + I_2 \longrightarrow 2KIO_3 + Cl_2$$
$$2KIO_3 + Ba(NO_3)_2 \longrightarrow Ba(IO_3)_2 + 2KNO_3$$

A mixture of 10g of iodine, 8.6g of potassium chlorate and 30ml of water are placed in a 100-ml Kjeldahl flask. One millilter of concentrated nitric acid is added and the mouth of the flask covered with an inverted beaker. The flask is now placed in a water bath at about 60°C; when the evolution of chlorine *just* begins it is immediately withdrawn. The vigorous reaction that follows may be moderated somewhat by momentary immersion of the flask in cold water. When the reaction subsides, gentle heat is applied until the iodine has dissolved and the excess chlorine has been driven off. The liquid is washed into a beaker with 60ml of hot water and heated on the steam bath to dissolve any solid that may have formed. A solution of 10.5g of barium nitrate in 100ml of hot water is slowly added and the mixture is cooled in ice. The product is filtered off and washed several times with a little cold water.

Yield = 19g (monohydrate)

Twenty grams of barium iodate monohydrate are added with mechanical stirring to 120ml of gently boiling 1N sulfuric acid. Heating and agitation are maintained for about one hour; a little water is added from time to time to keep the volume constant. The mixture is filtered and the residue is washed with 40ml of boiling water. The clear filtrate is evaporated on the water bath to a few milliliters of sirup, which is then stirred with 75ml of concentrated nitric acid while heating is continued. After a few minutes the vessel and contents are cooled in ice and the supernatant liquid is decanted from the solidified product. It is brought onto the filter with 15ml of glacial acetic acid and washed with a 10-ml portion of the same liquid. The product is drained well and transferred without delay to a vacuum desiccator where it is dried for several days over solid alkali.

$$Yield = 10\text{--}12g$$

(II)

$$3I_2 + 10HNO_3 \longrightarrow 6HIO_3 + 10NO + 2H_2O$$

Twenty grams of pure iodine and 100ml of fuming nitric acid are placed in a ground-glass 2- or 3-neck flask which is fitted with a short inlet tube that terminates above the surface of the liquid and an air condenser at least 50cm long. The reaction vessel is heated at 80°C in a water bath and a gentle (2 bubbles/sec) stream of dry air is passed in to remove the oxides of nitrogen that are formed (hood). If ordinary concentrated nitric acid is used, a slightly higher temperature (100–120°C) is required for the procedure. When the reaction is over and the liquid has assumed a pale-yellow color, it is evaporated to an oil on the steam bath under the hood. The residue is worked up as in (I).

$$Yield = 20\text{--}25g$$

(III)

$$I_2 + 5H_2O_2 \longrightarrow 2HIO_3 + 4H_2O$$

In a ground flask fitted with a long air-condenser are placed 25g of iodine, 50ml of concentrated nitric acid, and 15ml of 30% hydrogen peroxide (free of organic preservatives). Twenty-five milliliters of water are added and the vessel is heated at 70°C until the reaction begins, as shown by a partial disappearance of the iodine color. More hydrogen peroxide is cautiously added in small portions through the condenser until all the iodine has reacted; about 30–40ml will be required. The liquid is evaporated to a sirup in the hood and the product isolated as under (I).

Yield about 30g

Iodic acid is deliquescent because of its great solubility in water (286g/100ml at 25°C) so it must be kept in a dry place, preferably in the dark. Above 220°C, iodine pentoxide is formed by dehydration. The acid melts at 110°C to form $HIO_3 \cdot I_2O_5$.

References:
1. P:470.
2. GUICHARD, *Bull. soc. chim.*, (4), 5:723 (1909); *Ann. chim.* [ix] 7:8 (1917).
3. BAXTER AND ST. TILLEY, *Z. anorg. Chem.*, 61:295 (1909).
4. BRAY AND CAULKINS, *J. Am. Chem. Soc.*, 53:44 (1931).

91. Hydroxylamine O-Sulfonic Acid **

(I)

$$(NH_3OH)Cl + HSO_3Cl \longrightarrow NH_2OSO_3H + 2HCl$$

Fourteen grams of hydroxylammonium chloride (see No. 55) are placed in a 200ml beaker under the hood and 35g of chlorosulfonic acid (see No. 87) added slowly with caution. [CAUTION: The operator must wear gloves during this operation.] The reaction mixture foams up with the evolution of large volumes of hydrogen chloride; heat is given off. When the reaction has moderated and the contents of the beaker have cooled somewhat, the mixture is heated at 70–80°C for 10–15 minutes longer on the steam bath. Higher temperatures cause decomposition. The vessel is allowed to cool in a desiccator over solid alkali and then is placed in an ice bath. Fifty milliliters of absolute ether, previously cooled to 0°C or lower, are added dropwise with continual stirring; the excess chlorosulfonic acid reacts vigorously but the temperature of the mixture is not allowed to exceed 50°C. The white finely divided product is allowed to stand under the ether for about one hour in ice and is then suction-filtered through fritted glass, taking care to keep the filter cake moist. The flask is rinsed with 25ml of dry ether and the rinsing liquid is added to the filter funnel. The product is washed with seven 25ml portions of anhydrous ether and transferred moist to a vacuum desiccator where the excess liquid is removed. The hygroscopic material is stored in tightly stoppered bottles, preferably over P_2O_5.

$$Yield = 21g \quad (98\% \text{ purity})$$

(II)

$$(NH_3OH)_2SO_4 + 2SO_3 \longrightarrow 2NH_2OSO_3H + H_2SO_4$$

[If hydroxylammonium sulfate is not available it is prepared from the chloride as follows: Fifteen grams of hydroxylammonium chloride (No. 55) are covered with 15ml of water and 6ml of concentrated sulfuric acid are cautiously added under the hood. (CAUTION: As much hydrogen chloride escapes gloves should be worn.) The mixture is evaporated almost to dryness over a small flame and the cold residue triturated in a mortar with 15ml of alcohol. The product is suction-filtered, washed with 15ml more of alcohol, and dried *in vacuo*. Yield = 15g]

Forty-five grams of 30% oleum are placed in a 250-ml wide-mouthed flask and 12.5g of hydroxylammonium sulfate are carefully added in small portions with continual agitation. The reaction is highly exothermic and the flask is allowed to stand for one hour after being cooled to room temperature; the vessel is loosely stoppered during this time. The flask is cooled to 0°C in ice and ether is added as described in (I). The remainder of the procedure is also the same as above.

$$Yield = 15\text{--}17g \quad (92\text{--}98\% \text{ purity})$$

The acid is slowly hydrolyzed by water at 25°C; rapidly at higher temperatures. Warm alkaline solutions decompose the material to form sulfates and unstable imine (NH). This reaction may be used for the amination of several organic aromatic compounds. Aqueous acids cause reversion to the starting materials. The acid is soluble in cold methanol without reaction, but it esterifies when warmed; with ethanol it behaves similarly. Ether, chloroform, and carbon tetrachloride do not dissolve the sulfonic acid. With ammonia it forms hydrazine and shows gentle over-all oxidizing action.

References:

1. I, vol. 5:122.
2. WANNAGAT AND PFEIFFENSCHNEIDER, *Z. anorg. Chem.*, 297:151 (1958).

92. Sulfamic Acid **

(I)

a) $CO(NH_2)_2 + 2H_2SO_4 \longrightarrow NH_2SO_3H + NH_4HSO_4 + CO_2$

One hundred and twenty-five milliliters of concentrated sulfuric acid are mixed with an equal volume of 15–20% oleum in a one-liter Erlenmeyer flask and the mixture is cooled in an ice bath. A thermometer is placed in the liquid and 50g of urea are added in small portions with agitation and cooling; the temperature is kept below 45°C. The solution is now cautiously heated over a *small* flame and agitated; evolution of gas begins around 100°C and becomes fairly vigorous at 110°C. When the temperature has risen to 118–120°C the flame is removed and the flask is placed on an asbestos pad. The temperature rises slowly to 135°C, at which point the flask is briefly immersed in an ice bath until the liquid has cooled to 125°C; continual swirling is maintained. The flask is replaced on the pad; the reaction is self-sustaining at 125–130°C for about one-half hour. When the temperature starts to drop, the flask is heated at 125°C until the effervescence ceases rather abruptly, and is then cooled rapidly in an ice bath. A cold mixture of 200ml of water and an equal volume of concentrated sulfuric acid is then stirred in, and the product is allowed to crystallize for at least 2 hours in ice—preferably longer, or in the refrigerator overnight. The supernatant liquid is carefully decanted and the white crystals are washed twice by decantation with 250ml portions of 95% alcohol. The solid is brought onto the filter with 150 ml of alcohol and washed with three 30-ml volumes of the same solvent. The acid is dried in air; m.p. 205°C.

Yield = 56–69g

Failure to allow enough time for crystallization of product has produced yields as low as 34g.

b) $CO(NH_2)_2 + H_2SO_4 \cdot SO_3 \longrightarrow 2NH_2SO_3H + CO_2$

Thirty grams of urea are added in portions to 55ml of concentrated sulfuric acid contained in a 500-ml flask. The reaction mixture is continuously ice-cooled and stirred with a thermometer so that the temperature does not rise above 45°C during the addition. Under similar conditions, 100ml of 60% oleum are mixed in and the liquid is cautiously warmed on the steam bath until evolution of carbon dioxide becomes vigorous. At no time is the temperature of the reaction mixture allowed to rise over 135°C; it is cooled with ice if necessary. The flask is kept on the steam bath until effervescence ceases and is then cooled in ice for about three hours. The product is removed by suction on a glass filter, washed with 100ml of cold concentrated sulfuric acid, and drained dry for about thirty minutes. The acid is washed with four or five 100-ml portions of ice-cold methanol by stirring it on the filter and sucking it dry; excess wash liquid is removed *in vacuo*.

Yield about 85g

(II)

$(NH_3OH)_2SO_4 + 2SO_2 \longrightarrow 2NH_2SO_3H + H_2SO_4$

[A one-liter hydrogenation pressure bottle, or a one-quart soda bottle fitted with a screw-type pressure clamp, or an autoclave may be used in this experiment.]

A solution of 80g of hydroxylammonium sulfate (see No. 91, method II) in 240ml of water is cooled to —30°C or below in the pressure vessel, using a bath of dry ice and acetone. Under the hood, about 80ml of sulfur dioxide is condensed into the container by fitting a two-hole stopper, carrying both an inlet and an outlet tube, into the mouth of the pressure vessel; the gas should be passed in at such a rate that virtually none is lost by volatilization. The vessel is then securely sealed and placed behind a safety screen in the hood for 2–4 days at room temperature. The container is re-cooled to −30°C and the pressure seal is cautiously removed. [CAUTION: The operator must wear goggles and gloves during this operation.] When the excess sulfur dioxide has volatilized at normal temperature, the quantity still remaining in solution is removed by bubbling air through the mixture. The crystals of product are filtered off and the mother liquor is reserved. The solid acid is washed three times with 75ml of 95% alcohol and dried in air. About 125–150ml of concentrated sulfuric acid is added to the mother liquor slowly, from a tap-funnel, while stirring and cooling in ice. The ice-cold mixture is filtered after two hours and the solid is washed with three 20ml volumes of alcohol.

$$\text{Total yield} = 80\text{–}85\text{g}$$

If the reaction mixture is allowed to stand for only 24 hours the yield is reduced to 70g.

(III)

$$(CH_3)_2CNOH + SO_2 + H_2O \longrightarrow NH_2SO_3H + (CH_3)_2CO$$

[If acetoxime is not available, it may be prepared as follows: [2]

$$(NH_3OH)Cl + (CH_3)_2CO + NaOH \longrightarrow (CH_3)_2CNOH + NaCl + 2H_2O$$

A cold solution of 48g of sodium hydroxide in 70ml of water is added slowly, with cooling and constant stirring, to a mixture of 84g of hydroxylammonium chloride (No. 55), 75g of acetone, and 75ml of water. The product settles out as an upper layer which solidifies after cooling and standing for some time, preferably in ice overnight. The solid material is filtered off and dissolved in 250ml of ether; the mother liquor is extracted with three 50ml portions of the same solvent. The combined etheral extracts are freed from drops of aqueous solution by decantation and dried over about 5g of anhydrous sodium sulfate. The ether is carefully *distilled off* on the water bath; ordinary evaporation causes a loss of product because of its volatility. On cooling, the oxime solidifies and it is pressed on filter paper for rapid removal of the remaining traces of solvent. The product must be kept in tightly stoppered bottles as it sublimes readily. Yield= 65–75g; m.p. 59–60°C.]

About 40ml of liquid sulfur dioxide is condensed in a 250-ml pressure bottle containing a solution of 50g of acetoxime in 50ml of water. The procedure of method (II) is used and the sealed bottle is allowed to stand for at least 5 hours at room temperature. After re-cooling, the excess of sulfur dioxide is allowed to escape, the product is collected by filtration, washed with 75ml of alcohol, and with the same volume of ether.

Yield = 60g

Sulfamic acid is a stable, non-hygroscopic, monoprotic acid which is very convenient to use as a primary standard in acid-base titrations. The acid hydrolyzes fairly rapidly in boiling water to give ammonium bisulfate. It may be recrystallized from water at 70°C with rapid cooling to avoid decomposition. Sulfamic acid does not dissolve appreciably in oxygenated organic solvents, e.g., alcohols, ethers.

For the purification of commercial sulfamic acid for use as a primary acidimetric standard, see reference 4.

References:
1. J:365; I, vol 2:176ff; P:347ff.
2. B:158.
3. BAUMGARTEN, *Ber.*, 69:1929 (1936).
4. I, vol. 2:178.

93. Sulfuric Acid by the Chamber Process **

$$2SO_2 + NO + NO_2 + H_2O + O_2 \longrightarrow 2SO_2(OH)NO_2$$
$$2SO_2(OH)NO_2 + H_2O \longrightarrow 2H_2SO_4 + NO + NO_2$$

A one-liter bottle is fitted with a 3-hole stopper through which the following pieces of apparatus are connected:

1. A combustion tube about 10cm long carrying an air-inlet tube with a screw clamp and a gas-outlet tube bent at a right angle which leads down into the middle of the large bottle. A charge of 10g of powdered pyrites is placed in the combustion tube; a small plug of glass wool near the exit end retains any solid particles or unburnt sulfur.

2. A 25-ml distilling flask with a long side-arm bent at an angle and leading just below the stopper in the bottle. The flask is fitted with a capillary tube (not drawn out too fine) which leads almost to the bottom of the vessel; 10ml of concentrated nitric acid are introduced into the flask.

3. A filter flask is half filled with water as a gas flow indicator and fitted with a glass tube, one end of which leads just under the water surface in the flask and the other end made flush with the bottom of the stopper in the large bottle. The side arm of the flask leads to the water pump.

With the screw clamp open, the pyrites is gently heated with a wing burner in a slow stream of air drawn in by the aspirator. The clamp is then partially closed so that air also passes through the capillary into the nitric acid. The pyrites may now be heated more strongly; the current of air through the nitric acid is adjusted by means of the clamp so that red fumes of nitrogen oxides are always present in the bottle or "chamber." If not enough vapor of nitric acid is provided, colorless crystals of nitrosyl sulfuric acid ("chamber crystals") will form on the walls of the bottle.

When the pyrites is completely burned, the apparatus is disconnected and any oxides of nitrogen remaining in the bottle are carried away by a stream of air. The contents of the bottle are taken up with 75ml of water; if the solution is colored yellow-brown from dissolved nitrogen oxides, they should be removed by a current of air. The solution of sulfuric acid is made up to 100ml in a volumetric flask and the yield is determined by titration of an aliquot with base.

Reference: B:128.

Chapter 6

COORDINATION COMPLEXES

A. COORDINATION NUMBER 2

94. Diamminemercury (II) Chloride *

(I)

$$HgCl_2 + 2NH_3 \longrightarrow Hg(NH_3)_2Cl_2$$

Eight and one-tenth grams of mercuric chloride are dissolved in 150ml of dry ethyl acetate contained in a 250-ml filter flask fitted with a gas inlet tube reaching into the liquid. A steady stream of dry ammonia is passed in for 5–10 minutes until the precipitate settles well; the mixture should be frequently agitated during this step. After standing for 30 minutes, the white solid is filtered off and rinsed with 25ml of acetone to facilitate air drying.

$$Yield = 8-9g$$

(II)

$$HgCl_2 + 2NH_3 \longrightarrow HgNH_2Cl + HCl$$
$$NH_4Cl + HgNH_2Cl \longrightarrow Hg(NH_3)_2Cl_2$$

Fifteen grams of ammonium chloride and 0.63g of mercuric chloride are dissolved in 25ml of water. A second solution consisting of 6ml of concentrated aqueous ammonia and 15g of ammonium chloride in 250ml of water is also prepared. Both solutions are heated to 95°C and then thoroughly mixed. After standing for 24 hours the crystalline precipitate is filtered off without washing and dried in air.

$$Yield = 0.5g$$

157

If the ammonium chloride is omitted in this procedure only $HgNH_2Cl$ is formed.[2]

References:

1. P:184.
2. SAHA AND CHOUDHURI, *Z. anorg. Chem.*, 67:357 (1910).
3. FRANKLIN, *J. Am. Chem. Soc.*, 29:35 (1907).
4. NAUMANN, *Ber.*, 37:3603 (1904).
5. GERMAN AND JAMSETT, *J. Chem. Soc.*, 1337 (1939).

95. Diamminesilver (I) Sulfate *

$$2AgNO_3 + H_2SO_4 \longrightarrow Ag_2SO_4 + 2HNO_3$$
$$Ag_2SO_4 + 4NH_3 \longrightarrow [Ag(NH_3)_2]_2SO_4$$

Fifty grams of silver nitrate are treated with 155ml of molar sulfuric acid and *gently* heated in an evaporating dish under the hood until no more acid vapors are given off. The perfectly dry cold residue is dissolved in the minimum amount of concentrated aqueous ammonia and allowed to crystallize in a desiccator. The crude product is recrystallized from 5% aqueous ammonia and dried in air; large colorless columnar crystals.

Yield = 20–25g

The compound is only very slightly photosensitive and it shows a tendency to sublime in the storage bottle. Using silver chloride, no corresponding diammine can be prepared in the solid form, although a material of composition $2AgCl \cdot 3NH_3$ has been isolated from ammoniacal silver chloride solutions. There seems to be no danger of an explosion in this preparation.

Reference: B:164, 169.

96. Dipyridinemercury (II) Persulfate *

$$HgCl_2 + 2NaOH \longrightarrow HgO + 2NaCl + H_2O$$
$$HgO + 2HC_2H_3O_2 \longrightarrow Hg(C_2H_3O_2)_2 + H_2O$$
$$Hg(C_2H_3O_2)_2 + 2C_5H_5N + (NH_4)_2S_2O_8 \longrightarrow Hg(C_5H_5N)_2S_2O_8 + 2NH_4C_2H_3O_2$$

Five and four-tenths grams of mercuric chloride are dissolved in a hot solution of 5g of sodium chloride in 50ml of water. Fifty milliliters of a hot 5% solution of sodium hydroxide in water are added with stirring, the precipitated yellow mercuric oxide is filtered off by suction, and the material is washed three times with 25ml of hot water. The moist cake of oxide and the filter paper are suspended in 50ml of water and glacial acetic acid is added dropwise from a buret until the oxide just dissolves. The solution of mercuric acetate is filtered into 7g of *fresh* ammonium persulfate dissolved in 25ml of cold water, and 5ml of pure pyridine are slowly added with stirring. Colorless crystals of product begin to separate almost at once; the mixture is allowed to stand for 30 minutes to complete the precipitation. The solid is filtered off, washed with 20ml of cold water, and dried in air or in a desiccator over solid alkali.

$$Yield = 10g \quad (93\% \text{ based on mercury salt})$$

[If mercuric acetate is available, 6.4g of this salt may be dissolved in 50ml of water containing just enough acetic acid to clear up any turbidity and the preparation continued from that point on.]

The product may be recrystallized, if desired, by dissolving 1g in the minimum volume of cold $3M$ sulfuric acid and reprecipitating by the addition of a slight excess of pyridine.

COGNATE PREPARATION

96 a. Pyridinemercury (II) Chloride

$$HgCl_2 + 2C_5H_5N \xrightarrow{\text{heat}} Hg(C_5H_5N)_2Cl_2 \longrightarrow Hg(C_5H_5N)Cl_2 + C_5H_5N$$

Two and seven-tenths grams of mercuric chloride are dissolved in 50ml of 95% alcohol and 1ml of pyridine is added dropwise with stirring. The liquid and precipitate are heated to the boiling point on the steam bath, and just enough hot alcohol is added to dissolve the suspended solid; about 40ml should be required. On cooling, the product crystallizes in the form of colorless felted needles which are filtered out and dried in air.

For a possible dimeric formulation of the complex compound see reference 2.

$$Yield = 3g$$

References:
1. P:187.
2. P:170.

B. COORDINATION NUMBER 4

97. Alpha and Beta-Dichlorodiamminecobalt (II) ***

$$[Co(NH_3)_6]Cl_2 \longrightarrow [Co(NH_3)_2Cl_2] + 4NH_3$$

Alpha-form: (I)

Two grams of *dry* hexamminecobalt (II) chloride (see No. 107) are carefully transferred to a dry, accurately weighed, test tube; taking care that none of the crystals adhere to the sides of the tube. A plug of glass wool is inserted about 2 inches from the mouth of the test tube and the latter, with its contents, is reweighed, to four significant figures. The tube is then fitted with a vacuum-tight rubber stopper carrying a right-angled piece of glass tubing with a stopcock (*A*). The glass tubing is connected to an open-type manometer which, in turn, is joined to the side-arm of a 100-ml distilling flask; a screw clamp (*B*) is placed between the manometer and the flask. About 35ml of concentrated sulfuric acid are placed in the latter (to absorb ammonia), and a rubber stopper is inserted with a glass tube leading almost to the surface of the acid. The distilling flask is connected to the aspirator by means of a piece of pressure hose which is fitted with a second screw clamp.

The entire apparatus is evacuated to about 15mm, *A* is closed, and the test tube is placed in an oil bath maintained at 150°C. *Immediately* after the tube has been placed in the hot bath, *A* is opened *very* slowly and suction applied for one minute to draw off the ammonia. The gas is given off very vigorously at the start and if *A* is opened too quickly, powdered solid will be sprayed on the cool upper part of the test tube without decomposing completely. The color of the solid changes from yellow-pink to blue, the latter being the color of the *beta* compound. Stopcock *A* is closed and the test tube is allowed to remain in the bath for 30 minutes to give the unstable *beta* form enough time to change to the more stable *alpha* modification. The process of withdrawing ammonia together with the succeeding heating period is repeated two or three times more until the material in the test tube has assumed a pure pink color with no trace of blue. To check for complete decomposition, B is closed and A is slowly opened; the pressure should read 35–40mm. The apparatus may then be disconnected and the test tube reweighed as further proof that the change has been completed.

Alpha-form: (II)

A test tube, which has been filled and weighed as described in (I), is fitted with a glass-wool plug and a stopper carrying short gas-inlet and outlet tubes. A slow stream of pure dry ammonia is passed through the test tube, which is placed in an oil bath accurately maintained at 232–235°C. After two hours the tube is taken out and cooled rapidly during which time the ammonia is displaced by dry nitrogen. The tube is reweighed and heated again for one hour as above. This procedure is repeated until the weight is constant; m.p. 273±3°C.

At 150°C the hexammine has an ammonia pressure of well over one atmosphere while that of the diammine corresponds to only about 15mm. Method B may also be carried out in an Abderhalden drying pistol which is fitted with two outlets for maintaining a continuous flow of ammonia or nitrogen; the hexammine is placed in a combustion boat or small crucible. Boiling thymol (b.p. 233.5°C) is used as the heating agent. According to theory, every 1.000g of hexammine salt taken should lose 0.2933g of ammonia when decomposition is complete.

Beta-form

The apparatus of Alpha (I) is used; a water bath maintained at 72°C is used and the ammonia evolved from the hexammine is continuously pumped off after stopcock A has been cautiously opened. After 2 hours, during which time the test tube and contents are gently tapped from time to time to ensure uniform heating, no more of the hexammine should be discernible, even with the aid of a lens. The substance should be pure light blue in color. If appreciably less than the theoretical weight of ammonia has been given off, the tube and contents must be re-heated under vacuum to constant weight.

To show the transformation of the relatively unstable *beta* form to the *alpha* form, about 50mg of each compound is placed in a glass tube, 6mm in diameter and 10cm in length. The open ends are sealed *in vacuo* and the tubes are suspended for one hour in a bath at 180°C. The *alpha* form remains unchanged but the blue *beta* compound turns pink.

Again, one-half gram of each material is placed carefully in a glass tube, and the open ends are connected tightly to separate legs of an open U-tube manometer. Both tubes are then placed in a bath at 180°C. The *beta* compound develops an ammonia pressure about 10mm greater than does the *alpha* compound, clearly demonstrating the relative instability of the former. Over a period of two hours further heating, the pressure differential slowly drops as the *beta* is transformed into the *alpha* modification. When the change is complete, the mercury levels are even once more.

On the basis of color and stability, the pink *alpha* salt has been assigned the *cis*-formulation.

References:

1. B:185, 187, 188.
2. BILTZ AND FETKENHEUER, *Z. anorg. Chem.*, 89:121 (1914); 83:163 (1913).
3. COX et al., *J. Chem. Soc.*, 1556 (1937).
4. POWELL AND WELLS, *Ibid.*, 359 (1935).

98. Bis(ethylenediamine)copper (II) Diiodocuprate (I) **

$$CuSO_4 + 2C_2H_4(NH_2)_2 \longrightarrow [Cu\{C_2H_4(NH_2)_2\}_2]SO_4$$
$$[Cu\{C_2H_4(NH_2)_2\}_2]SO_4 + BaI_2 \longrightarrow [Cu\{C_2H_4(NH_2)_2\}_2]I_2 + BaSO_4$$
$$[Cu\{C_2H_4(NH_2)_2\}_2]I_2 + 2CuI \longrightarrow [Cu\{C_2H_4(NH_2)_2\}_2][CuI_2]_2$$

Three grams of anhydrous ethylenediamine are added with stirring to 5g of copper sulfate 5-hydrate in 20ml of water. To this deep blue solution, 8.5g of barium iodide 2-hydrate dissolved in 20ml of water are added slowly with stirring. The precipitated barium sulfate is removed by filtration with the aid of about 0.5g of Celite and washed twice with 5ml of water. The washings and filtrate are combined.

In a boiling solution of 48g of potassium iodide in 60ml

of water, 7.6g of copper (I) iodide is dissolved. The clear, hot liquid is added with stirring to the complex copper solution; precipitation begins immediately. After cooling in ice, the chocolate-brown material is filtered off and washed with two 10ml portions of ice-cold water. The product is dried in warm air; m.p. 267°C.

$$Yield = 13g$$

Hot water decomposes the substance to copper (I) iodide and diethylenediaminecopper (II) iodide. The material is insoluble in organic solvents.

COGNATE PREPARATIONS

98 a. Bis(propylenediamine)copper (II) Diiodocuprate (I) **

$$[Cupn_2][CuI_2]_2$$

3.7g of amine are used; olive-green product.

$$Yield = 12g$$

98 b. Diethylenetriamine Analogue **

$$[Cu_3den_4][CuI_2]_6$$

3.0g of amine are used; olive-green product.

$$Yield = 12.7g$$

98 c. Dipropylenetriamine Analogue **

$$[Cu_3dpn_4][CuI_2]_6$$

3.6g of amine are used; dark olive-green product, soluble in acetone.

$$Yield = 12g$$

98 d. Triethylenetetramine Analogue **

$$[Cutet][CuI_2]_2$$

3.0g of amine are used; the black-green product settles out as an oil which soon solidifies in the ice bath.

$$Yield = 8.2g$$

The color of these complexes seems to darken as the coordinating ability of the amine increases.

Reference: I, vol. 5:16.

99. Bis(ethylenediamine)copper (II) Nitrate *

$$Cu(NO_3)_2 + 2en \longrightarrow [Cuen_2][NO_3]_2$$

Twelve grams of copper nitrate 3-hydrate are dissolved in 75ml of 95% ethanol and the solution is cooled in ice. Seven grams of anhydrous ethylenediamine are added with stirring. The violet-blue product, which precipitates immediately, is washed with two 25-ml portions of ether.

Yield quantitative

COGNATE PREPARATION

99 a. Dipropylenetriamine Analogue *

$$[Cu_2dpn_4][SO_4]_3$$

Five grams of copper sulfate 5-hydrate are dissolved in 20ml of water and 3.5g of dipropylenetriamine are added with stirring. Acetone is added to the blue liquid until the product has been completely precipitated as an oil; the supernatant liquid should be almost colorless. The oil is repeatedly triturated with small portions of acetone in a mortar until it forms a solid; it is brought onto the filter with the same solvent and washed with a little ether. While the deep blue product is still moist, it is *rapidly* transferred to a vacuum desiccator and pumped dry. The material is extremely deliquescent. Losses in the preparation are only mechanical. The complex sulfate gives no precipitate with solutions of iodide, dithionate, ferricyanide, or persulfate ions. In concentrated aqueous medium, however, the addition of solid sodium fluoroborate causes partial precipitation of the relatively insoluble complex fluoroborate.

As a general rule, the solubility of copper ammine complexes in water and alcohols increases with the rise in coordinating power of the amine concerned; the molecular weight of the latter is also involved. The following general methods will serve to produce a large variety of 4-coordinated copper (II) complex salts:

1. Precipitating from a concentrated aqueous solution of the copper salt with amine, followed by alcohol to complete the separation of product.
2. Addition of the desired anion to an aqueous or alcoholic solution of the copper complex.
3. Precipitating an alcoholic solution of the copper salt with amine and adding acetone or ether if necessary.
4. Preparation of the desired copper ammine complex by metathesis in solution and addition of an organic precipitating solvent.

100. Tetramminecopper (II) Sulfate Monohydrate *

$$CuSO_4 + 4NH_3 \longrightarrow [Cu(NH_3)_4]SO_4$$

Twenty grams of copper sulfate 5-hydrate are dissolved in a mixture of 30ml of concentrated ammonia and 20ml of water. The resulting deep-blue solution is cooled in ice and stirred continuously while 30ml of alcohol is added dropwise from a buret or tap-funnel. The mixture is allowed to stand in the cold for at least 4 hours, preferably overnight; the supernatant liquid should be almost colorless. The crystalline product is filtered off, washed first with 25ml of a cold equivolume mixture of alcohol and concentrated aqueous ammonia, and then with 25ml each of 95% alcohol and ether. The salt is dried in air.

Yield almost quantitative

COGNATE PREPARATION

100 a. Tetramminecopper (II) Chloride Monohydrate **

$$[Cu(NH_3)_4]Cl_2$$

The procedure described for the sulfate must be slightly modified because the high solubility of the desired chloride in water makes it necessary to work in highly concentrated aqueous medium.

Ammonia gas is generated in the hood by allowing a solution of 25g of sodium hydroxide in 30ml of water to drop slowly on 30g of ammonium chloride contained in a small distilling flask. The gas is passed through an empty wash bottle to free it partially from water vapor, and then led through a wide (10–15mm) delivery tube and stopper into a warm solution of 17g of copper (II) chloride 2-hydrate in 15ml of water. The latter solution, conveniently contained in a small filter flask, becomes heated to the boiling point as a result of the ammonation; it should be cooled slightly in water occasionally to prevent too much evaporation. As soon as any precipitate that forms initially has dissolved (clear deep-blue solution) 8ml of alcohol are added to the cooled liquid.

Ammonia gas is passed in again to the saturation point, this time with ice-cooling. The deposited product is allowed to remain for 15–30 minutes longer in the ice bath to complete the crystallization and it is then filtered through a hardened paper or sintered glass funnel. The salt is washed with 25ml of a mixture of 20ml of 95% alcohol and 5ml of concentrated ammonia and then with similar volumes of alcohol and ether, respectively. After it is drained at the pump for about 15 minutes, the preparation must be immediately stored in a tightly stoppered bottle as it loses ammonia on standing in air.

$$Yield = 15\text{--}18g$$

The addition of the organic washings to the mother liquor causes the precipitation of a few more grams of a finely-divided, and consequently lighter-colored, product.

References:
1. B:170; J:377.
2. Biltz et al., Z. anorg. Chem., 148:207 (1925).

101. Tetramminezinc (II) Fluoroborate *

$$Zn(C_2H_3O_2)_2 + 2NH_4BF_4 + 4NH_3 \longrightarrow [Zn(NH_3)_4][BF_4]_2 + 2NH_4C_2H_3O_2$$

To a solution of 4.6g of zinc acetate 2-hydrate in 20ml of water is added concentrated ammonia until the initially formed precipitate of hydroxide has just completely dissolved. The ammonia should be added in one milliliter increments. A saturated aqueous solution of 5g of ammonium fluoroborate (No. 23) is added to the zinc ammine solution with stirring. The mixture is allowed to stand in ice for 30 minutes, filtered, and washed with acetone to aid drying in air; white crystals.

$$Yield = 5-6g$$

COGNATE PREPARATIONS

101 a. Bis(ethylenediamine)zinc (II) Fluoroborate *

$[Znen_2][BF_4]_2$

This compound can be made from 4.4g of zinc acetate 2-hydrate in 20ml of water, 3g of anhydrous ethylenediamine, and 5g of solid ammonium or sodium fluoroborate. About 10ml of 95% alcohol aids in completing precipitation.

$$Yield = 5g$$

101 b. Bis(dl-propylenediamine)zinc (II) Fluoroborate *

$[Znpn_2][BF_4]_2$

The procedure for ethylenediamine is used; 3.7g of anhydrous propylenediamine are employed.

$$Yield = 5g$$

101 c. Diethylenetriamine Analogue *

$[Zn_3den_4][BF_4]_6$

3.0g of amine are used with the zinc salt.

$$Yield = 3.0g$$

101 d. Dipropylenetriamine Analogue *

$[Zn_3dpn_4][BF_4]_6$

3.6g of dipropylenetriamine are employed in the procedure.

$$Yield = 3.6g$$

The statements made regarding solubility and preparation of copper complexes (see No. 99) apply also to the formation of zinc ammines.

References:
1. P:181.
2. WILKE-DÖRFURT AND BALZ, *Z. anorg. Chem.*, 159:197 (1927).

102. Tetrapyridinecopper (II) Persulfate *

$$CuSO_4 + (NH_4)_2S_2O_8 + 4C_5H_5N \longrightarrow [Cu(C_5H_5N)_4]S_2O_8 + (NH_4)_2SO_4$$

A solution of 5g of copper sulfate 5-hydrate in 40-ml of water is mixed with 9g of *fresh* ammonium persulfate (or 11g of the potassium salt) in 40ml of water. The mixture is cooled in ice and stirred while 15ml of pure pyridine are added drop by drop from a buret. The violet-blue crystalline precipitate is suction-filtered, washed with two 15ml portions of 10% aqueous pyridine, and finally dried in a desiccator (*not in vacuo*, as the product loses pyridine).

Yield quantitative

References:
1. P:146.
2. BARBIERI AND CALZOLARI, *Z. anorg. Chem.*, 71:347 (1911).

103. Tetrapyridinesilver (II) Persulfate

$$2AgNO_3 + 3K_2S_2O_8 + 8C_5H_5N \longrightarrow 2[Ag(C_5H_5N)_4]S_2O_8 + 2KNO_3 + 2K_2SO_4$$

A solution of 1.25g of silver nitrate in 25ml of distilled water is mixed with 10ml of pure pyridine, and the mixture is stirred into 15g of *fresh* potassium persulfate dissolved in 500ml of cold distilled water. The liquid immediately assumes an orange color; the product soon begins to precipitate, and this is complete in about 30 minutes. After it is filtered, the orange material is washed with two 10ml portions of ice-cold water and then dried for an hour or two *in vacuo* over solid alkali.

Yield = 3.2–4.0g

The salt keeps well in a dark, tightly stoppered vial, but in ordinary moist air it slowly becomes colorless after about three days exposure.

References:
1. P:158.
2. BARBIERI, *Gazz. chim. ital.* (2), 42:7 (1912).
3. MORGAN AND BURSTALL, *J. Chem. Soc.*, 2594 (1930).

4. Cox *et al.*, *Ibid.*, 775 (1936).
For the magnetic properties of Ag (II) compounds see reference 5.
5. SUGDEN, *Ibid.*, 161 (1932).

COORDINATION NUMBER 6

1. HEXAMMINE SERIES

a) Chromium Compounds

104. Hexamminechromium (III) Nitrate ***

(I)

$$2CrCl_3 + Zn \longrightarrow 2CrCl_2 + ZnCl_2$$
$$2CrCl_2 + 10NH_3 + 2NH_4Cl \longrightarrow 2[Cr(NH_3)_6]Cl_3 + H_2$$
$$[Cr(NH_3)_6]Cl_3 + 3HNO_3 \longrightarrow [Cr(NH_3)_6][NO_3]_3 + 3HCl$$

A one-liter Erlenmeyer flask is substituted in the apparatus for reduction described in Experiment No. 35. The flask is charged with 145g of chromium (III) chloride 6-hydrate dissolved in a mixture of 150ml of concentrated hydrochloric acid and an equal volume of water. Fifty-five grams of zinc (coarsely granulated or in the form of rods) is added and the reduction procedure is then followed exactly as for chromium (II) acetate.

The blue reduced solution is run *under* the surface of a mixture of 700g of ammonium chloride and 750ml of concentrated aqueous ammonia contained in a 2-liter flask which is cooled in ice. The latter is now quickly filled almost to the brim with concentrated ammonia water and fitted with a stopper carrying a glass tube bent twice at right angles; the free end dips just under the surface of a water-filled beaker. A fairly brisk evolution of hydrogen from the mixture in the flask soon begins and this continues at a slowly decreasing rate for 18–24 hours. During this time the reaction flask is kept immersed to the neck in a vessel of water maintained at 15–25°C; yields of product appear to be highest around 15°C.

When evolution of gas has virtually ceased, as shown by the outlet tube in the beaker, the deep red liquid is poured off the solid residue, which consists of product and ammonium chloride. The decanted solution is mixed with its own volume of alcohol and allowed to stand for 3–4 hours to complete precipitation of the complex chloride. This is filtered off by suction on a large funnel; as the material is finely divided it drains rather slowly. The residue in the flask is transferred to a beaker and extracted by decantation with four 100ml portions of water; the remaining ammonium chloride should be only faintly colored.

The moist cake of hexammine chloride obtained here is dissolved in the combined aqueous extracts and then the whole solution is mixed with 400ml of concentrated nitric acid and cooled in ice. After standing in the cold for 2 hours, the orange-yellow crystals of nitrate are filtered off, drained well, and washed successively with 50ml of ice-cold concentrated nitric acid, with the same volume of cold 1:2 nitric acid-water, and finally, copiously with 95% alcohol until the washings are acid-free. The salt is dried in air.

$$\text{Yield} = 45\text{–}50\text{g}$$

[If chromic chloride is not available as a starting material for this procedure, the compound may be prepared in solution by reducing 80g of potassium dichromate with a mixture of 250ml of concentrated hydrochloric acid and either 100ml of 95% alcohol, or 110g of oxalic acid 2-hydrate. The reduced solutions are then used directly in the reduction procedure; only the zinc need be added.

$$K_2Cr_2O_7 + 3C_2H_5OH + 8HCl \longrightarrow 2CrCl_3 + 3CH_3CHO + 2KCl + 7H_2O$$
$$K_2Cr_2O_7 + 3H_2C_2O_4 + 8HCl \longrightarrow 2CrCl_3 + 2KCl + 6CO_2 + 7H_2O]$$

(II)

$$CrCl_3 + 6NH_3 \xrightarrow{\text{NaNH}_2} [Cr(NH_3)_6]Cl_3$$
$$[Cr(NH_3)_6]Cl_3 + 3HNO_3 \longrightarrow [Cr(NH_3)_6][NO_3]_3 + 3HCl$$

This procedure must be carried out in a well-ventilated hood.

About 75ml of dry liquid ammonia is condensed in a 250ml filter flask fitted with a stopper and inlet tube; the flask is cooled in a bath of dry ice and acetone. A small piece (about 0.1g) of clean metallic sodium and 50mg of ferrous ammonium sulfate are added, and when the blue color of the sodium has disappeared, 5g of finely powdered anhydrous chromium (III) chloride (No. 14) is added in 0.5g portions with continued cooling and gentle agitation.

Each portion of the salt is allowed to react before more is added. [CAUTION: Gloves should be worn during this operation.] The chromium (III) chloride must not be added in quantity at temperatures too low for a reaction because there might be a very sudden and violent decomposition when the ammonia warms up. After the addition has been completed, and the clear, slightly colored, supernatant liquid has been decanted, the residual ammonia is allowed to evaporate from the brown precipitate. A light-yellow powder of impure hexammine chloride remains.

Yield about 8g

The crude product is quickly dissolved in a mixture of 15ml of water and one milliliter of concentrated hydrochloric acid (pre-heated to 40°C), and then filtered, if necessary. The filtrate is immediately cooled in ice and treated with 5ml of concentrated nitric acid. The pure nitrate that crystallizes out is filtered and washed with alcohol and ether. As the orange product is photosensitive it should be dried and stored away from direct light.

Yield = 8g

If the procedure is conducted without sodium amide, a mixture of about 4g of hexammine nitrate and 3g of chloropentaminechromium (III) chloride is obtained after working up the ammonia residue.[5, 6, 7]

References:
  (I) 1. P:396.
       2. JÖRGENSEN, *J. prakt. Chem.* (2), 20:105 (1879); (2), 30:1 (1884).
       3. CHRISTENSEN, *Ibid.*, (2), 23:54 (1881).
  (II) 4. I, vol. 3:153.
       5. B:184.
       6. CHRISTENSEN, *Z. anorg. Chem.*, 4:229 (1893).
       7. LANG AND CARSON, *J. Am. Chem. Soc.*, 26:414 (1904).

105. dl-Tris(ethylenediamine)chromium (III) Chloride 3½-Hydrate **

$$Cr_2(SO_4)_3 + 6en \longrightarrow [Cren_3]_2[SO_4]_3$$
$$[Cren_3]_2[SO_4]_3 + 6Cl^- \longrightarrow 2[Cren_3]Cl_3 + 3SO_4^{--}$$

[If the anhydrous (98–100%) ethylenediamine is not available, it may be prepared from the aqueous 70% product as follows: One hundred grams of solid sodium hydroxide and 175ml of 70% ethylenediamine are heated in a flask with an air condenser on the steam bath overnight. (As the amine attacks corks and rubber stoppers readily, these should be covered with tin foil.) The two layers that form are separated after cooling and the upper one is heated again for several hours with 30g more of the solid alkali. When distilled, the yield of amine, boiling at 115–118°C, is almost quantitative. This method is also used to dehydrate propylenediamine; b.p. 118–120°C.

It is highly advisable to distill both amines in the presence of boiling chips, otherwise bumping causes a serious problem; it sets in vigorously and suddenly at the boiling point of the amine and may cause a large portion of material to be carried over mechanically into the receiver.]

Commercial hydrated chromium (III) sulfate is dehydrated in an oven at 100–120°C. When the salt no longer dissolves in water the process is complete.*

Ninety-eight grams of the anhydrous chromium (III) sulfate are heated with 100ml of dehydrated ethylenediamine under reflux (air) for 16–24 hours in an oil bath at about 105°C. The green chromium salt soon begins to lose its color and powdery character; the flask should be frequently shaken during the first few hours of heating to keep the unchanged sulfate constantly exposed to fresh portions of amine. Finally a brown mass is formed; virtually no excess liquid is present. After the heating period is over, the yellow brown mass is chipped out of the flask with a spatula and ground to a powder. It may be necessary to break the

---

* There is fairly wide variation in the ease with which water can be removed from various grades of the salt. Baker Analyzed brand melted initially in its own water of hydration and had to be stirred, broken up, and re-ground with continuous heating over a period of one to two days until completely dry. The best product was found to be the Mallinckrodt Flake brand of the salt, which lost its water without caking in a few hours of drying time.

flask in order to remove all the material. The crude product is washed twice with 75ml of absolute alcohol, once with 100ml of ether, and then dried in air.

Yield = 160–175g

Ninety-six grams of the complex sulfate are rapidly dissolved in a mixture of 90ml of water and 15 ml of concentrated hydrochloric acid (pre-heated to 60°C) and quickly filtered by suction into an ice-cold mixture of 80ml of concentrated hydrochloric acid and 130ml of 95% alcohol. About one hour of standing in the cold completes the crystallization of the product as orange yellow crystals. The salt is drained well on the filter and washed with three 30-ml portions of alcohol and with 50ml of ether. Drying in air in the absence of direct light is recommended as the salt is somewhat photosensitive.

Yield = 58–60g (negligible test for sulfate)

The crude chloride may be rapidly recrystallized from an equal weight of water at 60°C but this causes a 40% loss of material. The non-purified material is completely suitable for most further work.

COGNATE PREPARATIONS

105 a. dl-Tris(ethylenediamine)chromium (III) Bromide 4-Hydrate *

[Cren₃]Br₃·4H₂O

$[Cren_3]Br_3 \cdot 4H_2O$

Thirty grams of the complex chloride are dissolved in 100ml of water at 65°C and 45g of sodium or ammonium bromide are stirred in. The product precipitates immediately and is recovered by cooling in ice to complete the crystallization, then filtering by suction.

Crude yield = 38–40g

The material is recrystallized from 75ml of water at 65°C, filtered, washed with alcohol and ether, then air-dried.

Yield = 29–31g

105 b. dl-Tris(ethylenediamine)chromium (III) Thiocyanate Monohydrate *

$$[Cren_3][SCN]_3 \cdot H_2O$$

30g of chloride and 35g of ammonium or sodium thiocyanate are used, as for the bromide.

Crude yield = 29–30g

One hundred milliliters of water at 65°C are used for recrystallization.

Yield = 22–23g

If the thiocyanate is prepared for use in the thermal decomposition to trans-$[Cren_2(SCN)_2][SCN]$ (see No. 125), ammonium thiocyanate should be employed in the metathesis of the chloride and the crude salt should not be recrystallized from water.

105 c. dl-Tris(ethylenediamine)chromium (III) Iodide Monohydrate *

$$[Cren_3]I_3 \cdot H_2O$$

Thirty grams of the chloride and 67g of sodium or ammonium iodide in 100ml of water are employed.

Crude yield = 43–45g

After recrystallization from 250ml of water at 65°C,

Yield = 30–32g

105 d. dl-Tris(ethylenediamine)chromium (III) Trioxalatocobaltate (III) *

$$[Cren_3][Co(C_2O_4)_3]$$

Saturated solutions of 5g each of the bromide and the potassium salt in water are mixed. The green plates of product are cooled in ice, filtered, and washed with 10ml of ice-cold water.

Yield = 6g

The material is slightly soluble in warm water but it decomposes if the aqueous solution is heated to 100°C.

105 e. dl-Tris(ethylenediamine)chromium (III) Hexacyanoferrate (III)

[Cren₃][Fe(CN)₆]

$$[Cren_3][Fe(CN)_6]$$

From warm saturated solutions of 4g of the chloride and 3.5g of the potassium salt in water. Separation of the product is aided by scratching the walls of the vessel and cooling. The orange product is filtered off and washed with 20ml of ice-cold water.

Yield almost quantitative

105 f. Propylenediamine Analogue **

$$dl\text{-}[Crpn_3]_2[SO_4]_3$$

This material is prepared exactly as described for the corresponding ethylenediamine salt, using 30ml of pn and 21g of anhydrous chromium (III) sulfate.

Yield = 40–42g

As the crude sulfate is appreciably soluble in the 95% solvent, it should be washed on the filter with absolute alcohol.

For the conversion of the material into various derivatives with properties similar to those of the corresponding ethylenediamine salt see reference 2.

No reaction was observed when 36.5g of anhydrous dipropylenetriamine were heated with 27g of dehydrated chromium (III) sulfate on the steam bath. There was no sign of decomposition even after 4 hours at 200°C. A drop of water added as catalyst made no difference.

References:
1. I, vol. 2:196ff.
2. ROLLINSON AND BAILAR, *J. Am. Chem. Soc.*, 65:250 (1943).

b) Cobalt Compounds

106. Hexamminecobalt (III) Chloride **
(I)

$$4CoCl_2 + 4NH_4Cl + 20NH_3 + O_2 \xrightarrow{C} 4[Co(NH_3)_6]Cl_3 + 2H_2O$$

a) Two hundred and forty grams of cobalt (II) chloride 6-hydrate and 160g of ammonium chloride are added to 200ml of water. The mixture is shaken until most of the salts are dissolved. Then 4g of activated charcoal (preferably from the center of a package) and 500ml of concentrated aqueous ammonia are added. A vigorous stream of air (about 5 bubbles/sec) is sucked through the mixture for four hours. This operation is best carried out in a one-liter filter flask fitted with a stopper and a wide-bore (at least 10mm) air-inlet tube that reaches about one inch below the surface of the mixture. The side-arm of the flask is connected to the aspirator. During the aeration the initially red solution becomes yellow-brown; the product crystallizes out as the reaction proceeds.

The mixture of carbon and product is filtered, drained well, and then added to a solution of 25ml of concentrated hydrochloric acid in 1500ml hot water. When all the salt has dissolved (with further heating, if necessary) the carbon residue is filtered from the hot solution by suction. The filtrate is placed in ice and 400ml of ice-cold concentrated hydrochloric acid is stirred in. After the entire mixture has cooled to about 0°C, it is filtered and the pure product is washed, first with 100ml of ice-cold 60% alcohol and then with the same amount of 95% alcohol.

Yield = 230g

In procedures on a smaller scale at least one gram of activated charcoal should be used in the reaction.

b) Similar yields are obtained without the lengthy aeration by cooling the unoxidized reaction mixture to 10°C in ice, and *slowly* adding 95–100ml of 30% hydrogen peroxide from a dropping funnel. The liquid mixture must be kept cold and frequently agitated during the addition. When all the peroxide has been added, the yellow-brown solution is heated to 60°C on the steam bath and maintained at that temperature for 30 minutes; any pink tint observed earlier in the liquid must have disappeared at the end of that time. The product separates out towards the completion of the heating period and the reaction mixture is cooled to 0°C in ice. The carbon is removed and the product is purified as under *a*.

(II)

$$AgNO_3 + NH_4Cl \longrightarrow AgCl + NH_4NO_3$$
$$AgCl + 2NH_3 \longrightarrow [Ag(NH_3)_2]Cl$$
$$CoCl_2 + [Ag(NH_3)_2]Cl + 4NH_3 \longrightarrow [Co(NH_3)_6]Cl_3 + Ag$$

To a solution of 75g of silver nitrate in 200 ml of water is added a solution of 25g of ammonium chloride in an equal volume of water. The precipitated silver chloride is washed repeatedly by decantation with water and dissolved in the minimum volume of cold 20% aqueous ammonia (10 volumes of 28% ammonia and 4 volumes of water); about 500ml should be required. The diammine silver solution should be used without delay in the next step.

One hundred grams of cobalt (II) chloride 6-hydrate and 30g of ammonium chloride are dissolved in the minimum of water at 40°C and then 20% ammonia is added until the precipitate first formed just dissolves to a red-violet solution. This is mixed with the ammoniacal silver solution and allowed to stand for two to four days at room temperature. The precipitate of product and metallic silver is filtered off and the filtrate reserved. The product is extracted by stirring up the residue repeatedly with 50ml portions of water, allowing the undissolved material to settle, and filtering the extract. This procedure is continued until the residue is grayish and the extracts are only faintly colored. The combined extracts (about 500ml) are heated to 80°C and concentrated hydrochloric acid is added until the liquid becomes turbid; on cooling in ice the pure product crystallizes out.

The ammoniacal filtrate above is cooled in ice while concentrated hydrochloric acid is added until the liquid is *just* acid; any precipitate is then filtered off and washed with a little water until the washings are no longer colored. The combined washings and acidified filtrate are then mixed with an equal volume of concentrated hydrochloric acid and heated to 80°C on the steam bath. On cooling, the remainder of the hexammine chloride crystallizes out together with some chloropentamminecobalt (III) chloride. The mixed crystals are filtered off and stirred up with 25ml portions of water until the filtered extracts are no longer yellow but a pale purple. The combined extracts are cooled in ice while one-half their volume of concentrated hydrochloric acid is added; more hexammine chloride separates out. The undissolved purple residue from the last extraction amounts to about 15g of chloropentammine salt. For purification see No. 119.

Total yield of hexammine chloride is about 80g

(III)

$$[Co(NH_3)_6Cl]Cl_2 + NH_3 \longrightarrow [Co(NH_3)_6]Cl_3$$

A mixture of 10g of chloropentammine cobalt (III) chloride (No. 119), 8g of ammonium chloride, and 100ml of 20% ammonia are placed in a pressure bottle of 250ml capacity. The bottle and contents are heated in a boiling water bath for six hours behind a safety screen. Alternatively the bottle may be wrapped firmly in a towel for protection against accidental rupture. After cooling, the yellow-brown liquid is poured into a large evaporating dish and the excess ammonia is volatilized in the hood over a period of 24 hours; the ammonia may also be removed by bubbling air through the reaction mixture. A solution of 50ml of concentrated hydrochloric acid and 200ml of water is then added, and the mixture heated for one hour on the steam bath. While cooling rapidly in ice, 250ml more of concentrated HCl is added with stirring; the yellow precipitate is filtered from the ice-cold mother liquor.

The crude material is extracted with four 50ml portions of water until only a small purple residue of starting material remains behind. The combined extracts are mixed with one-half their volume of concentrated HCl, cooled in ice, and filtered.

Yield = 8–10g

References:
1. (I) I, vol. 2:217; J:378; P:530.
2. (II) B:176.
3. (III) B:175.
4. I, vol. 2:220, 221; (detailed references on all three and other methods).

COGNATE PREPARATIONS

106 a. Hexamminecobalt (III) Nitrate **

(I)

a) Seventy-three grams of cobalt (II) nitrate 6-hydrate are dissolved in 100ml of water to which are added, in the order mentioned, 80g of ammonium nitrate, 2g of activated charcoal, and 180ml of concentrated aqueous ammonia. The solution is oxidized by air or with 25ml of 30% hydrogen peroxide, as specified under parts a) and b) of Method (I) for the hexammine chloride. The mixture of product with carbon obtained is dissolved on the steam bath in about 1300ml of water and 15ml of concentrated nitric acid, and filtered hot into 200ml more of the acid. After cooling well in ice, the precipitated salt is washed on the filter with 95% alcohol and dried at 100°C.

Yield = 77–79g

b) The mixture of crude hexammine chloride and carbon from the cobalt (II) chloride oxidation, obtained in (I) for that compound, is dissolved on the steam bath in a mixture of 1.5 liters of water and 15ml of concentrated nitric acid. The hot liquid is filtered from the carbon into 450ml of ice-cold concentrated nitric acid and cooled further in ice. The salt is washed with three 75ml portions of 95% alcohol and dried at 100°C.

Yield about 300g

The product contains a trace of chloride.

(II)

$$CoCO_3 + 2HNO_3 \longrightarrow Co(NO_3)_2 + CO_2 + H_2O$$
$$2Co(NO_3)_2 + 12NH_3 + I_2 \longrightarrow 2[Co(NH_3)_6][NO_3]_2I$$
$$2[Co(NH_3)_6][NO_3]_2I + 4HNO_3 \longrightarrow 2[Co(NH_3)_6][NO_3]_3 + I_2 + 2NO_2 + 2H_2O$$

Twenty-four grams of cobalt carbonate are dissolved in a 600-ml beaker by cautiously adding concentrated nitric acid and warming gently until effervescence has ceased; about 25–30ml of acid are required. The solution is mixed with 70ml of water and filtered. Alternatively, 58g of cobalt (II) nitrate 6-hydrate are dissolved in 75ml of water and used in the next step. The nitrate solution is poured into 200ml of concentrated ammonia and the solution is heated with mechanical stirring to 95°C under the hood. Oxidation to the trivalent state is effected by the addition of 25.4g of iodine in small portions to the hot liquid over a period of 30 minutes. A yellowish precipitate of the difficultly-soluble hexammine iodonitrate forms during the reaction. The reaction mixture is cooled in ice and allowed to stand in the cold for 30 minutes; it is then filtered off.

The moist filter cake is added to a mixture of 40ml of concentrated nitric acid and 160ml of water, then heated to boiling in a beaker under the hood. The iodine that escapes may be recovered to some extent by placing two round-bottomed flasks filled with ice alternately over the mouth of the beaker. When no more iodine is given off, the mixture is cooled well in ice and filtered by suction. The product is washed three times with 30ml of 95% alcohol and dried at 100°C.

$$Yield = 22–25g$$

Reference: B:176.

106 b. Hexamminecobalt (III) Bromide **

$$CoCO_3 + 2HBr \longrightarrow CoBr_2 + CO_2 + H_2O$$
$$2CoBr_2 + 2NH_4Br + 10NH_3 + H_2O_2 \longrightarrow 2[Co(NH_3)_6]Br_3 + 2H_2O$$

Twenty-four grams of cobalt carbonate are added slowly to 95ml of constant-boiling (48%) hydrobromic acid (see No. 88) and the solution is filtered. The filtrate is added to a mixture of 2g of activated charcoal and 120ml of concentrated ammonia; the mixture is then cooled to 10°C in an ice bath. Twenty milliliters of 30% hydrogen peroxide are added dropwise from a buret with continual swirling. The mixture is heated to 60°C on the steam bath and maintained at this temperature for 20–30 minutes. After cooling in ice, the salt-carbon mixture is filtered and drained well. The crude product is dissolved on the steam bath in a mixture of 900ml of water and 10ml of 48% hydrobromic acid, and then filtered hot with suction. To the filtrate is added 50ml more of the acid and the reaction mixture slowly cooled to 0°C in an ice bath. The product is filtered, washed with two 50ml portions of 95% alcohol, and dried at 100°C.

$$Yield = 65g$$

Reference: I, vol. 2:219.

106 c. Hexamminecobalt (III) Sulfate 5-Hydrate *

$$4CoSO_4 + 2(NH_4)_2SO_4 + 20NH_3 + O_2 \longrightarrow 2[Co(NH_3)_6]_2[SO_4]_3 + 2H_2O$$

A slurry of 196g of cobalt (II) ammonium sulfate 6-hydrate in 100ml of water is added slowly with stirring to an ice-cold mixture of 250ml of concentrated aqueous ammonia and 4g of *fresh* activated charcoal.

When all the salt has dissolved, the solution is oxidized as described previously with a moderate stream of air for 24 hours. The crude product and carbon are filtered by suction, drained thoroughly, and dried in air.

The mother liquor is cooled in the refrigerator overnight and a further quantity of product is obtained. To the ice-cold filtrate are added 200ml of 95% alcohol and a small additional amount of the complex is precipitated. The relatively light-colored reddish pink filtrate of aquopentammine salt is finally discarded.

The entire crop of impure crystals is extracted for a total of seven or eight times with two separate 500ml portions of boiling water, and filtered while hot. After each extraction, the filtrate is cooled in ice and the liquid is decanted from the orange crystals.

The combined solids and aqueous extracts are filtered and

the product is dried in air. The filtrate from the recrystallization is evaporated on the steam bath to a volume of 100–
125ml (a trace of cobalt (III) oxide is filtered off during
the evaporation), cooled in ice, and filtered. After washing
freely with cold 50% aqueous alcohol, the crystals are dried
in the air.

Total yield = 155g (88%)

106 d. Hexamminecobalt (III) Sulfamate 2-Hydrate *

$$NH_3 + NH_2SO_3H \longrightarrow NH_4SO_3NH_2$$
$$2Co(NH_2SO_3)_2 + 2NH_4SO_3NH_2 + 10NH_3 + H_2O_2 \longrightarrow$$
$$2[Co(NH_3)_6][SO_3NH_2]_3 + 2H_2O$$

To 10ml of ice-cold concentrated (28%) aqueous ammonia are added 10g of sulfamic acid (see No. 92), in small
portions with continued cooling and stirring. The solution
of ammonium sulfamate is mixed with 15ml of concentrated
ammonia and 0.5g of activated charcoal. Ten grams of cobalt (II) sulfamate 2-hydrate are stirred into the ammoniacal mixture until all the salt has dissolved to form a
reddish solution. The reaction mixture is cooled to 10°C
in ice and 5ml of 30% hydrogen peroxide is slowly added
dropwise with agitation. The oxidized liquid is allowed to
stand at room temperature for 15 minutes and then heated
for 20 minutes at 50–55°C on the steam bath. After filtering
with suction while hot to remove the carbon, the filtrate is
cooled in ice and stirred while alcohol is added dropwise
from a tap-funnel until the supernatant liquid is only faintly
colored; 30–40ml of 95% alcohol are required. The crude
product is filtered off and dissolved in the minimum quantity of water. An equal volume of 95% alcohol is added
dropwise as before until no more yellow solid precipitates;
the supernatant liquid is reddish in color. The product is
filtered, washed with 25ml of 95% alcohol and an equal
volume of ether, then dried in air.

Yield about 10–12g

106 e. Hexamminecobalt (III) Aminomethanesulfonate *

$$NH_3 + HSO_3CH_2NH_2 \longrightarrow NH_4SO_3CH_2NH_2$$
$$CoCl_2 + 2NaOH \longrightarrow Co(OH)_2 + 2NaCl$$
$$2Co(OH)_2 + 6NH_4SO_3CH_2NH_2 + 6NH_3 + H_2O_2 \longrightarrow$$
$$2[Co(NH_3)_6][SO_3CH_2NH_2]_3 + 6H_2O$$

A solution of 9.5g of cobalt (II) chloride 6-hydrate in 50ml of water is cooled in ice and stirred while a cold solution of 3.5g of sodium hydroxide in 25ml of water is added. When the precipitate is pure pink in color it is filtered with suction and washed with ice-cold water until free of chloride. The moist filter cake is stirred into an ice-cold previously-prepared mixture of 13.5g of aminomethanesulfonic acid (see No. 85), 25ml of concentrated ammonia, and 0.5g of activated charcoal. When the cobalt (II) hydroxide has completely dissolved, the mixture is oxidized at 10°C by 5ml of 30% hydrogen peroxide and allowed to stand for 15 minutes. The reaction mixture is heated at 55–60°C for 10 minutes on the steam bath and filtered hot. To the ice-cold filtrate 60ml of 95% alcohol are added slowly with stirring, and the crude product is filtered off. It is re-dissolved in about 30ml of water and an equal volume of alcohol is added. After cooling in ice, the product is filtered off and washed, first with alcohol and then with acetone.

Yield = 11–13g

106 f. Hexamminecobalt (III) Hexathiocyanatochromate (III) *

$$[Co(NH_3)_6][Cr(SCN)_6]$$

A solution of 1.5g of the hexammine chloride in 30ml of water is added to a solution of 3g of anhydrous potassium hexathiocyanatochromate (III) (No. 63) in 10ml of water. The product settles out as pink plates in almost quantitative yield. If the two solutions used for metathesis are more concentrated, a non-crystalline powdery precipitate results.

The material decomposes in hot water with decomposition of the anion; it is not appreciably soluble in cold water.

107. Hexamminecobalt (II) Chloride ***

(I)

$$CoCl_2 + 6NH_3 \longrightarrow [Co(NH_3)_6]Cl_2$$

Two hundred milliliters of alcohol are refluxed vigorously for about 15 minutes, to drive out any dissolved air, and then cooled in ice while a fairly vigorous stream of ammonia is passed in for about 20 minutes under the hood. The solution should be stored in a tightly stoppered flask until required.

Fifteen grams of cobalt (II) chloride 6-hydrate are dissolved in 15ml of boiling water and this solution is mixed with 40ml of concentrated ammonia (previously heated to 70°C). The mixture is *immediately* filtered by suction into a 250ml filter flask and kept hot with a *small* flame while the alcoholic ammonia previously prepared is added directly through the suction funnel until a slight permanent turbidity forms in the filtrate; about 100ml will be required. The filter funnel is replaced by a stopper and the side-arm of the flask is closed with a piece of rubber tubing carrying a clamp. The flame is removed and the flask is rapidly cooled to room temperature in an ice-water bath; small pink crystals of product separate out.

After standing for about 10 minutes in the closed flask in order to complete crystallization, the product is filtered under an inert atmosphere, using the apparatus and technique described in Experiment 35 under chromium (II) acetate. The crystals are washed through the dropping funnel with 25ml of a cold 1:1 mixture of 95% alcohol and concentrated ammonia. The flow of inert gas is maintained and the material is left covered with a thin layer of wash liquid during the entire operation of filtration and washing (except after the last washing with ether).

Next, the product is washed with two 25ml portions of the alcoholic ammonia, made previously, and finally three times with 25ml of absolute ether. After the last washing with ether, the product is dried by suction for at least one-half hour in a strong current of inert gas and then quickly transferred to a vacuum desiccator for complete removal of adhering solvents.

Yield about 7g

(II)

Thirty-five grams of cobalt (II) chloride 6-hydrate are placed in a pressure bottle of 125–250ml capacity with 50ml of concentrated aqueous ammonia and 10ml of 95% alcohol. After the bottle and contents have been heated for one hour on the steam bath with the usual safety precautions, complete solution should have taken place. On *slow* cooling to room temperature, the complex chloride is obtained in relatively large crystals which are isolated as in (I), washing with three 20ml portions of ice-cold concentrated ammonia, two 50ml volumes of 95% alcohol, and 75–100ml of ether. This product is somewhat less susceptible to oxidation in air than the material obtained in (I), but it still must be handled with minimum exposure to oxygen.

Hexamminecobalt (II) chloride has a pale yellowish-pink color. A deeper yellow or brownish tint indicates that oxidation has taken place.

(III)

Fifty milliliters of absolute methanol are placed in a 125ml suction flask fitted with a stopper and inlet tube reaching almost to the bottom of the vessel. This is cooled in an ice-water bath while dry ammonia is passed into the alcohol with frequent swirling until absorption is complete. The solution is rapidly transferred to a stoppered 250ml flask and cooled in an ice bath while a solution of 15g of cobalt (II) chloride 6-hydrate in 150ml of dry methanol is added with gentle shaking. The pale-pink powdery product precipitates immediately, leaving an almost colorless supernatant liquid. To aid in complete precipitation and coagulation, the well-stoppered, ice-cooled flask is allowed to stand for 15–30 minutes. The material is then filtered as rapidly as possible by suction using a 40–60mm coarse-grade sintered funnel covered with a watch glass. In the meantime, the reaction mixture, as yet unfiltered, is kept cold and stoppered to minimize oxidation. Just as the last of the methanolic mother-liquor begins to drain from the precipitate, the latter is washed, first with 25ml of anhydrous ether, and then with the same volume of benzene. The solid should be kept constantly covered by the organic liquids. While the product is still moist with benzene, it is transferred quickly to a vacuum desiccator containing calcium chloride and a small separate dish holding a mixture of calcium oxide and ammonium chloride.

Yield, quantitative

References:
1. B:185.
2. BILTZ AND FETKENHEUER, *Z. anorg. Chem.*, 89:98, 130 (1914).
3. CLARK *et al.*, *J. Am. Chem. Soc.*, 42:2488 (1920).

108. dl-Tris(ethylenediamine)cobalt (III) Chloride 3-Hydrate *

(I)

$$4CoCl_2 + 10C_2H_4(NH_2)_2 + 2C_2H_4(NH_2)_2 \cdot 2HCl + O_2 \longrightarrow 4[Co(en)_3]Cl_3 + 2H_2O$$

Eighteen grams of anhydrous ethylenediamine are dissolved in 50ml of water and the solution cooled in ice while 17ml of 6M hydrochloric acid are added slowly. A solution of 24g of cobalt (II) chloride 6-hydrate in 75ml of water is poured into the solution of the partly neutralized amine. Oxidation is effected by bubbling air (4–5 bubbles/sec) through the mixture in a 250ml filter flask fitted with an inlet tube. After three hours, the dark-brown solution is evaporated on the steam bath until a crust begins to form on the surface; the volume will be 15–20ml. A mixture of 15ml of concentrated hydrochloric acid and 30ml of alcohol is added and the entire material cooled in an ice bath. The yellow-orange crystals of product are washed in the filter with alcohol until the rinsings are colorless and dried in warm air.

Yield = 30–31g

A little more of impure product can be obtained by adding more alcohol to the mother liquor. This may be purified by dissolving it in the minimum of water and re-precipitating with an equal volume of alcohol.

The chlorides of the other polybasic ammine complexes with cobalt described in (II) may easily be prepared in solution by a similar procedure, but only the ethylenediamine compound can be directly isolated as a solid. The other chlorides must be made indirectly from the nitrates, bromides, or iodides of the respective series.

(II)

$$[Co(NH_3)_5Cl]Cl_2 + 3C_2H_4(NH_2)_2 \longrightarrow [Coen_3]Cl_3 + 5NH_3$$

Five grams of chloropentamminecobalt (III) chloride (No. 119) is added to a solution of 6g of anhydrous ethylenediamine in 40ml of water. The mixture is heated on the steam bath for 3–4 hours; water is added from time to time to keep the volume constant. The complex chloride dissolves initially with the evolution of ammonia to yield a red-purple liquid containing basic bis(ethylenediamine) salts and finally a dark yellow-brown solution is produced. A small portion of the reaction mixture is tested by treatment with an excess of 95% alcohol; a yellow precipitate should be formed with only a very faintly reddish-colored supernatant liquid. The solution is then evaporated to a volume of about 10ml and cooled while 50–75ml of 95% alcohol is added with stirring. The voluminous yellow product is filtered off and washed with two 25ml portions of 95% alcohol to remove excess amine. The crude material is purified by dissolving it on the steam bath in the minimum volume of 1M hydrochloric acid; 15–20ml will be required. After it is cooled in ice about 50ml of alcohol are added; the supernatant liquid should be almost colorless; otherwise a little more alcohol should be added. The product is washed on the filter with 25ml of 95% alcohol and an equal volume of ether.

Yield = 7.5g

Details of the simple resolution of the racemic chloride by means of silver d-tartrate or barium d-tartrate are given in reference 2.

References:
1. I, vol. 2:221.
2. a) WERNER, Ber., 45:125 (1912); b) I, vol. 6:183.

COGNATE PREPARATIONS

108 a. dl-Tris(ethylenediamine)cobalt (III) Sulfamate *

$$[Coen_3][SO_3NH_2]_3$$

Twelve grams of cobalt carbonate are added in small portions to a suspension of 19.4g of sulfamic acid (see No. 92) in 30ml of water. The filtered solution is poured into a mixture of 18g of anhydrous ethylenediamine, 45ml of water, and 9.7g of sulfamic acid. After cooling in ice to room temperature, the mixture is oxidized in air for 3 hours as described in (I).

The solution, together with any solid product that may have settled out during the aeration, is evaporated to crystallization on the steam bath. The mixture is chilled in ice and filtered and the yellow product is washed with 50ml of cold 50% aqueous alcohol, with 95% alcohol, and with ether. The mother liquor and alcoholic washings are again evaporated to a volume of 15–20ml, 10ml of 95% alcohol being added to the liquid as it cools. More product is isolated as just described and the whole mass is dried in air.

Total yield = 41g

Several interesting compounds can be simply prepared by metathesis of equivalent amounts of a soluble dl-tris-(ethylenediamine) cobalt (III),

$$[Co(en)_3]^{3+}$$

and the corresponding potassium salt. Fairly concentrated aqueous solutions are best for rapid separation of the product.

a) Trioxalatoferrate (III); orange.
b) Hexacyanocobaltate (III); yellow-orange.
c) Trioxalatochromate (III); brown plates.
d) Octacyanomolybdate (IV); dark-brown oil, solidifies to a yellow-brown solid after rinsing with a little water and triturating with alcohol.

108 b. dl-Tris(propylenediamine)cobalt (III) Nitrate *

[Copn₃][NO₃]₃

This compound is prepared from 30g of cobalt nitrate 6-hydrate in 25ml of water and a mixture of 22g of anhydrous propylenediamine with 6ml of pure colorless concentrated nitric acid in 20ml of water. After aerating this for four hours, 15ml of concentrated nitric acid are added and the solution is evaporated to incipient crystallization. It is filtered hot, ice-cooled, and re-filtered. The bright orange product is washed with alcohol and with ether and the mother liquor is treated with 100ml of 95% alcohol. The crude precipitated material, which may be oily, is filtered or decanted. It is purified by re-precipitation from a saturated aqueous solution with an equal volume of 95% alcohol. The product is then dried in air.

Yield = 17.5g

108 c. dl-Tris(propylenediamine)cobalt (III) Bromide Monohydrate *

[Copn₃]Br₃·H₂O

Twelve grams of cobalt carbonate are dissolved in 34g of constant-boiling (48%) hydrobromic acid and filtered. This solution is poured into a cold mixture of 22g of *pn*, 17g of HBr, and 50ml of water. After four hours oxidation with air, the solution is evaporated to 80ml, cooled, and filtered. The yellow product is washed with 95% alcohol and with ether; the mother liquor is combined with the alcoholic washing and evaporated to a thick sirup. This is solidified by triturating with 95% alcohol; then it is dissolved in 10ml of boiling water, and cooled. More product is then isolated in the same manner: yellow powder.

Total yield = 27g

108 d. dl-Tris(propylenediamine)cobalt (III) Iodide Monohydrate *

$$[Copn_3]I_3 \cdot H_2O$$

Twelve grams of cobalt carbonate are dissolved in 45g of 57% hydriodic acid (No. 89), filtered, and added to 22g of *pn* and 22g of HI in 150ml of water. The pink precipitate of cobalt (II) salt that forms is ignored; vigorous oxidation with air for three hours rapidly converts it to a yellow product. After filtration, the mother liquor is evaporated and two more batches of material are isolated; the final volume is about 50ml.

Total yield = 45g

108 e. Tris(propylenediamine)cobalt (III) Thiocyanate *

$$[Copn_3][SCN]_3$$

$$4K_2Co(SCN)_4 + 10pn + 2pn \cdot (HC_2H_3O_2)_2 + O_2 \longrightarrow$$
$$4[Copn_3][SCN]_3 + 4KSCN + 4KC_2H_3O_2 + 2H_2O$$

Thirty-six grams of potassium tetrakis(thiocyanato)cobaltate (II) (No. 68) are dissolved in 75ml of water and added to a mixture of 22g of *pn*, 6ml of glacial acetic acid, and 60ml of water. The product, which settles out as orange crystals during the 3 hours of vigorous aeration, is washed freely with 95% alcohol and ether.

Yield = 14.5g

The deep red mother liquor contains $Copn_2(SCN)_2SCN$.

Reference: For a description of the properties of $[Copn_3]^{3+}$ complexes see

GMELIN, *Handbuch der anorganischen Chemie*, No. 58B (Kobaltammine), Verlag Chemie, G.m.b.H., Berlin, 1930.

108 f. dl-Bis(diethylenetriamine)cobalt (III) Bromide *

$$[Coden_2]Br_3$$

This is prepared from 12g of cobalt carbonate, 34g 48% hydrobromic acid, and 20.5g of *den* dissolved in 50ml of water; it is similar to the *pn* compound. After being oxidized for 2 hours, the mixture is set aside for 24 hours in an open evaporating dish to crystallize. The yellow product is filtered, washed first with 50ml of 95% alcohol, and then with an equal volume of ether. The combined mother liquor and washings are treated with 150ml of 95% alcohol; more material is isolated in this way and the entire solid is dried *in vacuo*.

$$\text{Yield} = 35\text{g} \ (70\%)$$

108 g. dl-Bis(dipropylenetriamine)cobalt (III) Bromide *
[Co*dpn*₂]Br₃

The same procedure as for the *pn* bromide (No. 108 c) is used to prepare this compound, except that 26.5g of *dpn* are substituted. Two hours of oxidation in air is sufficient. The deep yellow-brown liquid is allowed to evaporate spontaneously in an open dish for two days and is then poured into 400ml of acetone. The oily lower layer is poured into a large mortar and triturated with successive portions of fresh acetone until a yellow powder remains. This is brought onto the filter with the same solvent and transferred while still moist to a vacuum desiccator.

$$\text{Yield} = 36\text{g} \ (64\%)$$

The salt is quite deliquescent and is soluble in alcohol.

108 h. dl-Bis(dipropylenetriamine)cobalt (III) Iodide *
[Co*dpn*₂]I₃

The procedure for the *pn* iodide (No. 108 d) is employed, using 26.2g of amine and 50ml of water. A heavy pink precipitate of cobalt (II) salt forms from the initial mixing, but most of this disappears after 3–4 hours of oxidation with air. The liquid and residual solid are evaporated on the steam bath to about 60ml and then suction-filtered to remove undecomposed [Co*dpn*₂]I₂. On further evaporation, a heavy skin begins to form persistently on the surface of the solution; the cooled sirupy mass is poured into 500ml of acetone and the yellow precipitate of product is filtered off. After being washed with ether, the solid is vacuum-dried.

$$\text{Yield} = 22.5g$$

A little more of the product may be isolated if a large volume of ether is added to the water-acetone mother liquor. This may be dissolved in 50ml of water and precipitated as yellow

$$[Codpn_2][Fe(CN)_6]$$

by the addition of saturated aqueous potassium ferricyanide.

108 i. Tris(triethylenetetramine)dicobalt (III) Iodide *

$$[Co_2tet_3]I_6$$

The procedure for this compound is the same as for the preceding, using 22g of *tet* and 50ml of water. After three hours of oxidation, the tacky red-brown precipitate is recrystallized from boiling water to yield dark orange crystals which are washed on the filter with alcohol and with ether, then dried in air.

$$\text{Yield} = 10g$$

A second recrystallization yields an analytically pure product which is dried at 100°C. The air-dried material contains about four molecules of water; at 100–110°C, two of them are lost.

c) *Nickel Compounds*

109. Dinitrotetramminenickel (II) *

$$Ni^{++} + CO_3^{--} \longrightarrow NiCO_3$$
$$NiCO_3 + 2HC_2H_3O_2 \longrightarrow Ni(C_2H_3O_2)_2 + CO_2 + H_2O$$
$$Ni(C_2H_3O_2)_2 + 2NaNO_2 + 4NH_3 \longrightarrow [Ni(NH_3)_4(NO_2)_2] + 2NaC_2H_3O_2$$

Twelve grams of nickel chloride 6-hydrate, or 13.2g of the sulfate 6-hydrate, are dissolved in 100ml of hot water and poured into a well-stirred solution of 5.5g of anhydrous sodium carbonate in 150ml of boiling water. The mixture is heated at the boiling point with stirring until the blue green precipitate of nickel carbonate begins to settle well. After suction-filtering, the solid is washed with 50ml of boiling water and drained well. The moist carbonate is dissolved on the steam bath in 6ml of glacial acetic acid and 10ml of water. On cooling some nickel acetate crystallizes out and about five drops more of acetic acid is added to counteract possible hydrolysis of the salt. About 30ml of concentrated aqueous ammonia is poured into the mixture with cooling and the violet solution is stirred until solution is complete.

Sixty grams of ammonium acetate and 40g of sodium nitrite are added to 50ml of water; the stirred mixture is carefully warmed to 25–30°C. When solution is complete, the clear, rather viscous liquid is mixed well with the ammoniacal nickel solution and allowed to stand at room temperature. Precipitation of the red complex, which soon begins, is complete after about one hour. When the preparation has stood overnight, the faintly-colored viscous mother liquor is carefully decanted and the salt is brought onto the filter with 95% alcohol. It is washed with 50ml more of the solvent (both sodium nitrite and ammonium acetate are soluble) and dried in air.

$$\text{Yield} = 10\text{–}10.5\text{g}$$

The compound begins to lose ammonia over 100°C and it is converted to the unstable violet hexammine by exposure to the gas at low temperatures. Magnetic data on the red nitrite indicate that it should be formulated as a hexammine nickel complex of tetrahedral configuration.

References:
1. P:559.
2. EPHRAIM, *Ber.*, 46:3110 (1913).

COGNATE PREPARATION

109 a. Dinitrotetrapyridinenickel (II) *

$$[Ni(C_5H_5N)_4(NO_2)_2]$$

Five grams of nickel chloride 6-hydrate (or 5.5g of the sulfate 6-hydrate) are dissolved in 50ml of water and 7ml of pure pyridine are added. The liquid is stirred mechanically in an ice bath until the temperature has fallen to 5°C or below, and then a solution of 25g of sodium nitrite in 30ml of water is *slowly* added dropwise from a separatory funnel. The blue-green product precipitates during the addition; stirring and cooling are continued for about one hour longer. After the complex nitrite is filtered by suction from the practically colorless ice-cold mother liquor, it is washed with 10–15ml of ice water and dried at normal pressure over solid *alkali*. Washing with organic solvents or evacuation of the product removes pyridine with the formation of a basic salt.

$$\text{Yield} = 8.5\text{–}9g$$

The crude material is purified as follows:

All the product is dissolved in 40ml of water (previously heated to 80°C) to which one milliliter of pyridine has been added immediately before it is mixed with the solid. When the blue-green substance has dissolved, leaving only a small residue of cream-colored basic nitrite, the hot liquid is immediately filtered by suction and rapidly cooled in ice. During the cooling process the solution should be continuously agitated to minimize the formation of tenacious crusts on the walls of the vessel; these should be removed as needed.

$$\text{Yield} = 7.5\text{–}8g;\ \text{decomposition point} = 108\text{–}110°C$$

Reference: P:560.

110. Hexamminenickel (II) Chloride *

$$NiCl_2 + 6NH_3 \longrightarrow [Ni(NH_3)_6]Cl_2$$

Twenty-four grams of nickel chloride 6-hydrate are dissolved in 40ml of warm water and 50ml of concentrated aqueous ammonia are added. The deep violet solution is cooled in ice; a heavy crystalline mass of product separates out. About 100ml of cold 95% alcohol is added to the mixture to complete the deposition; the supernatant liquid should be almost colorless. After filtering, the product is washed with two 25ml portions of alcohol and dried in air.

Yield almost quantitative

References:
1. P:554.
2. HECHT, *Präparative Anorganische Chemie*, p. 161, Springer, Berlin, 1951.

COGNATE PREPARATIONS

110 a. Hexamminenickel (II) Bromide *

$$[Ni(NH_3)_6]Br_2$$

Twenty-six grams of nickel sulfate 6-hydrate or 24g of the chloride 6-hydrate are dissolved in 300ml of hot water and mixed with a hot solution of 11g of anhydrous sodium carbonate in 200ml of water. The mixture is heated at the boiling point with stirring until the nickel carbonate settles well and is then filtered. After solid has been washed with 100ml of boiling water and drained, it is dissolved in portions in 34g of constant boiling hydrobromic acid. The solution is evaporated to dryness on the steam bath and the residue is taken up in 20ml of water. When the dark yellow-green solution has cooled to 5°C or lower in an ice bath, 50ml of concentrated ammonia are added slowly from a tap-funnel. Stirring and cooling are maintained; the liquid soon thickens with crystals of the violet product and the supernatant liquid becomes almost colorless. The solid is drained well on the filter and dried in air.

Yield = 30g

References:
1. B:171.
2. HECHT, *Präparative Anorganische Chemie*, p. 262, Springer, Berlin, 1951.
3. SÖRENSEN, *Z. anorg. Chem.*, 5:363 (1894).
4. BILTZ AND FETKENHEUER, *Ibid.*, 83:163 (1913); 89:98 (1914).

110 b. Hexamminenickel (III) Fluoroborate *

$$[Ni(NH_3)_6][BF_4]_2$$

An ammoniacal solution of the hexammine chloride is prepared as in the preceding directions, using one-fourth of the specified amounts. The precipitated solid is redissolved by the addition of 15ml of water and the mixture is filtered into a solution of 3g of ammonium fluoroborate (No. 23) in 15ml of water. The almost invisible precipitate is filtered off, washed with 15ml of ice-cold 6M ammonia and then freely with acetone to aid in air-drying.

Yield = 5–6g

Many inorganic salts that contain a high percentage of fluorine, e.g., fluorophosphates and fluoroborates, have a refractive index close to that of water. Hence, heavy aqueous suspension of these types of compounds appear deceptively void of solid until filtered.

References:
1. P:554.
2. WILKE-DÖRFURT AND BALZ, *Z. anorg. Chem.*, 159:197 (1927).

110 c. Hexamminenickel (II) Perchlorate *

$$Ni(NH_3)_6[ClO_4]_2$$

Six grams of nickel chloride 6-hydrate are dissolved in 30ml of water and concentrated ammonia is added until the initial precipitate of hydroxide just *barely* dissolves; about 10ml should be required. Perchloric acid (72%) is slowly added dropwise with stirring until the liquid above the precipitated violet solid is colorless. Approximately 5ml are needed. The solid is washed first with 10ml of ice water on the filter and then dried in warm air.

Yield quantitative

Reference: See No. 2 under No. 110 a.

111. dl-Tris(ethylenediamine)nickel (II) Sulfamate *

$$NiCO_3 + 2HSO_3NH_2 \longrightarrow Ni(SO_3NH_2)_2 + CO_2 + H_2O$$
$$Ni(SO_3NH_2)_2 + 3C_2H_4(NH_2)_2 \longrightarrow [Nien_3][SO_3NH_2]_2$$

Ten grams of sulfamic acid (No. 92) are dissolved in 50ml of water, and nickel carbonate is added in small portions until effervescence is complete; 6–7g are required. The solution is filtered from any undissolved material and cooled in ice while 9.5g of anhydrous ethylenediamine are slowly stirred in. Alcohol is added until precipitation of the violet salt is complete. The product is filtered, washed with 95% alcohol and with ether, and dried in air.

Yield = 19–20g

COGNATE PREPARATIONS

111 a. dl-Tris(ethylenediamine)nickel (II) Chloride 2-Hydrate *

$$[Nien_3]Cl_2 \cdot 2H_2O$$

Twelve grams of nickel chloride 6-hydrate are dissolved in 15ml of water and cooled in ice while 10g of *en* are added, followed by 25ml of alcohol.

Yield = 15.5g

Reference: I, Vol. 6:200.

111 b. Bromide *: From nickel carbonate and 17g of 48% hydrobromic acid in 50ml of water as described for the sulfamate.

111 c. Iodide *: From nickel carbonate; 22g of 57% HI in 50ml of water are used.

111 d. Fluoroborate *: From 6g of the chloride in 20ml of water and 5g of ammonium fluoroborate in 25ml of water.

111 e. Perchlorate *: Eight grams of the chloride in 25ml of water and about 6 ml of 70–72% perchloric acid are employed.

The corresponding propylenediamine complexes are similarly prepared, using the equivalent amount of amine. The yield of all these preparations is over 90%.

111 f. Bis(diethylenetriamine)nickel (II) Fluoroborate *

$$[Niden_2][BF_4]_2$$

Two and six-tenths grams of nickel sulfate 6-hydrate are stirred with 10ml of water while 2.6g of *den* is added. Then 3g of sodium fluoroborate is mixed with the liquid and the violet precipitate is filtered and drained well. The product is soluble in acetone.

Yield = 3.2g

111 g. Dipropylenetriamine Analogue *

[Nidpn_2][BF$_4$]$_2$

Preparation as for the preceding; 3.2g of amine are used.

Yield = 3.6g

111 h. Bis(dipropylenetriamine)nickel (II) Sulfate *

[Nidpn_2]SO$_4$

This compound is prepared from 2.6g of nickel sulfate 6-hydrate and 3.2g of the amine in 10ml of water. The violet liquid is treated with acetone until the separation of the oily product is complete. The oil is triturated in a mortar with repeated 20ml portions of fresh acetone and it finally produces a violet solid. This is rapidly drained on the filter and transferred moist to a vacuum desiccator; very deliquescent solid.

Yield = 4g

The procedures described should serve as a general guide to the preparation of nickel ammine complexes.

PENTAMMINE SERIES

a) Chromium Compounds

112. Aquopentamminechromium (III) Nitrate **

(I)

$$2AgNO_3 + 2NaOH \longrightarrow Ag_2O + 2NaNO_3 + H_2O$$
(a) $2[Cr(NH_3)_5Cl]Cl_2 + 3Ag_2O + 5H_2O \longrightarrow 2[Cr(NH_3)_5H_2O][OH]_3 + 6AgCl$
$$[Cr(NH_3)_5H_2O][OH]_3 + 3HNO_3 \longrightarrow [Cr(NH_3)_5H_2O][NO_3]_3 + 3H_2O$$

Twenty grams of silver nitrate are dissolved in 100ml of distilled water and treated with a solution of 5g of pure sodium hydroxide in an equal volume of water. The brown precipitate is washed three times by decantation with 100ml of water and drained well in the precipitating vessel. Forty-five milliliters of water are added to the moist silver oxide, followed by 5g of chloropentamminechromium (III) chloride (No. 113). The mixture is stirred well for four minutes (longer reaction times cause decomposition with liberation of NH_3) and filtered by suction into 5ml of ice-cold concentrated nitric acid. If any precipitate of silver halide or unchanged pentammine salt forms at this point, the orange solution is re-filtered. Then 30ml more of nitric acid is added and the solution cooled to 5°C or below while 100ml of 95% alcohol are stirred in. After thorough cooling for 30 minutes, the mixture is filtered and the orange solid is washed with 25ml of 95% alcohol, followed by an equal volume of acetone. The product is air-dried in the absence of direct daylight.

$$\text{Yield} = 4.3g$$

(b) $[Cr(NH_3)_5Cl]Cl_2 + H_2O \longrightarrow [Cr(NH_3)_5H_2O]Cl_3$
$[Cr(NH_3)_5H_2O]Cl_3 + 3HNO_3 \longrightarrow [Cr(NH_3)_5H_2O]NO_3 + 3HCl$

Five grams of chloropentamminechromium (III) chloride (No. 113) are suspended in 75ml of hot water containing 15 drops of nitric acid ($15M$). The mixture is cautiously heated on the steam bath until all the solid has dissolved and then for 3–5 minutes longer; the red color of the liquid should have acquired a distinct orange tint by this time. Now the solution is set aside for one hour to cool spontaneously; if any appreciable amount of unchanged pentammine salt settles during this time, the liquid should be heated once more to 90°C and re-cooled. Finally, the solution is cooled in ice and filtered to remove any trace of unchanged starting material. Thirty milliliters of concentrated nitric acid are added with stirring and the preparation completed as under (a).

$$\text{Yield} = 3.5g$$

(II)

$2KCr(SO_4)_2 + 6NH_3 + 3H_2O \longrightarrow Cr_2O_3 + 3(NH_4)_2SO_4 + K_2SO_4$
$Cr_2O_3 + 10NH_3 + 3H_2O \longrightarrow 2[Cr(NH_3)_5OH][OH]_2$
$[Cr(NH_3)_5OH][OH]_2 + 3HNO_3 \longrightarrow [Cr(NH_3)_5H_2O][NO_3]_3 + 2H_2O$

One hundred grams of very finely powdered potassium chromium (III) sulfate (chrome alum) are mixed in a flask with 250ml of concentrated aqueous ammonia. Then 250g of ammonium nitrate are added and the mixture is warmed for one hour at 55–60°C on the steam bath with occasional swirling. After the mixture has been cooled at 20°C, a strong current of air is passed in for 30 minutes. The purple solution is carefully decanted from any unreacted solid and filtered. It is then slowly poured into a mixture of 100g of cracked ice and 250ml of concentrated nitric acid, keeping the temperature below 30°C during the neutralization. After standing one hour in the ice bath, the resulting orange crystals are collected by suction filtration and drained thoroughly. The solid is then dissolved in 150ml of water and 80ml of concentrated nitric acid is added; the solution is then thoroughly cooled in ice while 100ml of 95% alcohol is slowly stirred in. After standing in ice for at least 30 minutes, the pure product is filtered, washed with 50ml of 95% alcohol and the same volume of acetone, then air-dried.

Yield about 12g

References:
1. I, vol. 5:132; P:399.
2. CHRISTENSEN, *J. prakt. Chem.* (2), 23:27, 41 (1881).
3. WERNER, *Ann.*, 405:220 (1914).

COGNATE PREPARATIONS

112 a. Aquopentamminechromium (III) Chloride **
$[Cr(NH_3)_5H_2O]Cl_3$

This compound is prepared in the same way as in (I) for the nitrate except that 7ml of concentrated hydrochloric acid is used to catch the filtrate from the silver oxide. Any silver halide or unchanged starting materials are filtered off. The product is precipitated as an orange-red solid by cooling the filtrate in ice while 100ml of an ice-cold 1:3 mixture of concentrated hydrochloric acid and alcohol is added. After filtering, the material is washed with 95% alcohol and with ether.

Yield = 4g

As the compound is unstable it loses water after a few months, reverting to the chloropentammine chloride. It is photosensitive, like the nitrate and all the other aquopentammine series of salts.

112 b. Bromide **

(a) This is prepared as described in (I) under the nitrate; 50ml of 48% hydrobromic acid are used to neutralize the filtrate and the resulting solution is filtered if necessary. After cooling, 75ml of methanol are added and the orange product is filtered by suction. It is washed with alcohol and dried in the dark.

Yield = 4.8–5.1g

(b) Three and four-tenths grams of the nitrate are dissolved in a mixture of 8ml of water and 2ml of concentrated ammonia. Ten milliliters of 48% hydrobromic acid and an equal volume of 95% alcohol are added and the liquid is cooled in ice. The orange precipitate is washed with 25ml of alcohol and ether on the filter and dried in the dark.

Yield = 3.5g

112 c. Iodide *

(a) Proceed as for Method (I) under the nitrate; however, only 25ml of water are used with the silver oxide and the chloropentammine salt. The red solution is filtered into 50ml of 57% hydriodic acid, and 100ml of 95% alcohol are added; acetone may be used instead. The product is washed with acetone on the filter and dried in the absence of light.

Yield = 4g

112 d. Ferricyanide *

This compound is obtained in almost quantitative yield from equivalent quantities of the aquonitrate and the potassium salt in 20% aqueous solutions.

Reference: I, vol. 5:134.

113. Chloropentamminechromium (III) Chloride ***

$$2CrCl_3 + Zn \longrightarrow 2CrCl_2 + ZnCl_2$$
$$4CrCl_2 + 18NH_3 + 2NH_4Cl + O_2 \longrightarrow 2[Cr_2(NH_3)_{10}OH]Cl_5$$
$$[Cr_2(NH_3)_{10}OH]Cl_5 + HCl \longrightarrow 2[Cr(NH_3)_5Cl]Cl_2 + H_2O$$

[To prepare 2% zinc amalgam: Fifteen grams of pure zinc are shaken for about five minutes with 100ml of $1N$ hydrochloric acid to which a small crystal of copper sulfate has been added. The acid is decanted and 50ml of a saturated solution of mercuric chloride is poured over the metal. When the zinc has been well covered with a deposit of mercury, the metal is quickly washed twice by decantation with water. About 50ml of clean mercury are added and the amalgam is covered with 50ml of $N/10$ hydrochloric acid. After a few hours, with occasional shaking, the zinc has dissolved and the amalgam is ready for use. It is preserved under $N/10$ HCl in a loosely stoppered bottle until required.]

Twenty-nine grams of chromium (III) chloride 6-hydrate are dissolved in a warm mixture of 25ml of concentrated hydrochloric acid and 45ml of water. The filtered solution is transferred to a 250ml round-type dropping funnel with a long stem containing 35ml of the zinc amalgam and fitted with a 2-hole stopper carrying an inlet- and an outlet-tube for a source of any inert gas. The inlet (7mm i.d.) should reach to within one inch of the surface of the solution; the outlet (3mm i.d.) should be bent at an acute angle. In this way, the contents of the funnel are always under a slight pressure from the inert atmosphere and the carrying-over of spray is minimized.

With a good current of gas circulating through the reduction apparatus, the funnel is swirled continuously until the liquid is a clear blue with no green tint; this step requires about 30 minutes. It is important to remember that a good yield of product depends solely on complete reduction to the chromium (II) state. The flow of gas is increased and the amalgam is drained rapidly into a suitable vessel; any drops adhering to the inside of the funnel stem are tapped out. The tip of the stem is then placed well under the surface of a cold mixture of 300ml of concentrated ammonia and 150g of ammonium chloride, and the chromium (II) chloride solution is run in rapidly with good swirling. The amalgam and solution should be drained from the funnel as expeditiously as possible to keep re-oxidation at the minimum; once the reduced solution has been run into the ammonia, no further protection from the air is necessary.

The ammoniacal reaction mixture is transferred to a one-liter filter flask which is fitted with a stopper and a wide inlet-tube that reaches almost to the bottom of the vessel. A *vigorous* current of air is now drawn through the mixture for 20–30 minutes; any bluish tint should completely disappear and the suspension should be bright red in color. In the hood, the oxidized mixture is slowly poured into one liter of concentrated hydrochloric acid (in a 2-liter flask) and the liquid is heated for 15–20 minutes over a small flame with frequent agitation. When the solid has settled well on standing, the clear faintly-colored liquid is carefully decanted until the residual volume of the suspension is about 500ml. An equal volume of cold water is now added and the flask is shaken for a few minutes to dissolve as much ammonium chloride as possible. The mixture is *gently* swirled during the subsequent filtration, leaving the coarser particles of ammonium chloride behind and carrying over only the bright-red product. It is preferable to use a sintered-glass funnel of medium porosity for the filtration. The product is stirred separately with two 50ml portions of ice-cold 6N HCl (to remove any ammonium salt), drained well, then washed freely with cold 50% aqueous alcohol and with acetone to facilitate air-drying.

$$Yield = 20\text{--}24g$$

The same product is also formed when aquo-, nitro- or nitratopentammine, as well as hexamminechromium (III) salts, are gently boiled with 20 times their weight of 6M hydrochloric acid for about 45 minutes.

References:
1. P:398; I, vol. 6:138.
2. CHRISTENSEN, *J. prakt. Chem.* [2], 23:28, 54 (1881).
3. JÖRGENSEN, *Ibid.*, [2], 20:107 (1879).
4. CHRISTENSEN, *Z. anorg. Chem.*, 4:229 (1893) (liquid ammonia method). See also: B:184; LANG AND CARSON, *J. Am. Chem. Soc.*, 26:414 (1904).

COGNATE PREPARATIONS

113 a. Bromopentamminechromium (III) Bromide *

$$[Cr(NH_3)_5H_2O]Br_3 \longrightarrow [Cr(NH_3)_5Br]Br_2 + H_2O$$

Four and one-half grams of aquopentamminechromium (III) bromide (No. 112 b) are mixed with 20ml of water and 5ml of 48% hydrobromic acid. The mixture is heated on the steam bath for 30 minutes while three 5ml portions of the same acid are added over five minute intervals. The mixture is cooled in ice and filtered, and the reddish product is washed with 95% alcohol and then air-dried.

$$Yield = 4g$$

The material is also produced in quantitative yield by drying the aquopentammine bromide to constant weight at 100°C (1-2 hours).

113 b. Iodopentamminechromium (III) Iodide *

$$[Cr(NH_3)_5I]I_2$$

This compound is made from the aquopentammine iodide (No. 112 c) by heating the latter at 60-80°C until the theoretical weight has been lost (4-8 hours); the yield is quantitative.

References:
1. I, vol. 5:134.
2. CHRISTENSEN, *J. prakt. Chem.* [2] 23:34 (1881).
3. JORGENSEN, *Ibid.*, [2] 25:91 (1882).

114. Nitropentamminechromium (III) Chloride *

$$[Cr(NH_3)_5H_2O][NO_3]_3 + NaNO_2 + 2HCl \longrightarrow$$
$$[Cr(NH_3)_5NO_2]Cl_2 + NaNO_3 + 2HNO_3 + H_2O$$

Three and four-tenths grams of aquopentamminechromium (III) nitrate (No. 112) (or better, 2.8g of the aquochloride, No. 112 a) are dissolved in 50ml of water and 5g of sodium nitrite are stirred into the solution. Then 7ml of 4M hydrochloric acid are slowly added with continual agitation and the mixture is cooled in ice for 15 minutes. The orange product is washed on the filter with 10ml of cold 50% aqueous alcohol and then with 15ml of acetone to aid in air-drying.

$$Yield = 2g$$

When the salt is warmed with concentrated hydrochloric acid, the chloropentammine chloride is formed.

COGNATE PREPARATIONS

114 a. Nitropentamminechromium (III) Nitrate *

$$[Cr(NH_3)_5NO_2][NO_3]_2$$

A solution of 3.4g of the aquo-nitrate (No. 112) in 40ml of water is mixed with one ml of $1M$ nitric acid, and a clear solution of 4g of sodium nitrite in 6ml of water is added. The product precipitates almost at once; the mixture is allowed to stand in ice for 15 minutes to complete the crystallization. The orange material is washed with aqueous alcohol and acetone, as described for the proceeding compound, and dried in air.

$$Yield = 2.4g$$

References:
1. P:401; I, vol. 5:133.
2. CHRISTENSEN, *J. prakt. Chem.*, 23:74 (1881).

114 b. Thiocyanatopentamminechromium (III) Thiocyanate *

$$[Cr(NH_3)_5Cl]Cl_2 + 3KSCN \longrightarrow [Cr(NH_3)_5SCN][SCN]_2 + 3KCl$$

As starting materials, 5g of the chloropentammine chloride (No. 113), 7g of the aquopentammine nitrate (No. 112), or 5.5g of the aquo-chloride (No. 112 a) may be employed.

The complex is mixed with 34ml of water containing 35g of potassium thiocyanate and 17ml of glacial acetic acid. The entire mixture is heated cautiously just to the boiling point over a *small* flame with continual stirring. At this point, the liquid turns brownish rather suddenly and an orange precipitate forms. Heating is discontinued immediately and the mixture is cooled in ice and filtered. The product is washed with 25ml of cold 1:1 aqueous alcohol and finally with ether before air-drying.

$$Yield = 4g$$

Reference: WERNER, Ler., 39:2670 (1906).

b) Cobalt Compounds

115. Acetatopentamminecobalt (III) Nitrate *

$$[CO(NH_3)_5CO_3]NO_3 + 2HC_2H_3O_2 \longrightarrow$$
$$[Co(NH_3)_5C_2H_3O_2](NO_3)C_2H_3O_2 + CO_2 + H_2O$$
$$[Co(NH_3)_5C_2H_3O_2]C_2H_3O_2[NO_3] + NH_4NO_3 \longrightarrow$$
$$[Co(NH_3)_5C_2H_3O_2][NO_3]_2 + NH_4C_2H_3O_2$$

Five grams of carbonatopentamminecobalt (III) nitrate (No. 118) are added in small portions to a mixture of 15ml of water and 12g of glacial acetic acid. The reaction mixture is concentrated on a steam bath for 1½–2 hours; during this time the red crystalline product separates. After cooling to room temperature, 40ml of water are added and the solid is filtered off. The mother liquor is removed from the filter flask and reserved, then the salt is washed with 50ml of ice-cold water, followed by 95% alcohol and ether.

About 15g of ammonium nitrate are dissolved in the mother liquor and the precipitated solid is isolated as described previously.

$$Total\ yield = 5–5.5g$$

Reference: I, vol. 4:175.

116. Aquopentamminecobalt (III) Nitrate *

$$[Co(NH_3)_5CO_3]NO_3 + 2HNO_3 \longrightarrow [Co(NH_3)_5H_2O][NO_3]_2 + CO_2 + H_2O$$

Ten grams of carbonatopentamminecobalt (III) nitrate ½-hydrate (See No. 118) are suspended in 10ml of water and 20ml of 1:1 nitric acid and water are added slowly in small portions. When the effervescence has stopped, after about 10 minutes, 100ml of alcohol (methyl or ethyl) are mixed with the liquid. The red precipitate is filtered off, washed with 95% alcohol and with ether, and then air-dried.

$$\text{Yield} = 10.5\text{g}$$

Reference: I, vol. 4:174.

COGNATE PREPARATIONS

116 a. Chloride **

(I)

$$3Co^{++} + MnO_4^- + 15NH_3 + 5H_2O \longrightarrow 3[Co(NH_3)_5H_2O]^{+++} + MnO_2 + 4OH^-$$

$$[Co(NH_3)_5H_2O]^{3+} + 3Cl^- \longrightarrow [Co(NH_3)_5H_2O]Cl_3$$

To a solution of 20g of cobalt (II) chloride 6-hydrate in 360 ml of water are added 110ml of concentrated aqueous ammonia followed by a solution of 10g of potassium permanganate in 400ml of water. The entire mixture is shaken well and allowed to stand for 24 hours. Ten grams of Celite or Filter-Cel are added and the hydrated manganese dioxide is filtered off by suction. The red-violet filtrate is placed in an ice bath and neutralized by the slow addition of concentrated hydrochloric acid; this is indicated by testing a small diluted portion of the liquid with litmus paper. While cooling is maintained, an ice-cold 1:1 mixture of 95% alcohol and concentrated hydrochloric acid is added slowly from a dropping funnel until no more bright-red product precipitates; about 500ml should be required. The solid is filtered from the pale-colored liquid and washed with 50ml of alcohol followed by ether, and then air-dried.

$$\text{Yield} = 12\text{--}15\text{g}$$

(II)

Ten grams of chloropentamminecobalt (III) chloride (see No. 119) are dissolved in 300ml of 5% aqueous ammonia on the steam bath. The deep-red solution is filtered, if necessary, and then cooled to 5°C in an ice bath while concentrated hydrochloric acid is added dropwise from a tap-funnel with constant agitation. When the liquid has become distinctly acid, the product is filtered, washed first with 50ml of 1:1 aqueous alcohol and then with 95% alcohol.

$$Yield = 10g$$

The crude product, prepared by either of the two methods given, may be purified according to 1 or 2 as follows:

1) The impure material is dissolved in cold 2% ammonia, using 75ml for each 10g of aquo-chloride. The ammoniacal liquid is filtered to remove any small amount of hexammine salt, and then treated with HCl as described under Method (II).

Yield about 9g for each 10g of starting material used

2) The crude product is treated with 75ml of water and 50ml of 10% ammonia on the steam bath for every 10g of crude chloride. After the red liquid has been cooled to room temperature under running water, a saturated aqueous solution of oxalic acid is added carefully until the reaction mixture is *just* acid. The red-pink aquopentamminecobalt (III) oxalate 4-hydrate is filtered and washed with 25ml of cold water.

The solid is redissolved in 75ml of 2% ammonia and precipitated again as above with oxalic acid.

$$Yield = 9g$$

The oxalate is covered with 25ml of cold water and dissolved by the addition of 45ml of concentrated hydrochloric acid. After the solution has been thoroughly cooled in an ice bath, 100ml more of the concentrated acid is slowly added dropwise with frequent swirling; cooling is maintained during this time. The analytically pure aquo-chloride is washed on the filter with 25ml of cold 6M hydrochloric acid and finally three times with 20ml of alcohol.

$$Yield = 8g$$

References:
1. B:177, 178; P:536.
2. JÖRGENSEN, *Z. anorg. Chem.*, 17:460 (1898).
3. JÖRGENSEN, *J. prakt. Chem.*, 31:50, 89 (1885).

116 b. Bromide **

$$CoCO_3 + 2HBr \longrightarrow CoBr_2 + CO_2 + H_2O$$
$$2CoBr_2 + 8NH_3 + 2NH_4Br + H_2O_2 \longrightarrow 2[Co(NH_3)_5H_2O]Br_3$$

Five grams of cobalt carbonate are added in small portions to 12ml of 48% hydrobromic acid and when effervescence has ceased, the mixture is filtered into a solution of 10g of ammonium bromide in 50ml of concentrated aqueous ammonia. The residue on the filter should be rinsed with 2ml of water which is also run into the ammonia. After cooling the entire solution down to about 10°C in ice, 8ml of 30% hydrogen peroxide is added dropwise with constant swirling. The dark-red oxidized liquid is poured into a 125ml filter flask fitted with a stopper and inlet-tube. A vigorous current of air is led through the reaction mixture to volatilize much of the excess ammonia and the solution cooled in ice while concentrated hydrobromic acid (48%) is slowly stirred in until the rose-colored precipitate of product persists on stirring. At this point the solution should be acid. An equal volume of 95% alcohol is now added and the material is filtered off, washed with 95% alcohol, then air-dried.

Yield = 15g

Reference: I, vol. 1:186.

116 c. Iodide *

$$[Co(NH_3)_5CO_3]NO_3 + KI \longrightarrow [Co(NH_3)_5CO_3]I + KNO_3$$
$$[Co(NH_3)_5CO_3]I + 2HI \longrightarrow [Co(NH_3)_5H_2O]I_3 + CO_2$$

Ten grams of carbonatopentamminecobalt (III) nitrate ½-hydrate (No. 118) are dissolved in 40ml of water at 85°C and 12.5g of finely powdered potassium iodide are added. The solution is cooled to 0°C in ice and the red product is filtered off and drained well.

This solid is suspended in 25ml of water and 20ml of 28% hydriodic acid is stirred in. When evolution of gas has stopped, 100ml of alcohol are added to the mixture and the rose-colored solid is removed by filtration. It is washed with 95% alcohol and ether, then air-dried.

$$Yield = 13g$$

Reference: I, vol. 4:173.

116 d. Sulfate *

The aquo-oxalate is prepared as described under the chloride, moistened with 10ml of water, and dissolved in the minimum volume of 1:4 dilute sulfuric acid. The complex sulfate is then precipitated with alcohol, filtered, and washed with more alcohol.

Yield over 90% of theory

Reference: JÖRGENSEN, Z. anorg. Chem., 17:462 (1898).

The aquopentammines show varying degrees of stability with respect to loss of water on heating; the chloride, bromide, and iodide are among the most labile of the series, and the oxalate is the most stable.

117. Bromopentamminecobalt (III) Bromide *

(I)

Proceed as for aquopentamminecobalt (III) bromide (see No. 116 b). The aerated oxidized solution is cooled in ice and faintly acidified with concentrated hydrobromic acid. Then 10ml more of the acid are added and the mixture is heated on the steam bath for 1½–2 hours. After cooling the slurry in ice, the solid is filtered off and washed with 20ml of water followed by three 10ml portions of 95% alcohol. The violet product is dried at 100°C.

$$Yield = 14–15g$$

(II)

The complex bromide is obtained in 80–90% yield when 0.03 mole of any of the following salts is heated on the steam bath for 2 hours with 25ml of 48% hydrobromic acid:

(1) No. 118 *: $[Co(NH_3)_5CO_3]NO_3 \cdot \frac{1}{2}$-hydrate (8.3g)

(2) No. 116 *: $[Co(NH_3)_5H_2O][NO_3]_3$ (10.4g)

(3) No. 116 b *: $[Co(NH_3)_5H_2O]Br_3$ (12.0g)

(4) No. 116 a *: $[Co(NH_3)_5H_2O]_2[C_2O_4]_3 \cdot 4H_2O$ (9.9g)
   (only 0.015 mole used)

(5) No. 123 a *: $[Co(NH_3)_5NO_2][NO_3]_2$ (9.4g)

The solid is filtered from the cooled reaction mixture and washed, first with 20ml of ice-cold water, then freely with 95% alcohol.

(III)

$$[Co(NH_3)_4Br_2]Br + NH_3 \longrightarrow [Co(NH_3)_5Br]Br_2$$

Ten grams of *trans*-dibromotetramminecobalt (III) bromide (No. 130) are dissolved in 50ml of 10% aqueous ammonia on the steam bath; the greenish salt dissolves to give a red solution. Then the liquid is treated with 50ml of concentrated hydrobromic acid and kept on the water bath for 1–2 hours. The product is filtered off and isolated, as under (II).

Yield = 9g

By heating the aquopentammine bromide to constant weight (2 hours) at 100°C, the bromopentammine bromide is obtained in quantitative yield.

Reference: B:179; I, vol. 1:186.

118. Carbonatopentamminecobalt (III) Nitrate $\frac{1}{2}$-Hydrate *

$$4Co(NO_3)_2 + 4(NH_4)_2CO_3 + 16NH_3 + O_2 \longrightarrow$$
$$4[Co(NH_3)_5CO_3]NO_3 + 4NH_4NO_3 + 2H_2O$$

A solution of 150g of cobalt nitrate 6-hydrate in 75ml of water is mixed with 225g of ammonium nitrate, 225ml of water, and 375ml of concentrated aqueous ammonia (28%).

[It is better to prepare the cobalt nitrate solution by dissolving 60g of cobalt carbonate in portions in 70ml of concentrated nitric acid and filtering the solution; as the crystalline nitrate is deliquescent it may contain considerably more water than indicated by the 6-hydrate.]

The entire reaction mixture, contained in a one-liter flask fitted with stopper and inlet-tube (10mm) is aerated by bubbling a slow stream of air through the liquid for 24 hours. The oxidized solution is then kept at $-10°C$ for 12–24 hours; the freezing compartment of a refrigerator is quite suitable. While the mixture is still very cold, it is filtered by suction; the product is thoroughly drained, then washed with 150ml of 95% alcohol, and finally with ether. The mother liquor is reserved and the washings are rejected. After air-drying, the material is thoroughly ground.

$$\text{Yield} = 83\text{–}90g$$

Although this product is impure, it serves well for other syntheses. It may be recrystallized, with a 66% recovery, from 200ml of water at 90–95°C, washed with 95% alcohol and with ether, then dried at 50°C.

The mother-liquor from the preparation is cautiously added in small portions to one liter of concentrated hydrochloric acid under the hood. As this causes heavy foaming the operation should be carried out in a 3-liter beaker or flask. Without cooling the mixture, it is heated for one hour on the steam bath, cooled in ice, and filtered. The solid is washed with 50ml of ice-cold water and then freely with 95% alcohol and ether.

Yield of chloropentamminecobalt (III) chloride
(No. 119) = 20g

References:
1. I, vol. 4:171.
2. WERNER AND GOSLINGS, Ber., 36:2380 (1903).

119. Chloropentamminecobalt (III) Chloride *

(I)

$$CoCO_3 + 2HCl \longrightarrow CoCl_2 + CO_2 + H_2O$$
$$4CoCl_2 + 4(NH_4)_2CO_3 + 12NH_3 + O_2 \longrightarrow$$
$$4[Co(NH_3)_4CO_3]Cl + 2H_2O + 4NH_4Cl$$
$$[Co(NH_3)_4CO_3]Cl + 2HCl \longrightarrow [Co(NH_3)_4(H_2O)Cl]Cl_2 + CO_2$$
$$[Co(NH_3)_4(H_2O)Cl]Cl_2 + NH_3 \longrightarrow [Co(NH_3)_5H_2O]Cl_3$$
$$[Co(NH_3)_5H_2O]Cl_3 \longrightarrow [Co(NH_3)_5Cl]Cl_2 + H_2O$$

Twenty grams of cobalt carbonate are dissolved in portions in 30ml of concentrated hydrochloric acid and the solution is filtered; alternatively, 40g of cobalt (II) chloride 6-hydrate may be dissolved in 35ml of warm water. The cobalt solution is mixed with 250ml of 10% aqueous ammonia, 50g of ammonium carbonate, and 250ml of water. After thorough agitation, the entire mixture is placed in a one-liter suction flask and a vigorous stream of air is drawn through the purple liquid for at least three hours, whereupon the color changes to deep red; aeration overnight does no harm.

Fifty grams of ammonium chloride are now added and the oxidized mixture is evaporated to a thick paste on the steam bath. Concentrated hydrochloric acid is carefully added until the effervescence of carbon dioxide ceases and the material reacts faintly acidic. Then concentrated ammonia water is added until the acid has been neutralized. After adding 10–15ml more of ammonia, the material is diluted to 400ml with water and heated for one hour on the steam bath. Much insoluble product, as a purple suspension, is already evident at this stage of the preparation. The cooled slurry is transferred to a one-liter flask and 300ml of concentrated hydrochloric acid are slowly mixed in with swirling. Now the flask and contents are reheated on the water bath for one hour longer; on cooling in ice, virtually the entire product crystallizes out, leaving only a faint green-colored supernatant liquid. The solid is filtered off, washed thoroughly with four 25ml portions of cold $6M$ hydrochloric acid, then with 95% alcohol. It is dried at 100°C.

$$Yield = 34\text{--}37g$$

The material so obtained is pure enough for all syntheses. If an analytically pure product is desired it may be prepared with very little loss by recrystallization as follows:

The solid is dissolved in 300 ml of 2% ammonia, warming on the steam bath if necessary. After filtering, any residue is extracted twice with 50ml portions of warm 2% ammonia. The combined ammoniacal extracts are mixed with 300ml of concentrated hydrochloric acid and heated for one hour on the water bath. After cooling in ice, the complex salt is isolated as described.

$$Yield = 30\text{--}34g$$

(II)

See Method II for No. 117. In the case of the aquopent-ammine bromide, 8.4g of the corresponding chloride is used instead. The conditions are one hour of heating on the steam bath with 25ml of 12M hydrochloric acid. Isolation of the product is the same as given. The yields are all in the 85–95% range.

(III)

For the equations involved, see the last three listed under Method (I).

Three grams of carbonatotetramminecobalt (III) nitrate ½-hydrate (No. 128) or 2.6g of the chloride (No. 128, a) are mixed with 40ml of water, and 4.5ml of concentrated hydrochloric acid are slowly added. When the evolution of carbon dioxide has ceased, the red liquid is made slightly alkaline with concentrated ammonia and 5ml in excess are added. The solution is heated for 45 minutes on the steam bath, treated with 50ml of concentrated hydrochloric acid, and reheated for one hour as before. After cooling, the product is separated and washed freely with 95% alcohol.

$$\text{Yield} = 2\text{--}2.5g$$

Finally, the pentammine chloride is easily made in quantitative yield simply by heating aquopentamminecobalt (III) chloride (No. 116, a) to constant weight for 1–2 hours in an oven at 100°C.

(IV)

$$2CoCl_2 + 2NH_4Cl + 8NH_3 + H_2O_2 \xrightarrow{\text{Heat}} 2[Co(NH_3)_5H_2O]Cl_3$$

$$[Co(NH_3)_5H_2O]Cl_3 \xrightarrow{\text{HCl}} [Co(NH_3)_5Cl]Cl_2 + H_2O$$

Twenty-five grams of ammonium chloride are dissolved in 150ml of concentrated aqueous ammonia contained in a one-liter Erlenmeyer flask. The mixture is continuously agitated while 50g of finely powdered cobalt (II) chloride

6-hydrate are added in portions. A yellow-pink precipitate of hexamminecobalt (II) chloride forms as the reddish cobalt chloride dissolves and reacts exothermically. Any air-oxidation which occurs at this point may be ignored.

Without undue delay, 40ml of 30% hydrogen peroxide are added to the warm ammoniacal slurry in a thin stream from a burette. Continuous swirling is essential during the oxidation. All the cobalt (II) ammine dissolves to form a deep red liquid with foaming and further evolution of heat.

When the vigorous effervescence has virtually ceased, 150ml of concentrated hydrochloric acid are cautiously added to the hot well-stirred solution of aquopentammine salt. This operation is performed in the hood because of the heavy ammonium chloride fumes which are given off during the neutralization. Purple product precipitates heavily from the almost boiling reaction mixture leaving a pale green-blue supernatant liquid.

After heating for 15 minutes longer on the steam bath, the flask and contents are cooled to room temperature and suction-filtered, preferably on a fritted funnel of medium-porosity. The orange mother liquor may be discarded.

When the complex salt has been drained well it is washed, first with 100ml of ice-cold water in portions, followed by an equal volume of 6N hydrochloric acid previously chilled to 10°C or below. To facilitate drying, the product is then freely rinsed with 95% alcohol (methyl or ethyl) and with acetone or ether. Drying at 100°C for 1–2 hours completes the conversion of any aquopentammine chloride that may be present to the desired material.

$$\text{Yield} = 48\text{--}50\text{g } (92\text{--}95\%)$$

For use of the complex in preparing cobalt chloride for determining atomic weights, see references 4 and 5.

References:
1. B:172–4; J:378.
2. WILLARD AND HALL, *J. Am. Chem. Soc.*, 44:2220 (1922).
3. SÖRENSEN, *Z. anorg. Chem.*, 5:369 (1894).
4. RICHARDS AND BAXTER, *Ibid.*, 22:222 (1899).
5. BAXTER AND COFFIN, *Ibid.*, 51:171 (1906).

COGNATE PREPARATIONS

119 a. Hydrogen Sulfate Analogue **

$$2[Co(NH_3)_5Cl]Cl_2 + 3H_2SO_4 \longrightarrow [Co(NH_3)_5Cl]_2(HSO_4)_2SO_4 + 4HCl$$

[CAUTION: The operator should wear gloves during the trituration here.]

Five grams of the pentammine chloride (No. 119) are triturated with 12g of concentrated sulfuric acid in a mortar placed under the hood; hydrogen chloride escapes in considerable quantity. The purple mass is dissolved in 40ml of water (pre-heated to 70°C), and filtered. On cooling, the product crystallizes out as reddish prisms. If the mixture is allowed to cool slowly and the product remains under the mother liquor for three days, relatively large crystals can be grown. The salt is filtered, washed with 95% alcohol, and dried at 100°C.

$$Yield = 3g$$

When 95% alcohol is added to the filtrate a fine crystalline precipitate of more product may be obtained.

119 b. Mercury (II) Chloride Double Salt *

$$[Co(NH_3)_5Cl]Cl_2 \cdot 3HgCl_2$$

This compound is prepared as long rose-red needles by mixing saturated aqueous solutions of the chlorochloride and mercury (II) chloride.

Yield quantitative

References:

1. B:174.
2. JÖRGENSEN, J. prakt. Chem. [2], 18:210 (1878).
3. BILTZ AND ALEFELD, Ber., 39:3371 (1916).

120. Fluoropentamminecobalt (III) Nitrate **

$$[Co(NH_3)_5CO_3]NO_3 + 2NH_4HF_2 \longrightarrow [Co(NH_3)_5F]FNO_3 + 2NH_4F + CO_2 + H_2O$$
$$[Co(NH_3)_5F]FNO_3 + NH_4NO_3 \longrightarrow [Co(NH_3)_5F][NO_3]_2 + NH_4F$$

Into a non-vitreous vessel are weighed 3.4g of 48% hydrofluoric acid and this is mixed with a solution of 3g of ammonium fluoride in 25ml of water. Ten grams of carbonatopentamminecobalt (III) nitrate ½-hydrate (No. 118) are added in small portions with stirring. When effervescence has ceased, the contents of the vessel are transferred to a 100ml glass beaker containing 15g of ammonium fluoride.

NOTE: A glass container should be used only if a heat-resistant vessel is not available as the former is slightly etched during the subsequent digestion.

The reaction mixture is now heated at 80–90°C on a *gentle* steam bath for one hour. Because of decomposition, slight quantities of ammonia are evolved during this time. After cooling to room temperature, 75ml of water are added and the liquid is stirred well to redissolve any pink solid that may have settled out on standing. The solution is filtered by suction; insoluble decomposition product remains behind. Twenty grams of ammonium nitrate are dissolved in the filtrate; the reaction mixture almost solidifies with precipitated pink crystals. When the contents of the vessel have cooled to 0°C or below in an ice-salt bath, the product is filtered off and washed with 10ml of ice-cold water, with 95% alcohol, and with ether, and then dried in an ordinary desiccator.

$$\text{Yield} = 6\text{–}7\text{g}$$

Reference: I, vol. 4:172.

121. Iodopentamminecobalt (III) Nitrate *

$$[Co(NH_3)_5H_2O]I_3 \longrightarrow [Co(NH_3)_5I]I_2 + H_2O$$
$$[Co(NH_3)_5I]I_2 + 2NH_4NO_3 \longrightarrow [Co(NH_3)_5I][NO_3]_2 + 2NH_4I$$

The 13g of aquopentamminecobalt (III) iodide obtained in No. 116(c) are heated in an oven at 60–80°C until the material has lost 0.5g in weight; this corresponds to the loss of a molecule of water. The dark purple iodo-iodide (12.5g) is ground in a mortar for 3–5 minutes with a *solution* of 50g of ammonium nitrate in 50ml water. The residue is collected on a filter, returned to the mortar, and reground as before with a fresh portion of aqueous ammonium nitrate. The salt is filtered and washed with ice-cold water in

10ml portions until the filtrate is no longer orange but very faintly greenish. The product is rinsed freely with 95% alcohol and ether and dried *in vacuo*.

$$Yield = 7–7.8g$$

The corresponding **iodo-chloride** and **bromide** may be prepared similarly by grinding the iodide twice with fresh portions of (a) 18.5g of ammonium chloride in 50ml of water at 20°C; and (b) 37g of ammonium bromide respectively in 50ml of water at 20°C.

Reference: I, vol. 4:173.

122. Nitratopentamminecobalt (III) Nitrate *

(I)

$$CoCO_3 + 2HNO_3 \longrightarrow Co(NO_3)_2 + CO_2 + H_2O$$
$$2Co(NO_3)_2 + 2NH_4NO_3 + 8NH_3 + H_2O_2 \longrightarrow 2[Co(NH_3)_5H_2O][NO_3]_3$$
$$[Co(NH_3)_5H_2O][NO_3]_3 \longrightarrow [Co(NH_3)_5NO_3][NO_3]_2 + H_2O$$

Five grams of cobalt carbonate are suspended in 25ml of water, and 12ml of 35% nitric acid are added in small portions to control the effervescence. When all the carbonate has dissolved the liquid is filtered to remove a small dark colored residue.

[A solution of cobalt (II) nitrate may also be prepared by dissolving 12.5g of the 6-hydrate in 35ml of water. Two grams of ammonium nitrate are added followed by 50ml of concentrated aqueous ammonia.]

The mixture is cooled to 10°C in an ice-bath while 5ml of 30% hydrogen peroxide is slowly added dropwise to the continuously swirled solution. When the oxidized liquid has warmed to 20°C, it is gently heated for about 10 minutes on the steam bath until a brown-red color is fully developed. The solution is now transferred to an evaporating dish and heated on the steam bath under the hood for 30 minutes to volatilize much of the excess ammonia. Any brown-black insoluble cobaltic oxide is now filtered off and the filtrate is cooled in ice while 50ml of 35% nitric acid is slowly added.

The bright red liquid is now heated to boiling over a small

flame with constant stirring; red crystals of product begin
to form in quantity. It is preferable to digest the mixture
for one hour on the steam bath. After the mixture has been
thoroughly cooled in ice and filtered, the solid is washed,
first with 25ml of 1:3 nitric acid and water, then freely
with acetone, and it is air-dried.

$$Yield = 7g$$

A small amount of hexammine nitrate contaminates the
product.

References:
1. P:536.
2. JÖRGENSEN, *J. prakt. Chem.*, 23:227 (1881).

(II)

$$[Co(NH_3)_4CO_3]NO_3 + 2HNO_3 + H_2O \longrightarrow [Co(NH_3)_4(H_2O)_2][NO_3]_3 + CO_2$$
$$[Co(NH_3)_4(H_2O)_2][NO_3]_3 + NH_3 \longrightarrow [Co(NH_3)_5H_2O][NO_3]_3 + H_2O$$
$$[Co(NH_3)_5H_2O][NO_3]_3 \longrightarrow [Co(NH_3)_5NO_3][NO_3]_2 + H_2O$$

Ten grams of carbonatotetramminecobalt (III) nitrate
½-hydrate (No. 128) are covered with 100ml of water and
treated dropwise with concentrated nitric acid until evolution of carbon dioxide has ceased; 5–6ml will be required.
The red liquid is made alkaline with concentrated ammonia
and then 15ml are added in excess. The mixture is heated
on the steam bath for 45 minutes and then treated with
125ml of concentrated nitric acid. After digesting for one
hour longer on the boiling water bath, the mixture of
crystals and liquid is cooled in ice and isolated as in (I).

$$Yield = 9–11g$$

(III)

The compound may also be produced by treating 0.03 mole
of materials (1), (2), and (5) as described in (II) for No.
117 with 25ml of 15M nitric acid for 1–2 hours on the steam
bath. The yields are of the order of 80–90%. The complex
nitrate is washed as in the first method given here. By
simply heating aquopentamminecobalt (III) nitrate (see
No. 116) for 18 hours at 100°C a quantitative yield of

product is obtained; 10g of the salt should lose 0.5g of water and yield 9.5g of the desired salt.

Reference: B:172; I, vol. 4:174.

123. Nitropentamminecobalt (III) Chloride *

$$[Co(NH_3)_5Cl]Cl_2 + H_2O \longrightarrow [Co(NH_3)_5H_2O]Cl_3$$
$$[Co(NH_3)_5H_2O]Cl_3 + NaNO_2 \longrightarrow [Co(NH_3)_5NO_2]Cl_2 + NaCl + H_2O$$

Ten grams of chloropentamminecobalt (III) chloride (see No. 119) are dissolved on the steam bath in a mixture of 110ml of water and 10ml of concentrated ammonia; any black residue of cobalt (III) oxide is filtered off.

[Alternatively, 10.7 g of the aquopentammine chloride (No. 116, a) may simply be dissolved in 125ml of warm water. The red solution is made barely acid with the drop-wise addition of concentrated hydrochloric acid; in the case of the ammoniacal solution about 12ml will be required.]

After the solution is cooled to about 50°C, 13g of sodium nitrite are added in small portions; foaming occurs and solid yellowish nitrito salt (see second product following) settles out. The mixture is heated on the steam bath until the precipitate has completely redissolved. On cooling the brown-yellow solution in ice, iridescent crystals of the same color form in quantity. To the cold slurry, 250ml of concentrated hydrochloric acid at 5°C are slowly added. After recooling to 5°C or below, the product is filtered off, washed with 25ml of cold concentrated HCl, and then freely with 95% alcohol and with ether. The complex is air-dried.

Yield = 8–9.5g

References:

1. JÖRGENSEN, Z. anorg. Chem., 17:463 (1898).
2. HARKINS, J. Am. Chem. Soc., 38:2646 (1916).

COGNATE PREPARATIONS

123 a. Nitropentamminecobalt (III) Nitrate *

(I)

$$[Co(NH_3)_5CO_3]NO_3 + NaNO_2 + 2HNO_3 \longrightarrow$$
$$[Co(NH_3)_5NO_2][NO_3]_2 + NaNO_3 + CO_2 + H_2O$$

Ten grams of carbonatopentamminecobalt (III) nitrate ½-hydrate (see No. 118) are suspended in 25ml of water and 10g of sodium nitrite are dissolved in the mixture. Under the hood, 10ml of 35% colorless nitric acid are added very slowly and the slurry is stirred for 15 minutes at room temperature until effervescence has ceased. Two hundred milliliters of methanol are added, the solid is filtered off and washed, first with more of the solvent, then with ether.

$$Yield = 10g$$

(II)

The same salt is also made from the carbonatotetrammine nitrate ½-hydrate (No. 128) by suspending 9.5g of the complex in 25ml of water and adding 7ml of concentrated nitric acid. When no more carbon dioxide is evolved, a mixture of 100ml of water and 10ml of concentrated aqueous ammonia is added and the liquid is heated for 45 minutes on the steam bath. The cooled solution of aquopentammine nitrate is just acidified with concentrated nitric acid and the procedure completed as under (I).

$$Yield = 7-9g$$

References:
1. I, vol. 4:174.
2. JÖRGENSEN, Z. anorg. Chem., 5:147 (1894).

123 b. Nitritopentamminecobalt (III) Chloride *

$$[Co(NH_3)_5Cl]Cl_2 + NaNO_2 \longrightarrow [Co(NH_3)_5ONO]Cl_2 + NaCl$$

Ten grams of chloropentamminecobalt (III) chloride (see No. 119) are treated with dilute ammonia as for the nitro-chloride described previously, and to the faintly acid filtrate are added 10g of sodium nitrite. When the latter has dissolved, 10ml of 6M hydrochloric acid are mixed with the ice-cold solution; the chamois-colored salt that precipitates immediately is allowed to stand under the chilled mother-liquor for 2–3 hours. The solid is filtered off, washed first with 10ml of ice-cold water, and then with 95% alcohol until the washings are acid-free.

$$Yield = 8g$$

During several weeks of standing the complex changes to the nitro salt; this occurs instantaneously if a 10% solution of the compound is mixed with an equal volume of concentrated hydrochloric acid.

Reference: JÖRGENSEN, *Z. anorg. Chem.*, 5:168 (1894).

123 c. Nitrosylpentamminecobalt (III) Salts **

$$[Co(NH_3)_5NO]X_2$$

These pink salts are obtained simply by bubbling nitric oxide, NO (generated from sodium nitrite and dilute sulfuric acid) into ammoniacal solutions of cobaltous salts in the presence of air.

In the absence of air, the corresponding cobalt (II) complexes are formed containing neutral NO groups; the black iodate and chloride are known (reference 4).

For all details see the following papers:

References:
1. WERNER AND KARRER, *Helv. Chim. Acta*, 1:54 (1918).
2. MILWARD et al., *J. Chem. Soc.*, 1938:233.
3. GHOSH AND RAY, *J. Indian. Chem. Soc.*, 20:409 (1943).
4. I, vol. 4:168.

3. TETRAMMINE SERIES

a) *Chromium Compounds*

124. cis and trans-Dichloro bis(ethylenediamine)chromium (III) Chloride ***

cis salt: $[Cren_3]Cl_3 \longrightarrow [Cren_2Cl_2]Cl + en$

[As the decomposition in this reaction is catalyzed by the presence of ammonium chloride, the starting material must be specially treated beforehand by any one of the following methods:

(a) Dissolve 30g of ammonium chloride in the mixture of 95% alcohol and hydrochloric acid used for the decomposition of 96g of $[Cren_3]_2[SO_4]_3$, as described in No. 105.

(b) Recrystallize at 60°C from a saturated (at 20°C) aqueous ammonium chloride solution.

(c) Grind the tris(ethylenediamine)chloride with 2% of its weight of ammonium chloride. This procedure is inferior to the others.]

Five to ten grams of tris(ethylenediamine)chromium (III) chloride 3½-hydrate are spread in a thin even layer on an open Petri dish embedded in a sand bath that carries a thermometer. The bath is maintained at 210°C until the product has lost at least 25% of its original weight (theory = 30.6%). The evolution of amine soon begins and the yellow salt slowly darkens over a period of an hour or two, finally yielding a red-violet material.

The complex salt may be sufficiently purified by simply washing with a *little* ice-cold concentrated hydrochloric acid —about 3ml of acid for each gram of material.

If desired, it may be recrystallized as follows: 4g of the crude material are quickly dissolved in 15ml of water at 70°C and the filtered solution is immediately cooled in ice. Four milliliters of ice-cold concentrated hydrochloric acid are added and the red-violet salt is washed on the filter with 95% alcohol and with ether.

Yield about 3g

The material exists as a monohydrate.

Reference: I, vol. 2:200.

trans salt ** $[Cren_2(SCN)_2]SCN + Cl_2 \longrightarrow [Cren_2Cl_2]Cl$ (partial)

Five grams of recrystallized *trans*-dithiocyanatobis-(ethylenediamine)chromium (III) thiocyanate (see No. 125) are added to 10ml of cold water in a test tube with a side-arm fitted with a stopper and gas inlet tube. The tube and contents are cooled in ice and a stream of chlorine is led in at about 3 bubbles/sec. The orange liquid changes to a brown-red color during the chlorination. The passage of gas is continued only until decomposition is complete, i.e., no further exothermic reaction when the cooling bath is removed. This requires at least 15 minutes. The mixture is filtered and the green residue is triturated with methanol and washed with ether.

Yield = 0.5–1.0g (Crude; contains sulfate)

If the chlorination is continued too long, or run at higher temperatures, only the *cis* compound results.

Reference: PFEIFFER, *Ber.*, 37:4282 (1904).

COGNATE PREPARATION

124 a. Cis-Dichlorobis(ethylenediamine)chromium (III) Bromide *

$cis[Cren_2Cl_2]Br$

Five grams of the *cis*-dichloro-chloride are quickly dissolved in 25ml of water and 50ml of 48% hydrobromic acid are added. After cooling in ice, the red-violet product is filtered off and washed with 95% alcohol and ether.

Yield = 4.5g

125. trans-Bis(thiocyanato)bis(ethylenediamine)- chromium (III) Chloride **

$$[Cren_3][SCN]_3 \xrightarrow{heat} [Cren_2(SCN)_2]SCN + en$$

(a) The starting material is prepared as described in No. 105 b, using ammonium thiocyanate for the metathesis of the triethylenediamine chloride. It should not be recrystallized again from water.

Ten grams of *dl* tris(ethylenediamine)chromium (III) thiocyanate monohydrate are heated at 130–135°C in an open Petri dish as for the *cis*-dichloro chloride (No. 124). The heating may be performed in a sand bath or thermostat oven. When the material has lost at least 16% of its original weight (theory = 18.4%) the decomposition is complete for practical purposes. The crude material is *quickly* recrystallized from water at 50–60°C, filtered, then dried in air.

Yield = 4.5g–5.5g

$$[Cren_2(SCN)_2]SCN + HCl \longrightarrow [Cren_2(SCN)_2]Cl + HSCN$$

(b) Five grams of crude unrecrystallized orange bis-(thiocyanato) thiocyanate are warmed with 70ml of concentrated hydrochloric acid to 40–50°C under the hood until effervescence almost ceases. The warm mixture is quickly filtered through asbestos or sintered-glass and the filtrate is cooled in ice to 5°C. The orange product is washed on the filter with 95% alcohol and ether and air-dried in the absence of direct light. The product must be acid-free.

$$Yield = 3g$$

References:
(a) I, vol. 2:202.
(b) PFEIFFER, *Ber.*, 37:4272 (1904).

COGNATE PREPARATION

125 a. cis-Bis(thiocyanato)tetramminechromium (III) Bromide *

$$[Cr(NH_3)_4(H_2O)Cl]Cl_2 + 2KSCN$$
$$\longrightarrow [Cr(NH_3)_4(SCN)_2]Cl + 2KCl + H_2O$$
$$[Cr(NH_3)_4(SCN)_2]Cl + HBr \longrightarrow [Cr(NH_3)_4(SCN)_2]Br + HCl$$

One and one-half grams of *cis*-chloroaquotetramminechromium (III) chloride (No. 126 b) are added to 4g of potassium thiocyanate in 30ml of water containing 10 drops of glacial acetic acid. The mixture is slowly heated over a small flame just to the boiling point and held there for 3–5 minutes. The clear hot liquid is immediately cooled in ice and 30ml of concentrated colorless hydrobromic acid are stirred in. After recooling to 5°C, the product is filtered and washed free of acid with 95% alcohol followed by acetone to facilitate air-drying.

$$Yield = 1.3g$$

Reference: PFEIFFER, *Z. anorg. Chem.*, 55:366 (1907).

126. Oxalatotetramminechromium (III) Nitrate *

$$[Cr(NH_3)_5H_2O][NO_3]_3 + H_2C_2O_4 \longrightarrow$$
$$[Cr(NH_3)_4C_2O_4]NO_3 + HNO_3 + NH_4NO_3 + H_2O$$

Three grams of oxalic acid 2-hydrate are dissolved in 30ml of an equivolume mixture of water and ethanol. The solution is cooled and 6g of aquopentamminechromium (III) nitrate (No. 112) are stirred in. The mixture is continually stirred for 5 minutes on the steam bath; the orange solid changes to a reddish tint during this time. The product is cooled, and 5ml of 95% alcohol are added; it is then filtered and washed with 25ml more of alcohol.

$$Yield = 5.5g$$

If desired, the complex may be recrystallized as follows; (loss is considerable):

Four and one-half grams of the material (No. 126) are dissolved in 120ml of hot water, faintly acidified with a few drops of acetic acid. The resulting solution is allowed to cool spontaneously to about 40–50°C and then crystallization is initiated by adding 1ml of concentrated nitric acid. After cooling to 5°C the product is washed on the filter with 95% alcohol and with acetone.

$$Yield = 2g$$

References:
1. P:401.
2. WERNER, *Ann.*, 405:220 (1914).
3. PFEIFFER, *Ber.*, 38:3599 (1905).

COGNATE PREPARATIONS

126 a. Oxalatotetramminechromium (III) Bromide *

$[Cr(NH_3)_4C_2O_4]Br$

Prepared similarly to the nitrate. Six grams of finely powdered aquopentammine bromide (No. 112 b) are used with the same amounts of oxalic acid and the alcohol-water mixture. Heating on the steam bath requires 10 minutes; brick-red powder.

$$Yield = 5.5g \text{ (unrecrystallized)}$$

126 b. cis-Chloroaquotetramminechromium (III) Chloride *

$$Cl_2 + H_2C_2O_4 + HNO_3 \ [Cr(NH_3)_4C_2O_4]NO_3 + 3HCl + H_2O \longrightarrow [Cr(NH_3)_4(H_2O)Cl]$$

Three and one-half grams of crude oxalatotetramminechromium (III) nitrate are mixed with 70ml of concentrated hydrochloric acid and the mixture allowed to stand for 24 hours at room temperature with occasional agitation. A deep-violet colored solution soon develops through the

formation of readily soluble $[Cr(NH_3)_4Cl_2]^+$; this under-
goes slow hydrolysis to form the rose product which is only
sparingly soluble in the acid. After cooling in ice, the material is washed on the filter with 95% alcohol and air-dried.

$$Yield = 2.3g$$

The product may be recrystallized by dissolving the salt
in 13–15 times its weight of cold water and adding cold concentrated hydrochloric acid until crystallization begins. The
pure salt has almost the same color as the chloropentammine chloride but is much more soluble in water.

For the outline of a direct method of preparation from
ammonium dichromate and hydrochloric acid, followed by
ammonia, see reference 2.

References:

1. P:402.
2. HECHT, *Präparative Anorganische Chemie*, p. 185, Springer,
Berlin, 1951.

126 c. cis-Bromoaquotetramminechromium (III) Bromide *

$$cis\text{-}[Cr(NH_3)_4(H_2O)Br]Br_2$$

This compound is prepared from 5.5g of oxalatotetram-
mine bromide (No. 126 a) and 75ml of 48% hydrobromic
acid as for the chloroaquo chloride.

$$Yield = 4.5g$$

A quicker method involves warming the mixture at 40°C
for almost 15 minutes; solution takes place and the desired
rose-colored product settles out on cooling in ice.

126 d. Oxalatobis(ethylenediammine)chromium (III) Bromide *

$$2K_3[Co(C_2O_4)_3] + 3en \longrightarrow$$
$$[Cren_2(C_2O_4)][Cren(C_2O_4)_2] + 3K_2C_2O_4$$
$$[Cren_2(C_2O_4)][Cren(C_2O_4)_2] + HBr \longrightarrow$$
$$[Cren_2(C_2O_4)]Br + H[Cren(C_2O_4)_2]$$

Seventy-five grams of potassium trioxalatochromate
(III) 3-hydrate (No. 70) are heated with 240g of 10% (by

weight) ethylenediamine over a small flame. The color of the stirred liquid changes from green to red-violet and after 15–20 minutes a red precipitate starts to form in quantity. The heating is discontinued and the mixture is allowed to cool *spontaneously* to about 45°C after which it is chilled in an ice bath. The solid is filtered off, washed first with ice-cold water until the rinsings are almost colorless, and then with alcohol followed by ether.

Yield = 29g

The air-dried solid is ground *well* in a large mortar for about three minutes with 30ml of concentrated hydrobromic acid. The residual orange solid is thoroughly drained on the filter, and washed with cold 66% alcohol, then with 95% alcohol, and with acetone.

Yield = 19g (almost quantitative)

This crude solid may be recrystallized from about 500ml of water at 50°C, when cooled in ice very well-formed crystals of the pure salt (7g) result. The orange salt is washed on the filter with 95% alcohol and with ether, and then dried in the dark.

Reference: PFEIFFER, *Ber.*, 37:4288 (1904).

126 e. Oxalatobis(ethylenediamine)chromium (III) Iodide *

[Cren$_2$C$_2$O$_4$]I

Twenty grams of potassium trioxalatochromate (III) 3-hydrate are digested with 35ml of 10% ethylenediamine at 90°C for 15 minutes on the steam bath. After cooling in ice, the red double salt (see preceding) is filtered off and washed free of mother liquor. A fritted glass funnel is very suitable in this case. The salt is repeatedly stirred on the filter with 10ml portions of concentrated hydrochloric acid and drained until only a grey-green residue (about 3g) remains; three to four extractions are required. The violet-red filtrate is diluted to 100ml with water and 50g of potassium iodide are stirred in until dissolved. After cooling in ice for about one hour, the orange product is filtered off, washed with 20ml of ice-cold 66% alcohol, then with 95% alcohol, and with acetone. The solid is dried in the dark.

Yield = 11g

Reference: WERNER, *Ber.*, 44:3135 (1911).

126 f. cis-Bromoaquobis(ethylenediamine)chromium (III) Bromide *

$$cis\text{-}[Cren_2(H_2O)Br]Br_2$$

Two and one-half grams of oxalatobromide (126 d) are allowed to stand for 24 hours with 10–15ml of concentrated hydrobromic acid; shake occasionally. An equivolume mixture of alcohol and ether is added to the red-violet mixture until precipitation is complete; the entire mixture is cooled in ice. The reddish solid is washed with 95% alcohol and with ether, and then dried in air.

Yield about 1.5g

The solid is very soluble in water.

Reference: PFEIFFER, *Z. anorg. Chem.*, 56:281 (1907).

b) Cobalt Compounds

127. Carbonatobis(ethylenediamine)cobalt (III) Nitrate *

$$trans\text{-}[Coen_2Cl_2]NO_3 + Na_2CO_3 \longrightarrow [Coen_2CO_3]NO_3 + 2NaCl$$

A solution of 15.6g of *trans*-dichlorodiethylenediamminecobalt (III) nitrate (No. 131 a) in 200ml of hot water is treated with 5.3g of anhydrous sodium carbonate and evaporated on the steam bath to 75ml. The deep red solution is cooled in ice and filtered, then the red solid is washed with methanol and air-dried.

Yield = 10g

More product can be isolated from the mother liquor, but it will be contaminated with sodium chloride.

Reference: PFEIFFER, *Ber.*, 60:308 (1927).

COGNATE PREPARATIONS

127 a. Chloride *

[Coen₂CO₃]Cl

$[Coen_2CO_3]Cl$

Fifty grams of acid-free *trans*-dichlorodiethylenediamine-cobalt (III) chloride (No. 131) are dissolved in the minimum of water at 90°C. If the hot green solution is allowed to stand for a short time it begins to turn purple because of hydrolysis to the *trans*-chloroaquo chloride. To the hot liquid are added 18.5 of anhydrous sodium carbonate and the mixture is stirred until solution is complete. The red liquid is then thoroughly cooled in ice, filtered, and thoroughly drained.

Yield about 40g

The salt may be recrystallized from hot water.

Reference: WERNER, *Ann.*, 386:72 (1912).

127 b. Bromide *

$[Coen_2CO_3]Br$

Ten grams of the carbonato nitrate are dissolved in 25ml of hot water and 8g of potassium bromide are stirred in. The red salt crystallizes out on cooling in ice. It is air-dried after filtering.

Yield = 9.5g

127 c. Sulfitobis (ethylenediamine) cobalt (III) Chloride *

$[Coen_2SO_3]Cl$

(a) A saturated solution of the carbonato chloride in cold water is treated with a stream of sulfur dioxide in a filter flask fitted with a gas inlet. The vessel is kept cold in an ice-water bath. When the evolution of carbon dioxide is over and the liquid has turned yellow-brown, the reaction is complete. 95% alcohol is *slowly* added with cooling until the yellowish solid has fully separated. The yield is over 90%.

(b) Five grams of the acid-free *trans*-dichloro chloride (No. 131) are dissolved in 50ml of water and 2.5g of anhydrous sodium sulfite are added. The green solution which turns brownish-yellow, is stirred until the sulfite has dissolved. While this is cooling in ice one hundred milliliters of 95% alcohol are added slowly and the solid that precipitates is filtered off and drained well. The yellow product is recrystallized by dissolving it in 15ml of hot water, cooling it in ice, and adding 15ml of methanol. The purified material is washed on the filter with methanol and ether.

$$\text{Yield} = 4.5g$$

Reference: WERNER, *Ann.*, 386:81 (1912).

127 d. Sulfatobis(ethylenediamine)cobalt (III) Bromide *

$$[Coen_2SO_4]Br$$

From a burette 27.0ml of 1.00N sulfuric acid are added to a solution of 4.3g of the carbonatobromide (127 b) in 85ml of water. The red solution is evaporated to a very viscous residue on the steam bath. After triturating with methanol in a mortar, the violet product, now in the form of a fine powder, is filtered and rinsed with acetone.

Yield, quantitative

Reference: DUFF, *J. Chem. Soc.*, 453 (1922).

128. Carbonatotetramminecobalt (III) Nitrate 1/2-Hydrate *

$$2Co(NO_3)_2 + 6NH_3 + 2(NH_4)_2CO_3 + \tfrac{1}{2}O_2 \longrightarrow$$
$$2Co(NH_3)_4CO_3NO_3 + 2NH_4NO_3 + H_2O$$

One hundred grams of cobalt (II) nitrate 6-hydrate are dissolved in 100ml of hot water; or 40g of cobalt carbonate are added in portions to a mixture of 50ml of concentrated nitric acid and 50ml of water. The filtered cobalt solution is added to a mixture of 200g of ammonium carbonate in one liter of water and 500ml of concentrated aqueous ammonia. The resulting liquid is transferred to a 2-liter suction flask fitted with a stopper and an inlet tube which reaches almost to the bottom of the vessel. Air is drawn through the deep-violet solution for 3 hours after which time the color has become dark red.

Alternatively, the reaction mixture may be rapidly oxidized by cooling it to 10°C in an ice bath and adding 25ml of 30% hydrogen peroxide slowly from a burette with continued cooling and agitation. The solution from the peroxide oxidation is allowed to stand for 10–20 minutes and then worked up as follows.

The dark red liquid is evaporated on the steam bath to a volume of 500ml while 10g of solid ammonium carbonate are added every 30 minutes. Any black cobaltic oxide that may form is filtered off by suction while the solution is hot and it is then further concentrated to 350ml. The addition of ammonium carbonate is continued during this time; the overall time for the evaporation is 6–7 hours. After cooling in ice, the red product is filtered and the filtrate is set aside. The solid is washed with 75ml of 95% alcohol.

$$Yield = 48–58g$$

If the filtrate is evaporated to 100ml with addition of ammonium carbonate, as before, and cooled in ice, 6–9g of crude material is obtained.

This crop of crystals is contaminated with some carbonatopentammine nitrate which is removed by dissolving the complex in 15 times its weight of water and adding 2–3 volumes of 95% alcohol.

$$Yield = 5–7.5g$$
$$Overall\ Yield = 56–63g$$

Reference: I, vol. 6:173.

COGNATE PREPARATIONS

128 a. Chloride *

[Co(NH₃)₄CO₃]Cl

Forty grams of cobalt carbonate are combined with a mixture of concentrated hydrochloric acid and 40ml of water are used; or a solution of 80g of cobalt chloride 6-hydrate in 100ml of hot water. The oxidized solution is evaporated similarly to the nitrate until the volume is 500ml and then 1250ml of alcohol are added. After cooling in ice, the salt is filtered off and washed, first with 50% alcohol, then with 95% alcohol.

Yield = 48–50g

128 b. Sulfate (3-Hydrate) *

$$[Co(NH_3)_4CO_3]_2SO_4 \cdot 3H_2O$$

This compound is prepared from 40g of cobalt carbonate and 20ml of concentrated sulfuric acid in 130ml of water; or from 94g of cobalt sulfate 7-hydrate in 150ml of water. The procedure is the same as for the nitrate.

Yield = 60–64g

The bromide, iodide, and oxalate may all be prepared similarly by using ⅓ mole of the corresponding cobalt salt or 40g of the carbonate dissolved in the equivalent amount of dilute acid.

References:

1. B:172; J:378.
2. VORTMANN, Ber., 10:1456 (1877).
3. VORTMANN AND BLASBERG, Ibid., 22:2648 (1889).
4. JÖRGENSEN, Z. anorg. Chem., 2:279–283 (1892).

128 c. Chloroaquotetramminecobalt (III) Sulfate *

$$[Co(NH_3)_4(H_2O)Cl]SO_4$$
$$[Co(NH_3)_4CO_3Cl + 2HCl \longrightarrow [Co(NH_3)_4(H_2O)Cl]Cl_2 + CO_2$$
$$[Co(NH_3)_4(H_2O)Cl]Cl_2 + H_2SO_4 \longrightarrow [Co(NH_3)_4(H_2O)Cl]SO_4 + 2HCl$$

Twenty grams of cobalt carbonate are dissolved in a mixture of 30ml of concentrated hydrochloric acid and an equal volume of water; or 40g of cobalt (II) chloride 6-hydrate in 60ml of water are used. The cobalt solution is added to a mixture of 100g of ammonium carbonate in 300ml of water and 250ml of concentrated aqueous ammonia. The entire mixture is oxidized with air for two hours, or treated dropwise with 10ml of 30% hydrogen peroxide at 10°C.

While the liquid is evaporating to 200ml on the steam bath, 5g of solid ammonium carbonate is added every 20–30 minutes. The solution is filtered hot to remove any cobalt

(III) oxide; then it is thoroughly cooled in ice while 250ml of 6M hydrochloric acid is *slowly* added from a tap-funnel with continuous agitation. This is followed under similar conditions by 150ml of concentrated hydrochloric acid. The red liquid (with crystals of carbonato salt) is slowly heated to 60°C (not above) until all the solid has dissolved; then it becomes deep violet-blue in color. Violet chloro-aquo chloride begins to separate, and crystallization is completed by cooling overnight in the ice-box. The crystals are filtered off, washed with 50ml of ice-cold 6M HCl, followed by 95% alcohol and ether, then air-dried.

$$\text{Yield} = 30\text{--}36g$$

The solid is contaminated with small amounts of chloropentammine chloride and dichlorotetrammine chloride, which are removed during the conversion to the sulfate as follows.

Twenty grams of the crude material is shaken with 600ml of water at 15–20°C until nothing more dissolves. The contaminating salts are filtered off and 40g of solid ammonium sulfate are stirred into the filtrate. When the latter has dissolved, the mixture is ice-cooled until separation is complete. The blue-violet product is removed by filtration and washed, first with 25ml of ice-cold water, and then with 95% alcohol.

$$\text{Yield} = 15\text{--}16.5g$$

References:
1. P:545; I, vol. 6:176.
2. JÖRGENSEN, *J. prakt. Chem.*, (2), 42:211 (1890).

129. Diaquotetramminecobalt (III) Nitrate *

$$[Co(NH_3)_4CO_3]NO_3 + 2HNO_3 + H_2O \longrightarrow [Co(NH_3)_4(H_2O)_2][NO_3]_3 + CO_2$$

Ten grams of carbonatotetramminecobalt (III) nitrate ½-hydrate (No. 128) are cautiously added in small portions to 50ml of ice-cold concentrated nitric acid. The slurry must be well stirred during this time to break up larger particles of the starting material. When evolution of carbon dioxide has ceased the red-violet mixture is treated with 50ml of acetone and cooled in ice. The product is filtered, pressed well, and washed with 95% alcohol and with ether.

Drying *in vacuo* over solid alkali gives an almost quantitative yield of product.

Reference: Vortmann, *Ber.*, 15:1893 (1882).

Cognate Preparation

129 a. Chloride *

$[Co(NH_3)_4(H_2O)_2]Cl_3$

Five grams of pure carbonatotetramminecobalt (III) chloride (No. 128, a) are dissolved in 25ml of water and 10ml of 6M hydrochloric acid are added dropwise with stirring until evolution of gas has ceased. Then the red-violet liquid is cooled to 5°C and 100ml of ice-cold concentrated hydrochloric acid is added; the product separates almost completely. The supernatant acid solution is carefully decanted and the solid is brought onto the filter with alcohol and washed with the same solvent until the rinsings are quite *free* of acid. The product is air-dried.

Yield = 5.5g

Reference: Hecht, *Präparative Anorganische Chemie*, p. 173, Springer, Berlin, 1951.

129 b. Dinitratotetramminecobalt (III)
Nitrate Monohydrate *

Five grams of the carbonato nitrate ½-hydrate are added in portions to 60ml of concentrated nitric acid and warmed on the steam bath until all the solid has dissolved. Cooling in ice precipitates the product, which is washed thoroughly on the filter with alcohol and ether, and then dried *in vacuo* over alkali.

Yield = 2g

Reference: Birk, *Z. anorg. Chem.*, 164:241 (1927).

129 c. Bromoquotetramminecobalt (III) Bromide *

$[Co(NH_3)_4(H_2O)Br]Br$

Ten grams of the carbonato nitrate ½-hydrate [or the sulfate 3-hydrate (see No. 128 Cognates)] are mixed with 50ml of water, and 15g of 48% hydrobromic acid (No. 88) are slowly added. When evolution of gas has ceased, 25g more of the acid is mixed with the red-violet solution and the whole is heated on the steam bath at 60°C until the liquid is colored dark-violet and crystals of the same color begin to form. Twenty grams of ammonium bromide are stirred into the liquid. (Any solid previously present in the reaction mixture should have dissolved before this point.) The solution is allowed to stand in the cold overnight, then filtered and the product is washed free of acid with 95% alcohol. The material may contain small amounts of the dibromotetrammine bromide (No. 130).

Yield about 10g

Reference: WERNER, *Ber.*, 38:2011 (1905).

129 d. Trichromatotetramminecobalt (III) *

$$[\{Co(NH_3)_4\}_2\{CrO_4\}_3]$$

A solution of 13.5g of diaquotetramminecobalt (III) nitrate in 200ml of water at 30°C is treated with 100ml of N potassium chromate.

$$2[Co(NH_3)_4(H_2O)_2][NO_3]_3 + 3K_2CrO_4 \longrightarrow$$
$$\{[Co(NH_3)_4]_2(CrO_4)_3\} + 6KNO_3 + 4H_2O$$

The product precipitates immediately and separation is completed after standing 15–30 minutes in ice. The dark-yellow solid is washed on the filter with small portions of cold water until the washings are almost colorless and then irrigated with acetone to facilitate air-drying.

Yield = 7g

Reference: BRIGGS, *J. Chem. Soc.*, 73 (1919).

130. trans-Dibromotetramminecobalt (III) Bromide *

$$[Co(NH_3)_4CO_3]NO_3 + 3HBr \longrightarrow [Co(NH_3)_4Br_2]Br + HNO_3 + CO_2 + H_2O$$

Twenty grams of carbonatotetramminecobalt (III) nitrate ½-hydrate (No. 128) are added in portions to 80g of 48% hydrobromic acid (No. 88) in a capacious vessel. The mixture is constantly agitated over a *small* flame, whereupon the color changes first to red-brown, then to pale brown, and finally to a dull green. When there is no more change in color (15–20 minutes), discontinue heating immediately and cool the slurry in ice. The grass-green product is filtered off on a hardened paper or sintered glass, and washed with 25ml portions of ice-water until the filtrate is no longer violet (due to the bromoaquo salt) but runs through virtually colorless. After rinsing with 95% alcohol and with ether, the material is vacuum-dried over solid alkali to remove traces of water and acid.

$$Yield = 24–27g$$

Until now it has been impossible to isolate the *cis*-dibromo salt presumably because of the relatively large volume of the bromine atom.

Reference: B:179.

131. cis- and trans-Dichlorobis(ethylenediamine)cobalt (III) Chloride **

$$4CoCl_2 + 8en + 6H_2O + O_2 \longrightarrow 4[Coen_2(OH)H_2O]Cl_2$$
$$trans\text{-}[Coen_2(OH)H_2O]Cl_2 + 2HCl \longrightarrow Coen_2Cl_2Cl\cdot HCl + 2H_2O$$
$$trans\text{-}[Coen_2Cl_2]Cl \xrightarrow[\text{in solution}]{\text{heat}} cis\text{-}[Coen_2Cl_2]Cl$$

One hundred and sixty grams of cobalt (II) chloride 6-hydrate in 500ml of water are added to a mixture of 540ml of water with 60g of anhydrous ethylenediamine. The reddish solution is transferred to a 2-liter suction flask fitted with a stopper and a gas-inlet tube reaching almost to the bottom of the vessel. A vigorous stream of air is drawn through the liquid for 6 hours; the color becomes dark ruby-red.

The oxidized solution is placed in a large evaporating dish and 350 ml of concentrated hydrochloric acid are added. The volume is concentrated to 550ml on the steam bath in the hood, and then cooled in ice; the salt [Coen_2Cl_2]Cl·HCl· $2H_2O$ is obtained as bright-green plates which are thoroughly drained on the filter. Any crusts of product that form earlier in the evaporation are ignored.

$$Yield = 93–103g$$

If the mother liquor is further evaporated to 300ml additional impure product is obtained, which is contaminated with tris(ethylenediamine)cobalt (III) chloride and ethylenediamine dihydrochloride. After it is dried at 100°C, the yield is about 18g of solid.

The main product, just described, is ground in a large mortar with methyl alcohol; the color changes to a pale green as the acid of crystallization is lost. Drying at 105–120°C completes the conversion to the neutral anhydrous trans-salt.

Yield = 83–93g

Cis-Form

The neutral trans-salt is dissolved in the minimum of water at 90°C and evaporated to dryness on the steam bath, (or preferably in an air bath at 103–105°C). The residue is re-treated with the same volume of hot water as before, and the evaporation is repeated.

The yield is about 70g of a pure violet powder which is less soluble in water than the corresponding trans-salt. Any of the latter that contaminates the product may be washed out with a very little ice-cold water until the residue is no longer dark-colored but pure violet.

The cis dichloro salt may be readily resolved as the d-α-bromocamphor-II-sulfonate. Only the l-form is recoverable.[5]

References:

1. I, vol. 2:222.
2. JÖRGENSEN, J. prakt. Chem. [2], 39:24 (1898).
3. WERNER, Ber., 34:1733 (1901).
4. USPENSKY AND TSCHIBISOFF, Z. anorg. Chem., 164:329 (1927).
5. (a) I, vol. 2:224; (b) BAILAR AND AUTEN, J. Am. Chem. Soc., 56:774 (1934).

COGNATE PREPARATIONS

131 a. trans-Nitrate *

trans-[Coen₂Cl₂]NO₃

A saturated solution of the green chloride (No. 131) in ice-cold water (to minimize hydrolysis) is immediately suction-filtered into a large excess of cold concentrated nitric acid. The green nitrate precipitates immediately in crystalline form. It is only slightly soluble in cold water and almost insoluble in nitric acid. It is washed with alcohol and ether.

Yield over 90%

131 b. trans-Dichlorobis(propylenediamine)cobalt (III) Chloride **

trans-[Copn$_2$Cl$_2$]Cl

One hundred and fifty grams of cobalt (II) chloride 6-hydrate are dissolved in one liter of water and added to a solution of 50g of anhydrous propylenediamine in two liters of water. The slightly cloudy brownish-red liquid is vigorously air-oxidized for 6–8 hours.

The red solution that results is treated with one liter of concentrated hydrochloric acid and evaporated in the hood to a volume of about 850ml. After cooling in ice overnight, the dark-green hydrochloride of the product separates and is filtered off on a fritted glass funnel. The solid is drained thoroughly, converted to the neutral *trans*-salt by dissolving it in the minimum volume of alcohol at room temperature, and slowly adding ether until precipitation of the powdery pale green salt is complete. The mother liquor is colored blue. The salt is dried *in vacuo* over solid alkali.

Yield = 35–37g

A similar procedure applied to diethylenetriamine and dipropylenetriamine yielded only green hygroscopic solids which dissolved in alcohol with a green color, and in water to form brown solutions. They were insoluble in acetone and are presumably the following diaminecobalt (III) complexes as double salts with cobalt chloride:

[Coden$_2$]Cl$_3$·CoCl$_2$ and [Codpn$_2$]Cl$_3$·CoCl$_2$

131 c. cis-Dichlorotriethylenetetraminecobalt (III) Chloride *

cis-[CotetCl$_2$]Cl

Forty grams of cobalt (II) chloride 6-hydrate are dissolved in 125ml of water and added to a solution of 18g of triethylenetetramine in 160ml of water. The solution is air-oxidized for six hours and then treated with 90ml of concentrated hydrochloric acid. After evaporating on the steam bath to a total volume of 150ml (ignoring crystal formation) and cooling in ice, the purple complex is filtered off, drained well, and washed, first with 25ml of cold 6M hydrochloric acid, followed by 95% alcohol. It is dried *in vacuo* over alkali.

$$\text{Yield} = 12.5g$$

Reference: WERNER, *Ber.*, 40:2228 (1907).

131 d. Chlorothiocyanatobis(ethylenediamine)cobalt (III) Salts *

cis- and *trans*-[Coen$_2$(SCN)Cl]$^+$

trans-[Coen$_2$Cl$_2$]Cl + KSCN $\longrightarrow$ *trans*-[Coen$_2$Cl$_2$]SCN + KCl

trans-[Coen$_2$Cl$_2$]SCN $\xrightarrow[\text{H}_2\text{O}]{\text{Heat}}$ *cis*- and *trans*-[Coen$_2$(SCN)Cl]Cl

$\xrightarrow[\text{2) KSCN}]{\text{1) Filter }cis\text{-}}$ *trans*-[Coen$_2$(SCN)Cl]SCN

Twenty grams of neutral *trans*-dichlorobis(ethylenediamine)cobalt (III) chloride (No. 131) are suspended in 30ml of water and 6.8g of potassium thiocyanate is added to the green solution. A green precipitate of the thiocyanate immediately forms. The mixture is warmed on the steam bath; the suspension turns grey, and finally all the solid dissolves to yield a bluish-red solution. After the vessel is cooled in ice and the walls are scratched, the *cis*-product crystallizes out; it is filtered off and then washed with 15ml of ice-cold water.

$$\text{Yield} = 11.5g$$

When the mother liquor, without the washings, is treated with 6.8g more of KSCN, the *trans* thiocyanate precipitates out; this is washed first with 50% aqueous alcohol, and then with 95% solvent.

$$\text{Yield} = 8\text{--}10g$$

Reference: WERNER, *Ann.*, 386:133ff. (1912).

131 e. Chloro(anilino)bis(ethylenediamine)cobalt (III) Chloride *

$$[Coen_2(C_6H_5NH_2)Cl]Cl_2$$

Five grams of neutral *tr*-dichloro chloride are stirred to a smooth paste with 5ml of water, and 5ml of pure aniline are added. The mixture is allowed to stand for one hour; the color changes from green to red and the reaction mixture almost solidifies. The material is triturated with methanol to a light-red powder, filtered, and washed with ether. The yield is almost quantitative.

The *p*-toluidine homologue is produced similarly from 5g of the complex, 2g of the amine, and 3ml of water. After standing for two days, during which time any large particles that form must be ground up, the material is isolated as described.

Reference: GMELIN, *Handbuch der Anorganischen Chemie*, No. 58B, Verlag Chemie, Berlin, 1930.

132. cis- and trans-Dichlorotetramminecobalt (III) Chloride **

$$cis \text{ Form: } [Co(NH_3)_4CO_3]Cl + 2HCl \xrightarrow{\text{alcohol}} cis\text{-}[Co(NH_3)_4Cl_2]Cl + CO_2 + H_2O$$

One hundred milliliters of absolute ethyl alcohol are placed in a gas-absorption flask and saturated at 0°C with hydrogen chloride under the hood. Eighty grams of this solution is shaken with 40g of finely powdered carbonatotetramminecobalt (III) chloride (No. 128 a) at room temperature until the evolution of carbon dioxide is complete. The gray-blue solid is immediately filtered off and washed with 100ml of absolute alcohol. A pale violet powdery solid remains which is dried *in vacuo* over alkali.

Yield quantitative (as the ½-hydrate)

The purification of the salt is tedious and attended by considerable loss, but it may be carried out as follows:

Five grams of the crude product is leached on the filter with about 5–10ml of ice-cold water. Any *trans*-dichloro material remains behind and the filtrate is run directly onto

4–5g of very finely powdered sodium dithionate 2-hydrate (see No. 47). The violet mixture is stirred until no more precipitate of the pale-purple dithionate forms. The latter is separated from the denser excess of sodium dithionate by making a slurry with a few ml of ice-water, and then filtered. Even with rapid work, only about 2g of cis-[Co(NH₃)₄Cl₂]₂S₂O₆ is obtained, because of attendant hydrolysis of the cation to the chloroaquo salt.

The dithionate precipitate then obtained is ground in a mortar with 4g of ammonium chloride and 4ml of water until the salt has become dark blue. The solids are filtered off and treated dropwise with ice-cold water until, with continued stirring, no more crystals of NH₄Cl are noticeable. The pale blue supernatant liquid is decanted; as long as ammonium chloride is present, the desired product is virtually insoluble in water. The solid is stirred with 5ml of ice-cold water until it dissolves and is then instantly suction-filtered into a slurry of 5g of ammonium chloride in 5ml of water. The reprecipitated complex chloride is freed from the denser NH₄Cl by gently swirling and is filtered off. It is freed from contaminating salt by moistening it on a clay plate with two successive 1ml portions of ice water, pressing the violet-blue product well dry each time.

Yield 1–1.5g

Reference: WERNER, *Ann.*, 386:103 (1912); *Ber.*, 40:4821 (1907).

$$\text{trans-Form: } [\text{Co(NH}_3)_4(\text{H}_2\text{O})\text{Cl}]\text{SO}_4 + \text{HCl} \longrightarrow [\text{Co(NH}_3)_4\text{Cl}_2]\text{HSO}_4 + \text{H}_2\text{O}$$
$$\text{trans-}[\text{Co(NH}_3)_4\text{Cl}_2]\text{HSO}_4 + \text{HCl} \longrightarrow \text{trans-}[\text{Co(NH}_3)_4\text{Cl}_2]\text{Cl} + \text{H}_2\text{SO}_4$$

(I)

Five grams of chloroaquotetramminecobalt (III) sulfate (No. 128 c) are added to 25ml of concentrated sulfuric acid and the mixture is allowed to stand two to three hours at room temperature. The violet solution is cooled in ice and 25ml of concentrated hydrochloric acid are added slowly from a tap-funnel under the hood. [CAUTION: Gloves should be worn during this operation as much hydrogen chloride is evolved.] After standing overnight in a stoppered flask at normal temperature, the almost colorless supernatant liquid is decanted from the green solid. The latter is brought onto the filter with 20% sulfuric acid, washed with a little of the same solvent, and then with alcohol.

Yield of *trans*-dichloro bisulfate, almost quantitative

(II)

Four grams of carbonatotetramminecobalt (III) chloride (No. 128 a) are treated at 0°C with 25ml of ice-cold concentrated hydrochloric acid to form the chloroaquochloride. When evolution of gas has ceased, the violet slurry is treated with 25ml of concentrated sulfuric acid dropwise under the hood; cooling is maintained. The mixture is allowed to remain in a closed vessel for two to three days until the solid is pure green in color. The *trans*-dichloro bisulfate is isolated as under (I).

$$Yield = 5g$$

The desired *chloride* is formed when a cold saturated solution of the bisulfate is filtered into an excess of cold concentrated hydrochloric acid or a saturated solution of ammonium chloride.

References:
1. P:546.
2. JÖRGENSEN, *Z. anorg. Chem.*, 14:415 (1897).
3. WERNER AND KLEIN, *Ibid.*, 14:29 (1897).

133. cis- and trans-Dinitrodiethylenediaminecobalt (III) Nitrate *

cis-Form: $K_3Co(NO_2)_6 + 2en \longrightarrow [Coen_2(NO_2)_2]NO_2 + 3KNO_2$
$2 \ cis\text{-}[Coen_2(NO_2)_2]NO_2 + 2HNO_3 \longrightarrow$
$$2 \ cis\text{-}[Coen_2(NO_2)_2]NO_3 + NO_2 + NO + H_2O$$

Twenty grams of sodium hexanitrocobaltate (III) (No. 73) are dissolved in 200ml of water and 15g of potassium acetate in 100ml of water are added. The light-yellow potassium salt that precipitates immediately is washed on the filter with alcohol and acetone.

Yield quantitative (22g)

Twenty grams of this material is added to a mixture of 5g of anhydrous ethylenediamine in 45ml of water. The mixture is heated on the steam bath and continuously stirred until the temperature rises to 60–70°C. The complex potassium salt begins to dissolve and a dark-brown solution is formed; further heating is unnecessary when the reaction starts. The mixture is filtered hot to remove traces of unreacted starting material and is then cooled to below 0°C in an ice-salt bath to precipitate the brown *cis*-dinitro nitrite. Twenty milliliters of 95% alcohol are added to the slurry to increase the amount of precipitate. The solid is filtered off and washed with acetone.

The nitrite is suspended in 15ml of water and 3ml of concentrated nitric acid are cautiously added dropwise under the hood. The mixture is warmed to 40°C and stirred until no more oxides of nitrogen are evolved. The yellow slurry is cooled in ice and filtered; the product is washed with methanol and with acetone.

Crude yield = 3.5g

The complex may be recrystallized twice from water below 60°C to yield about 2g of an analytically pure product.

trans-Form: $4Co(NO_3)_2 + 6en + 2en \cdot 2HNO_3 + 8NaNO_2 + O_2 \longrightarrow$
$4 \, trans\text{-}[Coen_2(NO_2)_2]NO_3 + 8NaNO_3 + 2H_2O$

Five grams of anhydrous ethylenediamine are dissolved in 12ml of ice-cold water, and 3ml of concentrated nitric acid are added. The cooled, partly neutralized, solution is mixed with 11.5g of cobalt (II) nitrate 6-hydrate, and 6g of sodium nitrite in 20ml of water.

When all the solids have dissolved, the mixture is transferred to a 50ml filter flask fitted with a stopper and a wide (10mm) gas-inlet tube, and air is drawn through the solution for 20–30 minutes. The yellow crystalline product begins to separate after a few minutes of aeration. When the oxidation is complete, the mixture is cooled to 0°C (or below) in an ice-salt bath, and filtered.

The crude product is recrystallized from the minimum volume of water at 95°C, washed with alcohol and ether on the filter, then air-dried.

Yield = 9–11g

The *trans* salt may be distinguished from the *cis* complex because it forms precipitates in aqueous solutions with chromate, oxalate, or thiosulfate ions; the *cis* salt reacts negatively under these conditions.

The *cis*-dinitro nitrate has been resolved into its optical isomers [2] as proof of configuration.

References:
1. I, vol. 4:176.
2. WERNER, *Ber.*, 44:2445 (1911); I, vol. 6: 195.

134. cis- and trans-Dinitrotetramminecobalt (III) Nitrate *

(I)

cis-Form: $[Co(NH_3)_4CO_3]NO_3 + 2HNO_2 \longrightarrow [Co(NH_3)_4(NO_2)_2]NO_3 + CO_2 + H_2O$

Ten grams of carbonatotetramminecobalt (III) nitrate ½-hydrate (No. 128) are dissolved in a mixture of 105ml of water and 8g of concentrated nitric acid. The salt dissolves with the evolution of carbon dioxide to form the diaquotetrammine nitrate which is deep-red in solution. Twenty grams of sodium nitrite are added in small portions to the liquid which is then heated on the steam bath until the color of the solution changes to a dark yellow-brown; the operation requires seven to eight minutes. The reaction mixture is immediately cooled in ice, under the hood, and a mixture of 80ml of concentrated nitric acid and 50ml of water is slowly added; heavy foaming occurs and oxides of nitrogen are evolved. After standing overnight, the mixture of neutral and acid product is filtered off and washed, first with 20ml of cold 1:1 water and nitric acid, followed by 95% alcohol.

The solid is recrystallized from 15ml of hot water containing a few drops of acetic acid and washed with 95% alcohol on the filter. Light-brown crystals are obtained.

$$\text{Yield} = 6.5\text{–}8g$$

(II)

$2[Co(NH_3)_4(H_2O)Cl]SO_4 + 4HNO_2 \longrightarrow$
$\qquad\qquad cis\text{-}[Co(NH_3)_4(NO_2)_2]_2SO_4 + H_2SO_4 + 2HCl + 2H_2O$

Ten grams of chloroaquotetramminecobalt (III) sulfate (No. 128 c) are added to a solution of 20g of sodium nitrite in 100ml of water followed by 3ml of glacial acetic acid. The color begins to change to a brown tint and the reaction is completed by heating for ten minutes on the steam bath. After cooling in ice, 25ml of alcohol are added to the dark brown liquid, which causes the dinitro sulfate to separate. The solid is washed on the filter with 10ml of ice-cold water, followed by 50ml of 95% alcohol.

$$Yield = 7g$$

The salt may be recrystallized as in Method (I).

References:
1. B:179; J:378; P:547.
2. JÖRGENSEN, Z. anorg. Chem., 5:162 (1894); 17:473 (1898); 11:430 (note) (1896).

trans-Form: $4CoCl_2 + 4NH_4Cl + 8NaNO_2 + 12NH_3 + O_2 \longrightarrow$
$4[Co(NH_3)_4(NO_2)_2]Cl + 8NaCl + 2H_2O$
$trans\text{-}[Co(NH_3)_4(NO_2)_2]Cl + NH_4NO_3 \longrightarrow$
$trans\text{-}[Co(NH_3)_4(NO_2)_2]NO_3 + NH_4Cl$

One hundred grams of ammonium chloride and 135g of sodium nitrite are dissolved in 750ml of water, and 100ml of concentrated aqueous ammonia are added. To this mixture is added a solution of 90g of cobalt (II) chloride 6-hydrate in 250ml of water, and the whole is transferred to a 2-liter suction flask with a stopper and gas-inlet tube at least 10mm in diameter. Air is drawn vigorously through the liquid which slowly becomes dark brown during the four hours required for the oxidation. The preparation is allowed to stand overnight; as the product is somewhat photosensitive, it is advisable to shield the reaction mixture from direct light.

The orange crystals are filtered off, and washed with 50ml portions of ice-cold water until the last part of the filtrate no longer gives a test for nitropentammine salt with 10ml of 5% aqueous ammonium oxalate solution. As a rule, the quantity of pentammine salt produced is small but it is unwise to neglect the test, which simply depends on the great difference in solubility of the pentammine and tetrammine oxalates. The crude solid, consisting of approximately equal parts of the dinitro chloride and nitrate (from the oxidation of nitrite), is washed with 95% alcohol and air-dried.

$$\text{Yield} = 55\text{–}70g$$

The solid is placed in a 3-liter flask and 2 liters of boiling water containing 5ml of acetic acid are added. The mixture is carefully heated over a free flame with continual agitation, until no more solid dissolves; all of the chloride present dissolves but much of the sparingly soluble nitrate remains behind. Prolonged heating should be avoided. Two hundred and fifty grams of ammonium nitrate are dissolved in the hot liquid and the mixture cooled immediately in ice. After standing in the cold for at least six hours, the product is filtered off, washed with 95% alcohol, and air-dried.

References:
1. B:180; J:378; P:537.
2. JÖRGENSEN, Z. anorg. Chem., 17:468 (1898).

The cis and trans dinitrotetrammine salts may be readily distinguished by gently boiling 0.5g of each salt with 10ml of concentrated hydrochloric acid. The cis salt gives a green precipitate of trans dichloro chloride, and the trans complex yields red chloronitro chloride (see next section).

COGNATE PREPARATIONS

134 a. cis-Chloride *

cis-[Co(NH₃)₄(NO₂)₂]Cl

One gram of the corresponding nitrate is dissolved in 30ml of warm water and 2g of ammonium chloride are added. One hundred milliliters of 95% alcohol are then stirred in slowly. After standing overnight, the yellow crystals are filtered off, washed with cold 50% aqueous alcohol, and with acetone.

$$\text{Yield} = 0.9g$$

Reference: B:180; HECHT, p. 181.

134 b. trans-Chloride *

To prepare the corresponding chloride, the crude crystals from the oxidation are dissolved in hot water (slightly acidified with acetic acid) allowing 400ml of water for each 20g of solid. This solution is then treated with 40g of ammonium chloride and cooled immediately. The salt is isolated as described previously.

Yield, variable

134 c. Chloronitrotetramminecobalt (III) Chloride *

$$[Co(NH_3)_4Cl(NO_2)]Cl$$

Eleven grams of crude *trans*-dinitrotetrammine chloride, obtained directly from the air-oxidation in (II) are warmed with 100ml of concentrated hydrochloric acid to 40–45°C in the hood. When a steady evolution of nitrogen oxides begins, the vessel is allowed to stand without further heating until *no* more gas is given off; it is advisable to shake the suspension occasionally. The color of the solid changes through orange to a brick-red as the reaction proceeds. After cooling in ice, the solid is washed on the filter with 95% alcohol and with ether, then air-dried.

Yield = 10g

Reference: JÖRGENSEN, *Z. anorg. Chem.*, 5:194 (1894); 7:290 (1894); 17:468 (1898).

134 d. Nitrothiocyanatotetramminecobalt (III) Chloride *

$$[Co(NH_3)_4(NO_2)SCN]Cl$$

Ten grams of *trans*-chloronitrotetrammine chloride (see preceding compound) are dissolved in 200ml of water at 80°C, and 8.5g of potassium thiocyanate are stirred in. The product settles out rapidly from the hot liquid. After this is cooled in ice, 50ml of cold concentrated hydrochloric acid are added to complete the separation of solid. The latter is filtered off, washed with 95% alcohol, and air-dried.

Yield = 10g

Reference: WERNER, *Z. anorg. Chem.*, 22:111 (1900).

135. Thiosulfatobis(ethylenediamine)cobalt (III) Bromide 3-Hydrate *

$$[Coen_2CO_3]Br + BaS_2O_3 \longrightarrow [Coen_2S_2O_3]Br + BaCO_3$$

A suspension of 4.2g of barium thiosulfate monohydrate (No. 37) in 100ml of water is mixed with 5g of carbonato-diethylenediaminecobalt (III) bromide (No. 127 b) and the mixture is stirred mechanically for one hour on the steam bath. The barium carbonate is filtered off and the red filtrate evaporated to dryness in an oven at 45–50°C over a period of two to three days.

Yield quantitative (6.5g)

For the preparation of the thiosulfatopentammine salts see references 2 and 3. This series of salts decomposes after several months with the evolution of H_2S.

References:
1. DUFF, J. Chem. Soc., 1922:453.
2. GMELIN, Handbook of Inorganic Chemistry, No. 58B.
3. RAY, Quart. J. Ind. Chem. Soc., 4:66–71 (1927).

4. TRIAMMINE SERIES

a) Chromium Compounds

136. Dichloroaquotriamminechromium (III) Chloride *

Two grams of triamminechromium (IV) oxide (No. 137) are covered with 30ml of cold glacial acetic acid and the stirred mixture is cooled in ice until it partly freezes. Then 20ml of ice-cold concentrated hydrochloric acid are stirred in and the slurry is cooled for 10–15 minutes in ice with occasional stirring. The blue-violet solid is filtered off, washed with 95% alcohol and with ether, and then dried for 15–30 minutes at 60°C.

Yield = 1.1g

A small quantity of chlorodiaquotriamminechromium (III) chloride may be isolated from the mother liquor by the addition of 95% alcohol and ether. This may be converted into No. 136 by drying at 100°C.

References:
1. WERNER, *Ber.*, 39:2663 (1906).
2. RIESENFELD, *Ibid.*, 39:4229 (1906).

COGNATE PREPARATION

136 a. Trichlorotriamminechromium (III) *

Five and one-half grams of triamminechromium (IV) oxide (No. 137) are added in small portions to 50ml of concentrated hydrochloric acid at 5°C with continual stirring. When the reaction is over, the gray-green precipitate is filtered off and washed with alcohol and ether. A further portion of blue-green solid may be obtained by keeping the mother liquor at −10°C overnight. The combined solids are dried at 150°C for 2 hours; the powdery material becomes greener in color.

Total yield = 2.5g

Reference: WERNER, *Ber.*, 43:2290 (1910).

137. Triammniechromium (IV) Oxide *

$$(NH_4)_2Cr_2O_7 + 4NH_3 + 2H_2O_2 \longrightarrow 2[CrO_4 \cdot 3NH_3] + 3H_2O$$

Thirty grams of finely powdered ammonium dichromate are dissolved in a mixture of 110ml of concentrated ammonia and 190ml of water. The yellow solution is allowed to stand at 0°C overnight and any precipitated ammonium chromate is rapidly filtered off from the cold liquid. While stirring continuously and maintaining the temperature of the solution at −5–0°C by means of an ice-salt bath, 25ml of 30% hydrogen peroxide are added dropwise from a buret. The reaction mixture becomes dark in color and is allowed to stand for at least 12 hours longer at 0°C. The dark-brown crystalline product is filtered off and washed with ice-cold alcohol and ether, then dried *in vacuo* over sulfuric acid.

Yield = 6g

References:
1. HOFMANN, *Ber.*, 38:3060 (1905).
2. RIESENFELD, *Ibid.*, 38:4070 (1905).
3. WIEDE, *Ibid.*, 30:2180 (1897).

b) Cobalt Compounds

138. Bromochloroaquoethylenediamineamminecobalt (III) Bromide *

[CoenNH₃Cl₂H₂O]Cl + 2HBr ⟶ [CoenNH₃ClBrH₂O]Br + 2HCl

Five grams of dichloroaquoethylenediamineamminecobalt (III) chloride (No. 139) are quickly dissolved in 25–30ml of water at 0–5°C and filtered into an equal volume of 48% hydrobromic acid cooled in ice. The olive-green product separates rapidly and, after standing in the cold for about 15 minutes, it is filtered off and dried *in vacuo* over solid alkali.

Yield = 2g

The material has the greatest known number of different coordinated groups around the central cobalt atom.

Reference: WERNER, *Ber.*, 38:4039 (1905).

COGNATE PREPARATIONS

138 a. Bromochloroaquotriamminecobalt (III) Bromide *

[Co(NH₃)₃H₂OClBr]Br

This compound is prepared similarly to No. 138, using 5.0g of dichloroaquotriamminecobalt (III) chloride (No. 139) and 35ml of water.

The filtrate is run into an equal volume of 48% hydrobromic acid. The chocolate-brown monohydrate of the desired product is precipitated; this is filtered off, pressed well, and dried for one hour at 110°C to remove the water of hydration. Olive powder.

Yield = 3–4g

Reference: WERNER, *Ber.*, 37:4705 (1904).

138 b. Bromochloroaquopropylenediamminecobalt (III) Bromide **

[CopnNH₃H₂OClBr]Br

Ten milliliters of absolute alcohol are saturated at 0°C

with dry hydrogen bromide (No. 88) and mixed with an equal volume of absolute alcohol.

Two grams of dichloroaquopropylenediamineamminecobalt (III) chloride (No. 139 b) are *quickly* ground up with 15ml of the ethanolic acid solution and transferred without delay to a small stoppered Erlenmeyer flask. The slurry is allowed to stand at room temperature overnight and then 10ml of absolute ether are added. The mixture is cooled in ice for about 30 minutes and then filtered on a sintered glass funnel. Without allowing the olive-green product to drain dry, the solid is washed carefully with 20–30ml of an equivolume mixture of absolute alcohol and dry ether until the washings run through virtually colorless. Unless all adhering traces of acid are washed out, the product absorbs water vapor vigorously from the air and becomes gummy. The moist material is expeditely transferred to a vacuum desiccator and dried over solid alkali.

$$\text{Yield} = 1.5g$$

139. Dichloroaquotriamminecobalt (III) Chloride **

$$2[Co(NH_3)_3(NO_2)_3] + 6HCl \longrightarrow 2[Co(NH_3)_3H_2OCl_2]Cl + 3NO + 3NO_2 + H_2O$$

[CAUTION: This entire experiment should be performed in the hood and rubber gloves should be worn as a protection from escaping hydrogen chloride.]

(a) An ice-cold mixture of sulfuric and hydrochloric acids should be prepared as follows: 200ml of concentrated hydrochloric acid are placed in a 500ml suction flask, fitted with a dropping funnel, and cooled in ice. One hundred milliliters of concentrated sulfuric acid are rapidly added dropwise with only occasional swirling to avoid excessive loss of hydrogen chloride vapors.

After standing in ice for 10–15 minutes longer, the mixture is transferred to a 500ml wide-mouth flask immersed in ice.

Twenty grams of trinitrotriamminecobalt (III) (No. 144) are ground well in a mortar.

(b) Twenty grams of urea (to remove oxides of nitrogen) are stirred into the acid mixture, followed by the trinitro complex in about 2g portions. During this time, cooling and agitation are maintained. The flask is now fitted with a 2-hole stopper carrying a thermometer that extends into the slurry and a gas-outlet tube about 6 inches long. The reaction mixture is allowed to warm up to room temperature; the color changes from yellow through red and brown to greenish. The evolution of gas (mainly nitrogen, with some oxides) becomes increasingly vigorous as the flask is now warmed to 35–40°C with frequent agitation. When the effervescence has largely abated, the temperature is raised to 50–55°C and maintained in this range until the suspension turns grass-green and no more gases are evolved; this requires from 30–45 minutes. The mixture is thoroughly cooled in ice, 250ml of cold 95% alcohol are added, and the re-cooled product is suction-filtered, preferably through a medium-size fritted-glass funnel. The olive-green crystals are washed with alcohol and acetone, then dried in air.

$$\text{Yield} = 14\text{--}17.5g$$

The product obtained here is entirely satisfactory for further syntheses, but it may be recrystallized, if desired, as follows [2c]

Ten grams of the complex are dissolved in 150ml of water that is acidified with several drops of hydrochloric acid. This solution is filtered, and 50ml of 6M HCl are slowly added. After this mixture stands for three hours without agitation, 50ml more of acid are added. During the next 12 hours, four more 50ml portions of acid are added at 3-hour intervals *without stirring or shaking*. The mixture is allowed to remain in the refrigerator for 24 hours, then filtered, washed with cold 6M HCl and with absolute alcohol, and dried in a desiccator over alkali.

$$\text{Yield} = 6\text{--}8.5g$$

References:
1. P:542; I, vol. 6:180.
2. (a) JÖRGENSEN, Z. anorg. Chem., 5:187 (1894); (b) 14:418 (1897); (c) 17:475 (1898).
3. MEYER et al., Ibid., 139:357 (1924).

COGNATE PREPARATIONS

139 a. Dichloroaquoethylenediamineamminecobalt (III) Chloride **

$[CoenNH_3H_2OCl_2]Cl$

The initial part of the procedure is similar to the preceding, except that 9g of powdered trinitroethylenediamineamminecobalt (III) (No. 143) and 9g of urea are used together with 50ml of concentrated sulfuric acid and 100ml of 12M hydrochloric acid. The mixture is allowed to warm to room temperature and stand at this point for about 30 minutes until all the solid dissolves, yielding a black-green solution. If necessary, the liquid is filtered with *gentle* suction through fritted glass, and cooled in ice while first 150ml of alcohol and then a similar volume of ether are slowly added with stirring. When the mixture has cooled to 5°C, it is filtered; the gray-green product is washed freely with 95% alcohol and with ether, then dried *in vacuo*.

Yield $= 7$g

Reference: WERNER, *Ber.*, 38:4037 (1905).

139 b. Dichloroaquopropylenediamineamminecobalt (III) Chloride ***

$[CopnNH_3H_2OCl_2]Cl$

Fifty milliliters of absolute alcohol are saturated with dry hydrogen chloride at 0°C.

[CAUTION: For the next step in the procedure wear gloves and work in the hood.]

Six grams of trinitropropylenediamineamminecobalt (III) (No. 143) are *rapidly* and *thoroughly* triturated in a mortar with three 15ml portions of the alcoholic HCl and immediately transferred to a small loosely-stoppered flask and allowed to stand overnight. The solid in the slurry should be grass-green in color by this time; otherwise the mixture is allowed to stand longer with occasional agitation. About 50ml of ether are added to the ice-cooled slurry and the olive-green solid is filtered off and washed thoroughly with 30–50ml of a 1:1 alcohol-ether mixture. During filtration, the solid should not be allowed to drain quite dry, as it is very deliquescent in this condition. While the product is still moist it is transferred to a vacuum desiccator and dried over solid alkali.

139 c. Dichloroaquotriamminecobalt (III) Hydrogen Sulfate *

$$[Co(NH_3)_3H_2OCl_2]HSO_4$$

Ten grams of dichloroaquotriamminecobalt (III) chloride are ground in the hood with 100g of ice-cold $9M$ sulfuric acid. [CAUTION: Gloves must be worn as hydrogen chloride is liberated.] The green slurry is filtered through sintered glass, washed freely with 95% alcohol and with acetone, and then dried *in vacuo*.

Yield = 10.5–11g

Reference: Jörgensen, Z. anorg. Chem., 14:418 (1897).

139 d. Chlorodiaquotriamminecobalt (III) Sulfate *

$$[Co(NH_3)_3(H_2O)_2Cl]SO_4$$

Five grams of the preceding material are stirred with 35ml of water at room temperature for about 30 minutes. The blue-violet solution is filtered and cooled in ice while 70ml of alcohol are added. When the product has separated completely, it is filtered off and washed with 95% alcohol and with acetone.

Yield about 2g

Reference: Jörgensen, Ibid., p. 421.

140. Chlorodinitrotriamminecobalt (III) *

$$2[Co(NH_3)_3(NO_2)_3] + 2HCl \longrightarrow$$
$$2[Co(NH_3)_3(NO_2)_2Cl] + NO + NO_2 + H_2O$$
$$NO + NO_2 + CO(NH_2)_2 \longrightarrow CO_2 + 2N_2 + 2H_2O$$

Ten grams of trinitrotriamminecobalt (III) (No. 144) are ground in portions with a solution of 5g of urea in 150ml of water. The slurry is transferred to a beaker under the hood and stirred mechanically while 100ml of concentrated hydrochloric acid is run in very slowly from a separatory funnel. The beaker and contents should be kept at 25°C during this step by cooling with a water bath. The latter may now be removed; evolution of gas is vigorous at first but it slackens after about 30 minutes. The temperature rises spontaneously to 35–40°C and the color of the mixture changes through orange to a bright red. After one hour, when all effervescence has ceased, the vermilion product is filtered off and washed with 95% alcohol and with acetone.

$$Yield = 8–9g$$

The solid may be recrystallized from 3M hydrochloric acid at 50°C. Above 60°C the compound hydrolyzes to $[Co(NH_3)_3(NO_2)_2H_2O]Cl$.

References:

1. P:541.
2. JÖRGENSEN, Z. anorg. Chem., 7:310 (1894); 13:180 (1897).

COGNATE PREPARATIONS

140 a. Bromodinitrotriamminecobalt (III) *

$$[Co(NH_3)_3(NO_2)_2Br]$$

Five grams of the dinitrochloro complex are stirred with 100ml of water and 5 drops of glacial acetic acid at 5°C until no more solid dissolves. While cooling and stirring is maintained, 50ml of 48% hydrobromic acid are added dropwise from a tap-funnel. After being stirred five minutes longer, the dark-red solid is washed on the filter with acetone.

$$Yield = 3.6g$$

Reference: JÖRGENSEN, Z. anorg. Chem., 7:315 (1894).

140 b. Tetranitrosulfatobis[triamminecobalt (III)] *

$$\{[Co(NH_3)_3]_2(NO_2)_4SO_4\}$$

Five milliliters of $9N$ sulfuric acid are added dropwise with stirring to a solution of 2.3g of dinitrochlorotriamminecobalt (III) in 45ml of water at 40°C containing two drops of acetic acid. A yellow precipitate forms which increases in quantity on cooling in ice. Then 25ml of 95% alcohol are stirred in and after the mixture has been chilled to 5°C, the solid is filtered off and washed with acetone.

$$Yield = 1.4g$$

Reference: As for preceding.

141. Nitrooxalatotriamminecobalt (III) *

$$[Co(NH_3)_3(NO_2)_3] + H_2C_2O_4 \longrightarrow [Co(NH_3)_3C_2O_4(NO_2)] + NO + NO_2 + H_2O$$

A mixture of 10g of trinitrotriamminecobalt (III) (see No. 144) and an equal weight of oxalic acid 2-hydrate in 80ml of water are heated on the steam bath in a covered flask or beaker for 30–60 minutes until no more gases are evolved upon frequent agitation. The solid is cooled in ice, filtered, and then washed freely with 95% alcohol and with acetone.

$$Yield = 6–8g$$

The same method may be used to prepare nitrooxalato-ethylenediamineamminecobalt (III):

$$[CoenNH_3(NO_2)C_2O_4]$$

However, in this case, the hot reaction mixture is filtered by suction before cooling.

Reference: WERNER, *Ann.*, 405:236 (1914).

COGNATE PREPARATIONS

141 a. Chlorooxalatotriamminecobalt (III) ½-Hydrate *

$$[Co(NH_3)_3C_2O_4Cl]\frac{1}{2}H_2O$$

Five grams of oxalic acid 2-hydrate are warmed at 50°C with 50ml of (1:1) alcohol-water until solution is complete.

Five grams of *finely* powdered dichloroaquotriamminecobalt (III) chloride (No. 139) is *sifted* into the solution and stirred well at 50°C for three to four minutes, taking care to break up any lumps. The gray-blue solid is cooled immediately, filtered off, and washed with 95% alcohol and with ether.

Yield = 3.6–4.3g

141 b. Chlorooxalatoethylenediamineamminecobalt (III)

[CoenNH₃(C₂O₄)Cl]

This compound is made by the same procedure except that 95% alcohol is used as the solvent. Also, for a quantitative yield, it is best to use anhydrous oxalic acid.

References:

1. P:544.
2. Jörgensen, Z. anorg. Chem., 11:434 (1896).

141 c. Oxalatoaquotriamminecobalt (III) Nitrate *

$[Co(NH_3)_2C_2O_4(H_2O)]NO_3$

$[Co(NH_3)_2C_2O_4Cl] + AgNO_3 + H_2O \longrightarrow [Co(NH_3)_2C_2O_4(H_2O)]NO_3 + AgCl$

One and one-half grams of chlorooxalatotriamminecobalt (III) ½-hydrate are stirred into 10ml of water containing 1g of silver nitrate. The mixture is heated at 60–70°C until the silver chloride has completely coagulated. After cooling and filtering, the purple filtrate is allowed to evaporate to dryness at room temperature.

For the preparation of the non-electrolyte, [Co(NH₃)₃-C₂O₄(SCN)], see reference 2.

Yield, quantitative

References:

1. Werner, Z. anorg. Chem., 15:162 (1897).
2. Werner, Ann., 405:236 (1914).

142. Trichlorotriamminecobalt (III) *

[Co(NH₃)₃Cl₃]

Dichloroaquotriamminecobalt (III) chloride (No. 139) is heated in a thin layer at 150°C in an oven until the loss in weight corresponds to one mole of water; i.e., 10g should lose 0.75g in weight. During the drying period the salt changes from an olive color to bright green; 1½–3 hours of heating are required. The complex is only very slightly soluble in cold water but hydrates after some time to re-form the starting material.

A complex series of reactions leading to very small yields of this compound can be outlined as follows:

$$[Co(NH_3)_3H_2OCl_2]Cl \xrightarrow{KOH} [Co_2(NH_3)_6(OH)_3]Cl_3 \xrightarrow[-30°C]{HCl} [Co(NH_3)_3Cl_3]$$

Reference: BIRK, Z. anorg. Chem., 175:411 (1928).

143. Trinitroethylenediamineamminecobalt (III) *

(I)

$$[Co(NH_3)_3(NO_2)_3] + en \longrightarrow [CoenNH_3(NO_2)_3] + 2NH_3$$

Twenty grams of trinitrotriamminecobalt (III) (No. 144) are stirred with 62g of 10% aqeous ethylenediamine in a 250ml flask and carefully heated over a free flame until the yellow solid has almost completely dissolved to give a deep yellow-brown solution with rather sudden and vigorous evolution of ammonia. When the reaction is over the mixture is cooled to room temperature and filtered to remove unreacted starting material. The filtrate is evapo-rated to crystallization (about 25ml) on the steam bath, cooled, and filtered, and the yellow solid is washed thor-oughly with 15ml of cold water, adding the washings to the mother liquor. The latter is then evaporated to a thick paste and washed three times with 10ml of cold water. The combined product is washed with 95% alcohol and with ether.

Crude yield = 9g

The solid may be recrystallized, if desired, from 30 times its weight of boiling water (faintly acidified with acetic acid); it should be cooled quickly. The remaining material in the product as prepared is converted to dinitrobis(ethyl-enediamine)cobalt (III) nitrite (see No. 133).

(II)

$$K[Co(NH_3)_2(NO_2)_4] + en \longrightarrow [Coen(NH_3)(NO_2)_3] + KNO_2 + NH_3$$

Twenty-four grams of potassium tetranitrodiamminecobaltate (III) (No. 146) are added to 300ml of water at 60°C and stirred until solution is complete. Then 5g of anhydrous ethylenediamine are stirred in at 60°C for about three minutes until precipitation of the yellow complex

$$[Coen_2(NO_2)_2][Co(NH_3)_2(NO_2)_4]$$

is complete. About 11g of the latter is removed by filtering while hot and then evaporating the filtrate to crystallization. The solid is washed with water, alcohol, and ether.

Crude yield = 12g

References:
1. WERNER, *Ann.*, 386:256 (1912); *Helv. Chim. Act.*, 1:10 (1918).
2. WERNER, *Ber.*, 38:4036 (1905).

COGNATE PREPARATIONS

In the preceding and all succeeding preparations, the product can easily be distinguished from the similar starting material by the far greater solubility of the product in concentrated hydrochloric acid.

143 a. Trinitropropylenediamineamminecobalt (III) *

$$[Copn(NH_3)_3(NO_3)]_3$$

Twenty-two grams of trinitrotriamminecobalt (III) and a mixture of 8.5g of anhydrous propylenediamine in 60ml of water are used. The procedure is exactly the same here as in (I) on No. 143, except that *two* crops of product are isolated before it is finally evaporated to a thick paste on the water bath.

Crude yield = 11g

Recrystallization as for the *en* compound (No. 143).

143 b. Diethylenetriamine Analogue *

$[Co_3den_2(NH_3)_3(NO_2)_9]$

Twenty grams of the trinitro non-electrolyte are added to 7g of diethylenetriamine and 63g of water. The filtered solution is evaporated to 20–25ml and allowed to cool slowly, breaking up any crusts of crystals formed. The solid is filtered off and washed with 40ml of water. When combined aqueous washings and mother liquor are evaporated to 20ml more product is isolated. The solids are washed with 95% alcohol and with ether.

Total yield = 6.0g

Recrystallization as for the preceding.

143 c. Dipropylenetriamine Analogue *

$[Co_3dpn_2(NH_3)_3(NO_2)_9]$

Twenty grams of trinitrotriamminecobalt (III) and 9g of amine in 10% aqueous solution are employed. This is evaporated and filtered and the washings are combined with the mother liquor; and these steps are repeated until no more water-insoluble material is obtained and the liquid has finally become a thick syrup. After the last evaporation, the cooled liquid is triturated with 25ml of cold water to isolate more product.

Combined yield = 6g

Two grams of the complex are quickly recrystallized from 60ml of boiling water containing two drops of acetic acid.

Yield = 1.6g

143 d. Triethylenetetramine Analogue *

$[Co_2tet(NH_3)_2(NO_2)_6]$

This compound is prepared similarly using 7.5g of amine and 60ml of water.

Yield = 7.9g

Recrystallization from 100ml of boiling water containing a few drops of acetic acid gave 5.5g of pure product.

144. Trinitrotriamminecobalt (III) **

$$2Co(C_2H_3O_2)_2 + 6NaNO_2 + 2NH_4C_2H_3O_2 + 4NH_3 + H_2O_2 \longrightarrow$$
$$2[Co(NH_3)_3(NO_2)_3] + 6NaC_2H_3O_2 + 2H_2O$$

Fifty grams of pure cobalt carbonate are prepared by slowly adding a saturated solution of the equivalent quantity of the chloride, nitrate, or sulfate to a hot solution of 60g of anhydrous sodium carbonate in 600ml of water. Some effervescence takes place. The mixture is digested at the boiling point with continual stirring for at least 15 minutes and then suction-filtered, washed freely with hot water, and pressed as dry as possible on the filter. Alternatively, 51g of technical cobalt carbonate may be dissolved in the minimum amount of 6M hydrochloric acid (about 140ml), filtered, and reprecipitated as described.

The purified cobalt carbonate is now dissolved in a hot mixture of 70ml of glacial acetic acid and 140ml of water. This solution is then added to a cold mixture of 105g of sodium nitrite, 500 ml of concentrated aqueous ammonia, and 3.5g of activated charcoal. The resulting solution is cooled to 10°C in ice while 280ml of 3% hydrogen peroxide are slowly added with good agitation. After standing for 20 minutes longer in the cold, the oxidized liquid, contained in a 2-liter Erlenmeyer flask, is heated over a free flame in the hood for one hour with frequent swirling; much ammonia escapes and the volume is kept constant by the addition of water as necessary. The hot liquid is filtered rapidly by suction to remove the charcoal, and the filtrate is cooled in an ice bath. The product that separates (crystallization is aided by scratching the walls of the vessel) is filtered, washed with alcohol and with ether, and then air-dried.

The mother liquor is treated with 3g more of charcoal and evaporated to 650–700ml over a flame with mechanical stirring. More product can be isolated from the filtrate if this is filtered while hot, and treated as previously described.

Total yield = 55–57g

The product may be rapidly recrystallized from thirty times its weight of boiling water faintly acidified with acetic acid. An analytically pure sample is obtained in this way, but for most syntheses the material obtained here is quite satisfactory.

References:
1. B:183; P:539; I, vol. 6:189.
2. ERDMANN, *J. prakt. Chem.*, 97:412 (1866).
3. JÖRGENSEN, *Z. anorg. Chem.*, 5:185 (1894); 7:308 (1894); 17:475 (1898).
4. DUVAL, *Compt. rend.*, 182:636 (1926).

5. DIAMMINE SERIES

145. Ammonium Tetrakis(thiocyanato)diammine chromate (III) Monohydrate *

(Reinecke's Salt)

$$NH_4[Cr(SCN)_4(NH_3)_2] \cdot H_2O$$

Two hundred grams of ammonium thiocyanate are placed in a suitably sized evaporating dish and gently heated at 140–150°C over a small flame until the salt completely fuses. While stirring with a thermometer 34g of finely-powdered ammonium dichromate are sifted onto the melt in small portions. The fusion is stirred well after each addition and a further portion of the salt is stirred in only when the vigorous frothing has subsided. The temperature of the reaction mixture rises to about 160°C during this time, especially at the beginning of the dichromate addition. External heating may be temporarily discontinued during the first part of the fusion but it should be resumed later in order to keep the temperature of the melt at about 160°C.

The purple liquid is allowed to cool and solidify in a desiccator to avoid deliquescence and it is then broken up quickly with a spatula and transferred to a beaker containing 125g of ice with which the solid is well stirred. Because of the presence of much excess ammonium thiocyanate the temperature falls below 0°C (negative heat of solution). When the mixture has spontaneously warmed, with occasional stirring, to the point where only a *small* piece of ice remains, the red solid is filtered off by suction and drained well without washing.

The crude solid is added to 500ml of water at 70°C and stirred continuously while the temperature is raised again to 60–65°C. The purple-red solution is then immediately filtered by suction into an ice-cooled flask, and rapidly cooled to 5°C. The complex salt is filtered off, drained well, and air-dried.

Yield = 50–60g

The red solid remaining on the filter is the so-called Morland's salt, or the guanidinium salt of the complex anion:

$$HNC(NH_2)_2 \cdot H[Cr(NH_3)_2(SCN)_4]$$

which is formed by the thermal decomposition of ammonium thiocyanate:

$$2NH_4SCN \longrightarrow HNC(NH_2)_2 \cdot HSCN + H_2S$$

If potassium dichromate is used instead of the ammonium salt, approximately an equal weight of a mixture of the potassium and ammonium salts of the reineckate anion is obtained. The free solid acid may be readily made by decomposing the barium salt with sulfuric acid followed by ether extraction.

For the preparation of the $[Cr(NH_3)_2(SCN)_3(NO)]^-$ anion, see reference 5(b).

References:
1. P:403.
2. REINECKE, Ann., 126:113 (1863).
3. WERNER AND HOBLIK, Ibid., 406:276 (1914).
4. WERNER AND KLEIN, Ber., 35:283 (1902).
5. WERNER AND RICHTER, (a) Z. anorg. Chem., 15:249 (1897); (b) Ibid., 243.
6. Organic Syntheses, vol. 15, p. 75, Wiley, New York, 1935.

COGNATE PREPARATION

146. Ammonium Tetranitrodiamminecobaltate (III) Monohydrate **

(Erdmann's Salt)

$$4CoCl_2 + 8NH_4Cl + 4NH_3 + 16NaNO_2 + O_2 \longrightarrow$$
$$4NH_4[Co(NH_3)_2(NO_2)_4] + 16NaCl + 2H_2O$$

One hundred grams of ammonium chloride and 135g of sodium nitrite are dissolved in 750ml of water and mixed with a solution of 90g of cobalt (II) chloride 6-hydrate in 250ml of water. Then 25ml of concentrated ammonia are added and the entire mixture is aerated *vigorously* for 1½ hours in a 2-liter filter flask fitted with a stopper and a gas-inlet tube.

The brown oxidized solution is filtered and allowed to evaporate spontaneously for at least five days in several large crystallizing dishes in layers of liquid about one inch deep. After this time, large brown crystals of product have formed as well as a fine orange-yellow contaminating crystalline powder:

$$[Co(NH_3)_4(NO_2)_2][Co(NH_3)_2(NO_2)_4]$$

This may now be removed, together with the bulk of the mother liquor, by gentle swirling and decantation; the coarse crystals of the desired material remain behind in the vessel. The ammonium salt is drained on the filter and ground up. It is then stirred with five successive 70ml portions of water at 45–50°C until only a small residue of the impurity mentioned remains behind. The combined aqueous extracts are filtered and concentrated by vacuum distillation (from a water bath at 40°C) to about 200ml. After the residual solution, together with any product that has settled out, has been allowed to evaporate further at room temperature for several days, the large glistening brown crystals are filtered off and air-dried.

Yield = 60–70g

References:
1. P:548.
2. JÖRGENSEN, Z. anorg. Chem., 17:476 (1898).

146 a. Potassium Tetranitrodiamminecobaltate (III) *

$$K[Co(NH_3)_2(NO_2)_4]$$

$$4CoCl_2 + 4NH_4Cl + 4NH_3 + 16NaNO_2 + O_2 \longrightarrow$$
$$4Na[Co(NH_3)_2(NO_2)_4] + 12NaCl + 2H_2O$$
$$Na[Co(NH_3)_2(NO_2)_4] + KCl \longrightarrow K[Co(NH_3)_2(NO_2)_4] + NaCl$$

A solution of 40g of cobalt (II) chloride 6-hydrate (0.168

mol.) in 100ml of water is added to a mixture of 60g of sodium nitrite (0.87 mol), 15g of ammonium chloride (0.28 mol), and 12ml of concentrated aqueous ammonia (ca. 0.18 mol), in 300 ml of water. The mixture is placed in a one-liter filter flask fitted with a stopper and a 10mm i.d. inlet tube reaching down to about one-half inch from the bottom of the flask. Air is drawn vigorously for 1½ hours through the suspension which is then suction-filtered (Celite or Filter-Cel is recommended) to remove the pink deposit of basic cobalt (II) salt.*

The filtrate, which is colored deep yellow-brown is treated with 30g of potassium chloride and allowed to stand in a large (12–15 inch) evaporating dish for 2 days.

The coarse brown crystals of product, admixed with a little light yellow powder, are filtered from the pale-colored mother liquor and dissolved in 250ml of water at 60°C by shaking for a few minutes.

The mixture is suction-filtered while hot; the yellow contaminant remains behind. The extract must be cooled in ice as soon as possible to avoid decomposition; lustrous yellow-brown crystals of product settle out slowly. These are filtered off, the filtrate is reserved, and the solid is washed with 95% alcohol.

To the filtrate are added 10g of potassium chloride; the remainder of the potassium salt soon precipitates as a yellowish microcrystalline powder. This material is filtered, washed with two 10ml portions of ice-water, followed by 95% alcohol.

Total yield = 16–21g (30–40% based on cobalt (II) chloride taken)

Reference: B:150.

6. MONOAMMINE SERIES

147. Sodium Pentacyanoammineferrate (II) x-Hydrate **

$$[Fe(CN)_5NO]^{2-} + 2OH^- \longrightarrow [Fe(CN)_5NO_2]^{4-} + H_2O$$
$$[Fe(CN)_5NO_2]^{4-} + NH_3 \longrightarrow [Fe(CN)_5NH_3]^{3-} + NO_2^-$$

* This represents 40–50% of the original amount of cobalt (II) salt; it is washed with water, dissolved in dilute hydrochloric acid, and precipitated as cobalt (II) carbonate by adding 10% aqueous sodium carbonate to the cobalt (II) chloride solution at the boiling point.

Thirty grams of sodium pentacyanonitrosylferrate (II) 2-hydrate (No. 74) are covered with 120ml of ice-cold water in a 250ml suction flask with a gas-inlet tube and a thermometer. The flask is cooled in an ice-salt bath while a steady stream of ammonia (3 bubbles/sec) is led in under the hood. Care must be taken that the temperature does not rise above 20°C during this time because decomposition would occur; the optimum range is 8–12°C. When no more gas is absorbed at this temperature, (indicated when the level of the liquid fails to rise in the inlet tube as the current of gas is interrupted), the dark yellow-brown solution is allowed to stand at 0°C for about 2 days. The amber-colored crystalline product separates with attendant evolution of gas,

$$(NH_3 + NO_2^- \longrightarrow N_2 + OH^- + H_2O).$$

This is filtered off, then dried *in vacuo.*

$$Yield = 25g$$

The salt may be purified by dissolving it in the minimum of water at 15–20°C and cooling in ice with stirring while 95% alcohol is added dropwise.

References:
1. HECHT, *Präparative anorganische Chemie,* p. 158, Springer, Berlin, 1951.
2. MANCHAT, *et al., Ber.,* 45:2876 (1912).
3. HOFMAN, *Z. anorg. Chem.,* 10:264 (1895).

7. POLYNUCLEAR SERIES

148. dl-Tris[tetrammine-μ-dihydroxocobalt (III)] cobalt (III) Bromide **

Five grams of *trans*-dibromotetramminecobalt (III) bromide (No. 130) are suspended in 20–25ml of water contained in a 150ml beaker. The mixture is cautiously warmed, with *continual* stirring, over a very small flame or hot plate. A purple liquid containing the green starting complex is formed as the latter hydrates to the bromoaquo salt. The suspension then turns brown and vigorous foaming begins. After 5–10 minutes the last traces of starting material dissolve rather abruptly, and effervescence also ceases, yielding a brown clear liquid. The solution is heated and stirred for one minute longer and is then rapidly cooled in ice. The black-brown crystals of the product that separate are filtered off and washed with 95% alcohol.

Yield, about 1g

This purely inorganic compound was resolved into its isomers by Werner as final proof that optical activity was the property of the central coordinating atom only.

For the preparation of the sulfate of the series, see reference 4.

References:

1. WERNER, *Ber.*, 40:2113 (1907).
2. WERNER, *Ibid.*, 47:3087 (1914) ; gives resolution.
3. MOELLER, *Inorganic Chemistry*, p. 265, Wiley, New York, 1952.
4. I, vol. 6:176.

149. Potassium bis[dioxalato-μ-hydroxocobaltate (III)] 3-Hydrate **

$$CoCO_3 + K_2C_2O_4 + H_2C_2O_4 \longrightarrow K_2[Co(C_2O_4)_2] + CO_2 + H_2O$$
$$K_2[Co(C_2O_4)_2] + H_2O_2 \longrightarrow K_4[Co_2(C_2O_4)_4(OH)_2]$$

To a mixture of 25g of potassium oxalate monohydrate and 7.5g of oxalic acid 2-hydrate dissolved in 80ml of hot water, are added 7.0g of cobalt carbonate in small portions, allowing the foaming to subside after each addition. A red-purple solution of potassium dioxalatocobaltate (II) is formed which is stable only in an excess of oxalate ions. The liquid is boiled for a few minutes, then filtered hot by gentle suction, and transferred to a 250ml beaker. Nine grams more of potassium oxalate are dissolved in the re-heated liquid and the solution is cooled to 60°C, while 30ml of 6% hydrogen peroxide are slowly added dropwise from a burette; the heat of oxidation maintains the temperature of the reaction mixture within the required range of 60–65°C and the addition of peroxide should be regulated accordingly. The solution turns deep green in color and considerable foaming occurs; towards the end of the reaction the green product begins to separate from the hot solution and unless this is removed periodically with a "policeman" it will adhere obstinately to the walls of the beaker.

When the addition is complete, the green slurry is cooled

to 20°C (*not* lower) and filtered at once. The solid is washed on the filter with cold 1:1 alcohol-water and finally with 95% alcohol. It is dried in air.

$$\text{Yield} = 7\text{–}10\text{g}$$

References:
1. P:551.
2. DURRANT, *J. Chem. Soc.*, 87:1787 (1905).
3. PERCIVAL AND WARDLAW, *Ibid.*, 101:2628 (1929).

COGNATE PREPARATION

149 a. Dioloctamminedicobalt (III) Chloride **

$$[Co(NH_3)_4H_2OCl]SO_4 + NH_3 + H_2O \longrightarrow [Co(NH_3)_4(OH)(H_2O)]SO_4 + NH_4Cl$$
$$[Co(NH_3)_4(OH)H_2O]SO_4 \longrightarrow [Co_2(NH_3)_8(OH)_2][SO_4]_2 + 2H_2O$$
$$[Co_2(NH_3)_8(OH)_2][SO_4]_2 + 4NH_4Cl \longrightarrow [Co_2(NH_3)_8(OH)_2]Cl_4 + 2(NH_4)_2SO_4$$

Twelve grams of chloroaquotetramminecobalt (III) sulfate (No. 128 c) are dissolved in 200ml of N aqueous ammonia, filtered if necessary, and treated *immediately* with 400ml of ice-cold 95% alcohol in portions. The hydroxoaquotetrammine complex precipitates as red crystals in the form of the monohydrate. These are filtered off, washed first with 67% alcohol, then with 95% alcohol and finally air-dried.

$$\text{Yield} = 10\text{g}$$

This salt is heated at 100°C to constant weight. The theoretical loss in weight (one molecule of water) for the 10g obtained is 0.65g. Five grams of the dioloctamminesulfate so produced are ground in a mortar with 25ml of water and 10g of ammonium chloride. If the dehydration at 100°C has been carried to completion, no smell of ammonia should be noticeable at this point. The deep-red solid is filtered off, and the contaminating undissolved ammonium chloride is removed by re-grinding the material with 20ml of water in a mortar. The filtered product is dissolved in 100ml of water; if a completely clear red solution is not formed, filtration is necessary. Four grams of ammonium chloride are stirred into the liquid; the desired salt precipitates almost quantitatively in pure form. It is dried *in vacuo*.

$$\text{Yield} = 3\text{g}$$

A little of the insoluble dithionate of the series may be precipitated from the faintly-colored mother liquor with sodium dithionate.

References:

1. JÖRGENSEN, Z. anorg. Chem., 16:184 (1898).
2. WERNER, Ber., 40:4116, 4820 (1907).

Chapter 7

COLLOIDS

150. Antimony (III) Sulfide *

A solution of 0.2g–0.3g of potassium antimonyl tartrate (tartar emetic) in 100ml of water is treated with hydrogen sulfide for a short time. An orange-yellow sol is formed which is dialyzed in running water for 2–4 days.

COGNATE PREPARATIONS

150 a. Arsenic Analogue *

As₂S₃sol

A saturated aqueous solution of arsenious acid is produced by boiling re-sublimed arsenic (III) trioxide with water for several hours. Fifty milliliters of this solution are diluted with water to 200ml and treated in the cold with hydrogen sulfide. The yellow-orange sol formed has a greenish tint in greater dilutions. It may be concentrated by adding more of the saturated arsenious acid solution and re-treating with H_2S. Any flocculated material is filtered off and the excess hydrogen sulfide is removed by bubbling carbon dioxide through the colloidal suspension. Finally the sol is purified by dialysis as described for No. 150.

150 b. Mercuric (II) Analogue *

HgSsol

One milliliter of a saturated aqueous solution of mercuric chloride is treated dropwise with a saturated solution of sodium sulfide 9-hydrate in water until complete solution has taken place:

$$HgCl_2 + 2Na_2S \longrightarrow Na_2[HgS_2] + 2NaCl$$

The solution of sodium dithiomercurate (II) is poured into one liter of water with vigorous stirring. After a short time, an initially dark-brown, then black, stable sol of mercuric sulfide forms.

151. Copper *

One gram of U.S.P. gum arabic is dissolved in 70ml of hot water. After cooling, 0.1g of copper sulfate 5-hydrate is dissolved in the liquid and 30ml of concentrated ammonia are added. The blue solution is warmed to 50°C and a few milliliters of a 0.0005% hydrazine hydrate solution are added. A copper sol is produced which is the color of the metal by reflected light and blue by transmitted light. The colloidal suspension must be dialyzed for several days immediately after it is prepared and it is stable for only a short time.

COGNATE PREPARATIONS

151 a. Blue Gold Sol *

A 0.001% solution of tetrachloroauric (III) acid in distilled water is treated in the cold with an aqueous 0.05% solution of either hydrazine hydrate, hydroxylamine hydrochloride, or phenylhydrazine hydrochloride.

151 b. Red Gold Sol or Silver Sol *

One hundred milliliters of a 0.001% solution of tetrachloroauric (III) acid (or silver nitrate) in distilled water is treated with several drops of 1% sodium carbonate 10-hydrate and heated to boiling in a flask. Every 30 seconds one drop of a *fresh* 1% tannin solution (U.S.P.) is added with agitation. When a deep red gold color has formed (or yellow-brown to red-brown for the silver) the colloidal solution is cooled and stabilized by the addition of a few milliliters of chloroform or toluene.

152. Iron (III) Oxide *

Six and one-half grams of powdered ammonium carbonate are dissolved in 100ml of water at 50°C and cooled. A filtered solution of 7.5g of ferric chloride 6-hydrate in 25ml of water is treated with ⅔ of the carbonate solution with stirring. About 1/10 of this largely neutralized solution is set aside and the remainder treated dropwise with the reserved ⅓ of the carbonate until a brown precipitate of hydrous ferric oxide is *just* permanently formed. The residual 1/10 ferric solution is then added in portions until this precipitate re-dissolves. After filtering off any flocculated oxide which may form after a little standing, the red-brown sol is dialyzed in running water until the dialysate is free of chloride. The sol is stable in the cold but is precipitated by boiling or electrolysis.

COGNATE PREPARATION

152 a. Vanadium (V) Oxide *

V_2O_5 sol

One gram of ammonium metavanadate is ground with 10ml of water in a mortar and 10ml of $2N$ hydrochloric acid is gradually added with continued grinding. The red-brown slurry of hydrated vanadium pentoxide is transferred to a sintered-glass funnel and rinsed with 10ml portions of distilled water. At first the washings are a clear yellow color but then the filtrate becomes a cloudy red-brown. The solid remaining on the filter is washed into a flask with 100ml of distilled water. After standing a few hours with occasional shaking, the solid has peptized to a clear orange-red sol. Old preparations (several months) of this colloid show a characteristic rod-like refractive power.

153. Silicic Acid *

Twenty grams of crystalline sodium silicate (meta-) are dissolved in 70ml of hot water and filtered if necessary. This solution is added dropwise to a mixture of 20ml of concentrated hydrochloric acid and 40ml of water containing two drops of phenolphthalein indicator. When the addition of the silicate solution produces a permanent pink color, the colorless sol is dialyzed until the dialysate is free of chloride.

154. Sulfur **

(I)

Separate solutions of 7.2g of sodium sulfite 7-hydrate (A)
and 6.4g of sodium sulfide 9-hydrate (B), each in 50ml of
water, are prepared. With a pipette, 1.5ml of A are added
to B. To the latter solution is added, dropwise and with constant stirring, a mixture of 2.7g of concentrated sulfuric
acid and 10ml of water until a *very* faint permanent turbidity is produced; about 8ml of the acid solution will be
required. Five and one-half grams of concentrated sulfuric
acid are added to the remainder of A and this is then quickly
stirred into the acidified sulfide-sulfite mixture. After standing one hour in a covered vessel, the liquid is filtered and the
residue is treated with 300ml of distilled water; a milky-
white colloidal sulfur solution is formed. Five to ten milliliters of this solution are diluted to 300ml with pure water,
producing a reddish opalescent sulfur sol. After standing
for one day, any traces of flocculated sulfur are filtered off.
The suspension is stable for a period of several weeks.

(II)

Finely-powdered roll sulfur is refluxed with an excess of
absolute alcohol for several hours to produce a saturated
solution. This is poured into a 100-fold volume of water to
produce the sol.

References:

1. B:39–50; J:380–382.
2. HECHT, *Präparative Anorganische Chemie*, pp. 202–207, Springer,
   Berlin, 1951.
3. GRUBITSCH, *Anorganisch-präparative Chemie*, pp. 355–372,
   Springer, Vienna, 1950.

Chapter 8

ORGANOMETALLIC COMPOUNDS

NOTE: For all preparations in this section, glassware must be thoroughly clean and dry; reagents must be of the highest purity available. These precautions are absolutely necessary to ensure highest yields.

155. Bisbenzenechromium (0) ****

$$3CrCl_3 + 2Al + AlCl_3 + 6C_6H_6 \longrightarrow 3[Cr(C_6H_6)_2][AlCl_4]$$
$$2[Cr(C_6H_6)_2]^+ + S_2O_4^{--} + 4OH^- \longrightarrow 2Cr(C_6H_6)_2 + 2SO_3^{--} + 2H_2O$$

A nitrogen-filled dry box is very suitable for all filling operations in this procedure.

PURIFICATION OF REAGENTS:

1) **Anhydrous chromium (III) chloride** (No. 14) is boiled for 15–30 minutes with $2N$ hydrochloric acid and then washed well with water, methanol, and ether in that order. The salt is ground fine in a mortar and dried at 105–120°C for two hours.

2) **Anhydrous aluminum chloride** (No. 10) must be freshly sublimed before use; it is ground and transferred into the reaction vessel as rapidly as possible. Material taken from a freshly-opened, powdered, and re-sublimed high-grade sample of the salt may also be employed.

3) **Aluminum powder** (100 mesh or finer) of the greatest commercial purity is rinsed with pure dry benzene as a precaution to remove organic impurities and dried at 105–120°C.

4) **Benzene** (thiophene-free) is refluxed for several hours with pelletized sodium and then distilled directly from the metal, rejecting a small fore-run and the residue in the pot.

PROCEDURE:

A 250ml 3-necked flask with ground-glass joints is fitted with a stopper in the center and two stopcock adapters on the sides. The flask is rapidly charged with 25g of the prepared chromium (III) chloride, 3.5g of aluminum powder, and 60g of aluminum chloride and then evacuated with a mechanical pump. The reaction vessel is then filled with pure, dry, oxygen-free nitrogen. With the inert gas flowing through the flask, 100ml of benzene is added, followed by 10 drops of dry mesitylene. One of the stopcock outlets is quickly substituted by a reflux condenser connected to a glass tube or rubber hose which leads just below the surface of a vessel containing mercury, and a Trubore stirrer is inserted into the middle neck of the flask. The flow of nitrogen is continued during these steps, but once the apparatus has been closed, the stream of gas may be shut off. All glass joints must be tight and well-greased to ensure against leakage. The mixture is stirred well and refluxed for 30–35 hours with periodic precautionary checking for trouble-free operation.

While the preceding reaction vessel is being cooled to room temperature, a 5-liter 3-necked flask is equipped with an efficient air-tight stirrer, a reflux condenser with a mercury pressure gauge, and a wide (10mm or larger) inlet tube fitted with a suitable length of clean Tygon tubing.

The flask is now filled with a cold solution of 220g of potassium hydroxide in 1300ml of air-free water, followed by 500ml of absolute methanol and two liters of purified benzene.

[The operations described next must follow in close succession for good results in the experiment.]

One hundred and forty grams of the purest sodium dithionite available are rapidly stirred into the 5-liter flask, which is cooled in an ice-water bath. The first reaction vessel is fitted with a wide outlet tube leading to the bottom of the small flask and connected by the Tygon tubing to the large flask. The stirrer is quickly removed from the

250ml flask, substituted by a *tight* ground-glass stopper, and the cool, yellow-green contents are *gently* swirled while being forced into the large reduction vessel under pressure of nitrogen. With due care, most of the solid material may be transferred in this way, provided that the small vessel is agitated sufficiently. If some solid remains, 50ml of benzene may be added and any residue left behind may be forced over as described.

The inlet tube in the large flask is now removed and substituted by a stopper. Next the mixture is stirred very rapidly for two hours at room temperature.

The upper layer (benzene) is carefully forced under nitrogen into a 3-liter flask containing about 25g of solid potassium hydroxide, using a technique similar to that just described. The remaining aqueous mixture is stirred again with 50–100ml of benzene and this second extract is added to the main solution of the product under nitrogen. The combined benzene layers are dried under nitrogen over the solid base for 15–30 minutes with gentle agitation from time to time. Then the solution is transferred as before to a second 3-liter flask or preferably, to a 5-liter resin kettle with a 2- or 3-necked cover.

The benzene is now stripped *in vacuo* on the steam bath; the brown-black to black residual product is readily scraped from the walls of the vessel.

$$\text{Crude Yield} = 23\text{--}31\text{g } (70\text{--}95\%)$$

For purification, the solid is washed (three times) with 100ml of absolute ether and sublimed at about 160°C with a vacuum pump; m.p. (under N_2) 284–5°C.

References:

1. I, vol. 6:135.
2. FISHER AND HAFNER, *Z. Naturforsch.*, 10b:665 (1955).

COGNATE PREPARATIONS

155 a. Bis(benzene)chromium (I) Iodide *

$$[Cr(C_6H_6)_2]I$$

$$4Cr(C_6H_6)_2 + O_2 + 2H_2O \longrightarrow 4[Cr(C_6H_6)_2]OH$$
$$[Cr(C_6H_6)_2]OH + KI \longrightarrow [Cr(C_6H_6)_2]I + KOH$$

Ten grams of Bis (benzene) chromium (0) are added to a mixture of 200ml benzene and 100ml water contained in a 500ml suction flask which is fitted with a stopper and an inlet tube that reaches almost to the bottom of the vessel. Air is drawn through the flask until the complex has dissolved and the benzene layer has become practically colorless. The yellow-brown aqueous layer is separated and filtered if necessary. It is then treated with a saturated solution of potassium iodide until no more precipitate forms. After cooling in ice the yellow product is filtered off, washed three times with 5ml of 95% alcohol, and finally with ether. The compound is dried *in vacuo*.

$$\text{Yield} = 10.5\text{g} \quad (65\%)$$

Reference: FISHER AND HAFNER, *Z. anorg. allgem. chem.*, 286:146 (1956).

155 b. Bis(biphenyl)chromium (0) ***

$$Cr(C_{12}H_{10})_2$$

The reagents used in this synthesis are purified as described under the benzene analogue; the biphenyl is sublimed and dried at 100°C for 30 minutes.

Ten grams of the prepared chromium (III) chloride, 8g of aluminum powder, 30g of aluminum chloride, and 27g of biphenyl are intimately mixed by shaking in a clean, dry, stoppered 250ml bottle. The mixture is rapidly poured into a 150ml beaker and covered with an even layer of three to four grams of biphenyl.

The beaker is immediately immersed in an oil bath preheated to 100°C. When the fusion mixture begins to melt and effervesce with evolution of hydrogen chloride heating is temporarily interrupted. The reaction heats up to 140–150°C. After ten minutes the fusion is stirred thoroughly with a thermometer; the temperature should not rise above 160°C. The bath is now maintained at 120°C for one-half hour to complete the reaction. It should be noted that a properly conducted fusion is the yield determining factor in this and the succeeding preparation.

The reaction melt is cooled to room temperature and added in portions to 100ml of methanol contained in a one liter beaker immersed in ice. Four hundred milliliters of a cold saturated sodium chloride solution are added with stirring and the precipitate rapidly filtered by suction on a 15cm funnel. The dark-colored acidic methanol-water filtrate (see next preparation) is discarded. The residue on the filter funnel is successively extracted with several 100ml portions of water until the extract is only very faintly colored. Between each extraction with water, air should be drawn through the filter cake for about 15 minutes to oxidize any remaining bis(diphenyl)chromium (0) to the + 1 valence state.

The combined orange-red aqueous extracts are added under nitrogen to a cold, well-stirred mixture of 500ml air-free water, 90g of potassium hydroxide, and 55g of the purest sodium dithionite available (see preceding preparation). The desired product precipitates immediately and after standing for one-half hour it is filtered off and dried for one or two days over phosphorous (V) oxide. The dry material is dissolved in absolute ether, filtered if necessary, and the solvent is removed *in vacuo*. Bronze colored crystals.

Yield = 10–12g (m.p.ca. 112°C)

Reference: FISHER AND SEUS, *Ber.*, 89:1814 (1956).

155 c. Bis(biphenyl)chromium (I) Iodide *

$$[Cr(C_{12}H_{10})_2]I$$

(I)

The same method as described in 155 a is used. Fifteen grams of bis(biphenyl)chromium (0) are employed. The yield is practically quantitative.

(II)

The fusion mixture outlined in 155 b is treated with cold methanol and aqueous sodium chloride as described. The first methanol-water filtrate is reacted separately with 3g of solid potassium iodide to precipitate a small additional amount of product. The successive leachings with water are carried out as in the previous procedure. To these combined extracts 10g of potassium iodide are added with stirring.

The orange-to-reddish-black product is filtered by suction, rinsed with cold water, and air-dried.

$$Yield = 22\text{--}25g$$

References:
1. See 155 b.
2. HEIN, *Ber.*, 54:2716 (1921).

155 d. Hexa(phenylisocyanide)chromium (0) *

$$3Cr(CH_3COO)_2 + C_6H_5NC \text{ (excess)} \longrightarrow$$
$$Cr(C_6H_5NC)_6 + 2Cr \text{ (III) complex}$$

A 100ml three-necked flask is fitted with a stirrer, a dropping funnel, and a two-hole stopper carrying an inlet- and an outlet tube for any inert gas such as nitrogen, hydrogen, or illuminating gas.

The flask is charged with 6g of chromium (II) acetate monohydrate (No. 35) and 40ml of absolute methanol. The stirrer and flow of inert gas are started and a solution of 20g of phenylisocyanide in 10ml of absolute methanol are added slowly through the dropping funnel. After the very dark red reaction mixture has stood overnight in a refrigerator the crystalline product is filtered off. It is washed twice with 10ml of ice-cold methanol and dried in air.

$$Yield = 5\text{--}6g$$

Reference: Malatesta *et al.*, *Gazz. Chim. ital.*, 82:516 (1952).

156. Bis(cyclopentadienyl)iron (II) ***

$$C_2H_5Br + Mg \longrightarrow C_2H_5MgBr$$
$$C_2H_5MgBr + C_5H_6 \longrightarrow C_5H_5MgBr + C_2H_6$$
$$6C_5H_5MgBr + 2FeCl_3 \longrightarrow 2(C_5H_5)_2Fe + (C_5H_5)_2 + 3MgBr_2 + 3MgCl_2$$

A 200ml 3-necked flask is fitted with a dropping funnel, a vapor-tight mechanical stirrer, and an efficient reflux condenser with a calcium chloride drying tube. Four grams of magnesium turnings (Grignard grade) are placed in the flask, and a solution of 18g of pure ethyl bromide (b.p. 38°C) in 15-20ml of sodium-dried absolute ether is poured into the funnel. Five to ten milliliters of the halide solution are added to the magnesium. Initiation of the reaction is indicated by the formation of a whitish turbidity on the surface of the metal together with a slight ebullition which gradually accelerates. If this does not occur within a few minutes, a small crystal of iodine may be added or the mixture may be warmed in a dish of water at 40–50°C.

As soon as the reaction starts, and *not* before, 40–50ml of anhydrous absolute ether are added through the condenser and stirring is begun. The remainder of the ethereal halide solution is added at such a rate that spontaneous refluxing is maintained. When all has been added, the reaction is completed by heating for 30 minutes on the steam bath; virtually all of the magnesium should have dissolved with the exception of a few tiny flakes. Fifty milliliters of pure dry thiophene-free benzene are added to the Grignard reagent and the dropping funnel is substituted by a thermometer reaching well into the solution. The cold water is run out of the condenser, the drying tube is removed, and the ether is distilled off in the hood on a steam bath until the internal temperature of the mixture reaches 60–65°C. The reflux condenser is refilled with water, the drying tube is replaced, and a solution of 11gm of freshly-distilled cyclopentadiene (b.p. 42°C) in 25ml of absolute benzene is added. The reaction mixture is now heated at 60–65°C on the water bath, with stirring, until the evolution of ethane is complete, as shown by leading the evolved gases into a small beaker containing a little mercury. This operation requires 4–6 hours.

A freshly prepared solution of 9g of anhydrous iron (III) chloride [1] [CAUTION: Very hygroscopic material!] in 25ml of absolute ether is quickly added to the cooled solution of cyclopentadienylmagnesium bromide with stirring and the closed flask is allowed to stand overnight at room temperature. The reaction is then refluxed for one hour with stirring, cooled in ice, and decomposed by the dropwise addition of about 50ml of cold 10% aqueous ammonium chloride. The organic layer is separated and dried over anhydrous magnesium sulfate. Evaporation of the solvents leaves an orange-brown residue weighing about 3.5g. This represents crude product; the material is purified by recrystallization from methanol to yield needles; m.p. 172–174°C.

The compound sublimes above 100°C; its vapor is stable to 400°C. It is readily soluble in benzene and less so in ether. Even at the boiling point, the substance is not affected by water, dilute aqueous sodium hydroxide, or concentrated hydrochloric acid.

To analyze for iron, a weighed amount of the complex is boiled with concentrated nitric acid under reflux, evaporated to dryness on the steam bath, and the residual iron (III) chloride is precipitated from a hot, very faintly acid solution with aqueous ammonia. After ignition at 800–900°C, the material is weighed as Fe_2O_3.

References:
1. B:77A; I, vol. 3:191; *Ibid.*, vol. 5:154.
2. HONIGSCHMID AND BIRKENBACH, *Ber.*, 56:1476 (1923).
3. KEALY AND PAUSON, *Nature*, 168:1039 (1951).

157. Tetraphenyllead (IV) **

$$C_6H_5Br + Mg \longrightarrow C_6H_5MgBr$$
$$4C_6H_5MgBr + 2PbCl_2 \longrightarrow (C_6H_5)_4Pb + Pb + 2MgCl_2 + 2MgBr_2$$

In a one-liter, three-necked, ground-glass flask fitted with a dropping funnel, a vapor-tight stirrer, and a reflux condenser with a drying tube, are placed 12g of magnesium turnings (Grignard) and 50ml of absolute ether (sodium-dried). A solution of 78g of pure bromobenzene (b.p. 155°C) in 150ml of dry ether is placed in the dropping funnel. A small crystal of iodine is added to the magnesium and the stirrer is started. About 20ml of the ethereal halide solution is added and the reaction mixture is warmed in a dish of water at 40–50°C until the reaction starts, as shown by the disappearance of the brown-violet color of iodine and the onset of spontaneous ebullition when the water bath is removed. The solution of bromobenzene is now added dropwise at such a rate that refluxing is maintained, and when addition is complete, the flask is heated on the water bath, with stirring, for one hour to complete the reaction.

After cooling, 400 ml of sodium-distilled benzene are added, followed by 63g of powdered, dry (105–120°C for two hours) lead (II) chloride in one portion. The mixture is then stirred and refluxed for 8 hours and cooled. Alternatively, the lead (II) chloride may be added to the

Grignard reagent without previous addition of benzene and the mixture is allowed to stand, protected from moisture, for two days at room temperature. In the alternate procedure the lead salt should be added in 10–20g portions with stirring and ice-cooling.

The contents of the flask are poured into a mixture of 350ml of water, 100g of ice, and 50ml of concentrated hydrochloric acid. The gray-black solid is filtered off and the filtrate is reserved. The solid is washed with water and dried at 100°C; it weighs 45–50g.

The organic layer is separated from the filtrate and dried over anhydrous magnesium sulfate.

Next, the dried gray solid is extracted four times with the same 300ml portion of boiling benzene. After each extraction the product is isolated by cooling in ice and filtered.

$$\text{Yield} = 19\text{--}23\text{g}$$

The spent benzene extract is combined with the dried organic mother liquor and evaporated to a volume around 100ml. If this is ice-cooled, more product may be isolated.

$$\text{Total Yield} = 26\text{--}29\text{g}; \text{ m.p. } 222\text{--}224°\text{C}$$

One recrystallization from benzene raises the melting point to 225°C.

For more elaborate preparative methods, see references 3 and 4.

References:
1. B:216.
2. GILMAN AND ROBINSON, *J. Am. Chem. Soc.*, 49:2316 (1927).
3. GILMAN *et al.*, *J. Org. Chem.*, 17:630 (1952).
4. C.A., 42:5870 (1948).

COGNATE PREPARATION

157 a. Diphenyllead Iodide *

$$(C_6H_5)_4Pb + 2I_2 \longrightarrow (C_6H_5)_2PbI_2 + 2C_6H_5I$$

Three grams of tetraphenyllead are dissolved in 60ml of warm chloroform. After cooling, a solution of 3g of iodine in 15ml of carbon disulfide is added dropwise until the color of iodine just persists. The mixture is allowed to evaporate spontaneously in a dish under the hood and the residue is extracted three times with 10ml of carbon disulfide. The filtered extracts are evaporated in a stream of clean air (hood) to a volume of 10ml and then 3ml of absolute alcohol are added. After cooling in ice, the yellow crystals are filtered off and washed with two 5ml portions of cold 95% alcohol.

$$\text{Yield} = 2.5\text{–}3.5\text{g}; \text{m.p. } 105\text{–}7°\text{C (dec.)}$$

$$(C_6H_5)_2PbI_2 \xrightarrow{\text{Heat}} (C_6H_5)_2 + PbI_2$$

Reference: No. 1 for preceding.

158. Tetraphenyltin (IV) **

$$C_6H_5Br + Mg \longrightarrow C_6H_5MgBr$$
$$4C_6H_5MgBr + SnCl_4 \longrightarrow (C_6H_5)_4Sn + 2MgBr_2 + 2MgCl_2$$

An ethereal solution of 0.5 mole of phenylmagnesium bromide is prepared as described in Experiment 157. Then 250ml of sodium-distilled toluene are added and the ether is distilled off through the empty reflux condenser in the hood, using a boiling water bath. The condenser is refilled with water, the drying tube replaced, and a solution of 25g of anhydrous tin (IV) chloride (No. 84) in 100ml of toluene is added dropwise with stirring.

The reaction mixture is refluxed for one hour with agitation; it is then cooled and added to 300ml of ice-cold 2N hydrochloric acid. Any solid that has precipitated is filtered off and dried.

The layer of toluene is separated from the acid solution and combined with an extract made by treating the dry residue on the filter with 100ml of boiling benzene. The organic mixture is cooled to room temperature and any product that forms is filtered off. The benzene-toluene layer is then washed with 100ml of water followed by a similar volume of 5% aqueous potassium fluoride. Any insoluble $(C_6H_5)_3SnF$ and $(C_6H_5)_2SnF_2$ that precipitate are filtered off. After a second washing with water, the hydrocarbon solution is evaporated on the steam bath. Several crops of crystals may be collected. The final volume is 50 ml; m.p. 224–5°C.

Total Yield = 33–37g (80–90% based on tin (IV) chloride)

Reference: CHAMBERS AND SCHERER, *J. Am. Chem. Soc.*, 48:1054 (1926).

COGNATE PREPARATIONS

The preceding method of preparation may be employed for all of the following tetra alkyl tin (IV) compounds by using 0.5 mole of the corresponding bromide for the Grignard reaction. Other necessary modifications are noted below. All yields are in the range of 50–80%.

158 a. Tetramethyl Tin (IV) **

The Grignard reagent is prepared from 0.5 mole of methyl iodide in a total of 200ml of sodium-dried di-*n*-butyl ether as detailed in No. 157. The tin (IV) chloride is added in 100ml of dry xylene (the commercial mixture of *ortho*, *meta*, and *para* isomers is quite satisfactory). One hour reflux is required. The product is isolated by fractional distillation, b.p. 78°C; air-stable liquid.

158 b. Tetraethyltin (IV) **: The final toluene solution of product should be fractionated through a six inch packed column to remove the fore-run of solvent; b.p. 181°C.

158 c. Tetra-*n*-butyltin (IV) **: The toluene is removed from the product *in vacuo* on the water bath and the residue distilled under vacuum; b.p. 145°C (10mm).

158 c. Tetracyclohexyltin (IV) **: The toluene solution is evaporated *in vacuo* and the residue is recrystallized from a mixture of benzene and 95% ethanol; m.p. 263°C.

For the preparation of various tetra aryl tins (IV) see: Bähr and Gelius, *Ber.*, 91:812 (1958).

As these compounds have low solubilities in the more common organic solvents, they serve as useful exercises in recrystallization, and for the determination of melting points over 300°C.

Among the organometallic tin (IV) analogues described are:

a) Tetramesityl—m.p. 320°C (dec.).
b) Tetra-l-naphthyl—310–320°C (dec.).
c) Tetrakis (9-phenanthryl)—360–370°C (dec.).
d) Tetrakis (2-biphenyl)—300–301°C.

INORGANIC LABORATORY PREPARATIONS

FOR SUPPLEMENTARY READING

LABORATORY MANUALS

1. W. JOLLY, *Synthetic Inorganic Chemistry;* Prentice-Hall, 1960.
2. R. E. DODD AND P. L. ROBINSON, *Experimental Inorganic Chemistry;* Elsevier, 1957.
3. H. F. WALTON, *Inorganic Preparations;* Prentice-Hall, 1948.

TEXTBOOKS

1. T. MOELLER, *Inorganic Chemistry—An Advanced Textbook;* Wiley, 1952.
2. J. KLEINBERG *et al., Inorganic Chemistry;* Heath, 1960.
3. E. S. GOULD, *Inorganic Reactions and Structure;* Holt, 1955.
4. S. Y. TYREE AND K. KNOX, *Textbook of Inorganic Chemistry;* Macmillan, 1961.
5. H. EMELEUS AND J. ANDERSON, *Modern Aspects of Inorganic Chemistry;* Van Nostrand, 1960.
6. W. M. LATIMER AND J. H. HILDEBRAND, *Reference Book of Inorganic Chemistry*, 3rd ed.; Macmillan, 1951.
7. D. M. YOST AND H. RUSSELL, *Systematic Inorganic Chemistry;* Prentice-Hall, 1944.
8. J. P. PARTINGTON, *Textbook of Inorganic Chemistry*, 6th ed.; St. Martins, 1950.
9. E. DEB. BARNETT AND C. L. WILSON, *Inorganic Chemistry;* Longmans, 1959.
10. R. HESLOP AND P. L. ROBINSON, *Inorganic Chemistry;* Elsevier, 1960.

11. H. REMY, *Treatise on Inorganic Chemistry* (translated by J. S. ANDERSON); Elsevier, 1956.
12. W. HUCKEL, *Structural Chemistry of Inorganic Compounds* (translated by L. LONG); Elsevier, 1950.
13. M. DAY AND J. SELBIN, *Theoretical Inorganic Chemistry;* Reinhold, 1962.

INDEX

QD
155
S3

10,551

CKKD

Date Due